Debris-Covered

Glaciers

Edited by

M. NAKAWO

Institute for Hydrospheric–Atmospheric Sciences, Nagoya University, Furo-cho, Chikusa-ku, Nagoya 464-01, Japan

C. F. RAYMOND

University of Washington, Geophysics Program, Box 351650, Seattle, Washington 98195-1650, USA

A. FOUNTAIN

Department of Geology, Portland State University, Portland, Oregon 97207-0751 USA

Proceedings of an international workshop held at the University of Washington in Seattle, Washington, USA, 13–15 September 2000. The workshop was supported by the International Commission on Snow and Ice of the International Association of Hydrological Sciences.

Financial sponsorship for this publication was provided by:

 The International Arctic Research Center, Fairbanks, Alaska, USA

 Glaciological Expedition in Nepal

IAHS Publication no. 264
in the IAHS Series of Proceedings and Reports

Published by the International Association of Hydrological Sciences 2000
IAHS Press, Centre for Ecology and Hydrology, Wallingford,
Oxfordshire OX10 8BB, UK
IAHS Publication no. 264
ISBN 1-901502-31-7

British Library Cataloguing-in-Publication Data.
A catalogue record for this book is available from the British Library.

The papers included in this volume have been peer reviewed and some were extensively revised before publication.

IAHS is indebted to the employers of the Editors for the invaluable support and services that enabled them to work effectively and efficiently.

The designations employed and the presentation of material throughout the publication do not imply the expression of any opinion whatsoever on the part of IAHS concerning the legal status of any country, territory, city or area or of its authorities, or concerning the delimitation of its frontiers or boundaries.

The use of trade, firm, or corporate names in the publication is for the information and convenience of the reader. Such use does not constitute an official endorsement or approval by IAHS of any product or service to the exclusion of others that may be suitable.

The camera-ready pages were produced at IAHS Press, Wallingford, UK, by Penny Kisby.

Publications in the series of Proceedings and Reports are available *only* from:
IAHS Press, Centre for Ecology and Hydrology, Wallingford, Oxfordshire OX10 8BB, UK
tel.: +44 1491 692442; fax: +44 1491 692448; e-mail: jilly@iahs.demon.co.uk

Printed in The Netherlands by Krips repro Meppel.

Preface

Shrinkage of glaciers has contributed to rising sea level over the last century. It is of global concern whether the rate of shrinkage could accelerate. Glaciers are also of local interest for human water use and potential hydrologic hazards. To address these issues requires accurate measurements of glacier mass balances worldwide and better understanding of their mass and energy exchange. Much of our understanding to date has been gained from relatively clean glaciers, largely free of debris cover. However, debris-covered glaciers comprise a significant fraction of the global population of glaciers and are particularly common in the Himalayas, Andes, Alaska and on stratovolcanoes worldwide.

Despite their relatively common occurrence, debris-covered glaciers have not been well studied, in part because we do not have practical methods to measure or predict the melting rate of the ice under the debris. This fundamental variable is crucial for mass balance calculations, response to climatic variations, and for water runoff. Moreover, the perimeter of debris-covered glaciers can be difficult to determine from ground-based and satellite observations. From a hydrological perspective, debris-covered glaciers commonly develop supraglacial lakes that can release disastrous floods.

In addition to issues directly concerning debris-covered glaciers, rock glaciers may be an end-member in the spectrum of glaciers, possibly originating from debris-covered glaciers. Current debate on the origin of rock glaciers and their possible genetic connection to debris-covered glaciers highlights fundamental issues regarding debris transport and energy balances.

With these issues in mind, the workshop was organized, aiming to synthesize our current understanding about debris-covered glaciers and rock glaciers. By drawing on experiences from different regions of the world we hope to highlight the underlying physical processes controlling the nature of debris-covered and rock glaciers. During the initial organizational phase of the workshop, we were anticipating about 30 participants. Much to our surprise, over 50 people responded to our call for papers with submitted abstracts. This response indicates the timeliness of the topic.

The workshop was held on the campus of the University of Washington in Seattle with sponsorship of the Geophysics Program. The 54 oral and poster presentations were delivered over three days. A fine banquet overlooking the ship canal was convened on the second night and a field trip to the debris-covered Emmons Glacier on Mt Rainer occurred on the Saturday following the meeting.

This volume of proceedings contains 28 papers. Each paper was reviewed by at least two referees with expertise in the topic of the paper. The organization of the papers in the volume follows the organization of the workshop. Because the proceedings volume was published prior to the workshop, we are not able to include the results of the stimulating discussion in this volume, which we hope to publish in another publication.

Organizing and Editing Committee
M. Nakawo, C. F. Raymond & A. Fountain

It is our pleasure to take this opportunity to thank to all the participants for their contribution to the workshop. We express our gratitude to Dr Gordon Young, Secretary General of the International Association of Hydrological Sciences (1995–June 2000), and Dr Liz Morris, President of the IAHS International Commission on Snow and Ice, for their support of this workshop. We would like to thank our colleagues who reviewed the manuscripts for this publication. It is through their efforts, spending much time examining each manuscript that the quality of this publication is achieved. Ms Penny Kisby and her staff at IAHS Press are responsible for the final editing of the proceedings and the crisp product that was produced. The publication cost was partly supported by the International Arctic Research Center and the Glaciological Expedition in Nepal. The travel support for the participants from developing countries was provided by Nagoya University and a donation from the members of the Glaciological Expedition in Nepal, for which we acknowledge the following personnel: Y. Ageta, T. Chetri, K. Fujita, H. Iida, S. Iwata, T. Kadota, O. Kobayashi, S. Kohshima, N. Naito, M. Nakawo, C. Narama, K. Rijan, A. Sakai, N. Takeuchi, Y. Takeuchi and T. Yamada.

Organizing and Editing Committee:
M. Nakawo, C. F. Raymond, A. Fountain

Contents

4   Supraglacial Lakes

5   Climate Variations

6   Biology and Hydrology

1 Distribution and Setting

Debris-Covered Glaciers (Proceedings of a workshop held at Seattle, Washington, USA, September 2000). IAHS Publ. no. 264, 2000.

Morphological evolution of the debris cover on Khumbu Glacier, Nepal, between 1978 and 1995

SHUJI IWATA

Department of Geography, Tokyo Metropolitan University, Hachioji, Tokyo 192-0397, Japan
e-mail: iwata-s@comp.metro-u.ac.jp

TATSUTO AOKI

Department of Geography, University of Tokyo, Bunkyo-ku, Tokyo 113-0033, Japan

TSUTOMU KADOTA

Frontier Observational Research System for Global Change, Sumitomo Hamamatsu-cho Building 4F, 1-8-16 Hamamatsu-cho, Minato-ku, Tokyo 105-0013, Japan

KATSUMOTO SEKO*

Institute for Hydrospheric–Atmospheric Sciences, Nagoya University, Furo-cho, Chikusa-ku, Nagoya 464-01, Japan

SATORU YAMAGUCHI

Institute of Low Temperature Science, Hokkaido University, Kita-ku, Sapporo 060-0819, Japan

Abstract The debris-covered area of Khumbu Glacier was topographically mapped in 1995 and the morphological evolution was determined by comparing the 1995 maps with those made in 1978. There had been significant changes in the surface morphology during this 17-year period: the area with a rough uneven surface with large relative relief had extended both upglacier and downglacier, and area of high ablation had increased. The glacier shrinkage in the ablation area where there was a thick debris cover was associated with an increase in surface relief and relative height, mainly caused by rapid ablation on exposed ice and lateral erosion at streams and ponds.

INTRODUCTION

There are many debris-covered glaciers which have ablation areas covered with supra-glacial debris and till in the Khumbu region of eastern Nepal. Many aspects of the debris-covered area of Khumbu Glacier were intensively investigated in 1978 (Watanabe *et al.*, 1980). In particular, members of the project carried out a series of topographic surveys (Iwata *et al.*, 1980), and completed a topographic sketch map covering the whole ablation area and large-scale detailed 1:1000 maps of research areas I–IV (Fig. 1 in Watanabe *et al.*, 1980). After a 17-year interval, during the post monsoon season in 1995, the authors investigated the ablation area of Khumbu Glacier and constructed maps comparable to those completed in 1978. A series of glaciological and geomorphological observations was also carried out. The evolution of the surface morphology is in itself an interesting phenomenon for geomorphologists but observations of surface morphological changes also gives clues to the dynamic behaviour of the glacier, in particular the relationship between ice flow, ablation, and debris supply.

* Present address not known.

This report describes the morphological evolution in the ablation area of Khumbu Glacier over a 17-year period obtained by comparing observations in 1995 with those in 1978, and discusses the significance for the evolution of ablating debris-covered glaciers.

KHUMBU GLACIER

Khumbu Glacier is a valley glacier originating from the southwest face of Qomolangma (Sagarmatha or Mt Everest, 8848 m), and flows in a southwest direction forming a 10-km-long, debris-mantled glacier tongue. The equilibrium line occurs at 5600 m a.s.l. (Watanabe *et al.*, 1980) in the icefall from whose foot the long and slender glacier tongue appears. Two main tributary glaciers join the mainstream: one is from the south of Lingtren and Khumbutse, and the other is from the western face of Nuptse (Fig. 1 in Fushimi *et al.*). The tributary glacier located just downstream of Gorak Shep is completely separated from the main glacier at present. Bare ice is exposed at Base Camp (5300 m a.s.l.) and extends downglacier 2–3 km below Base Camp as a slender bare ice band with ice pinnacles. The median part of the ablation area downglacier 5 km below Base Camp has a distinctive dark-coloured schistose debris cover supplied from the steep rock walls of the higher mountains (Fushimi *et al.*, 1980).

The ablation area is bounded by lateral and frontal moraines with distinct ridges formed during the Little Ice Age and Neoglacial periods (Iwata, 1976; Fushimi, 1981; Röthlisberger, 1986), and is mostly covered with a supraglacial debris mantle, except for limited areas in the upper part. The surface has a very complicated and chaotic topography: with striking glacier karst features, including funnel-shaped hollows with lakes, ice cliffs exposed on walls of hollows and on banks of lakes, and debris-covered cones (conical hills) and ridges. Khumbu Glacier is one of the most well-investigated debris-covered glaciers in the Himalayas. Various aspects of the debris-covered area have been described: surface morphology (Iwata *et al.*, 1980; Seko *et al.*, 1998); distribution, grain size, and production rates of supraglacial debris (Fushimi *et al.*, 1980; Nakawo *et al.*, 1986); ablation rates (Inoue & Yoshida, 1980; Nakawo *et al.*, 1999); and morphogenetic processes (Watanabe *et al.*, 1986).

METHOD

Field observations, measurements and surveys were carried out during the post monsoon season (October and November) of 1995. Sketch maps of the topography of the whole ablation area were made to clearly show the irregular morphology of the debris-covered glacier surface, and to compare the morphology in 1995 to that in 1978. Methods and data sources of the mapping in 1995 (the 1995 map) are as follows:
(a) stereoscopic observation of SPOT images taken in November 1995,
(b) field observation by Iwata in October 1995, and
(c) supplementary interpretation of stereo-pairs of vertical aerial photographs taken in December 1992.
The sketch map indicating the situation in 1978 (the 1978 map: Appendix, Separate Sheet 1 in Iwata *et al.*, 1980) was used as the base map. The completed map shows the distribution of sharp and gentle ridges, convex and concave slopes, valley lines, bare-ice areas, ice cliffs, ponds or lakes, and streams on the debris-covered surface (Fig. 1).

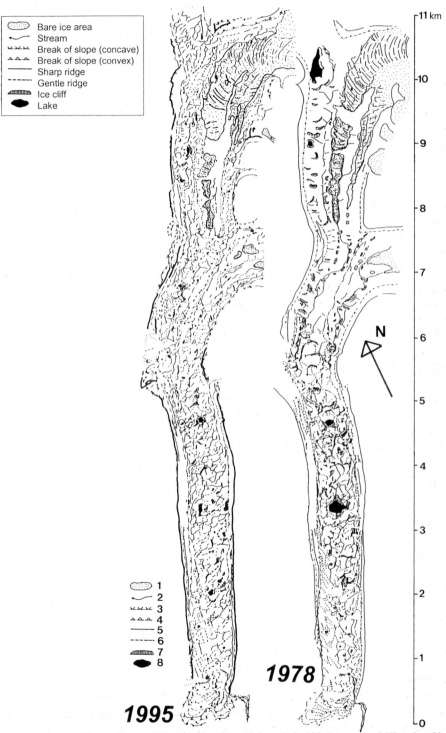

Fig. 1 Topographic sketch maps of the whole ablation area of Khumbu Glacier in 1978 (Iwata *et al.*, 1980) and 1995.

The 1978 map was mainly compiled by simple terrestrial photogrammetry of about 400 stereo-pairs of photographs taken from lateral moraine ridges (Iwata *et al.*, 1980). Therefore relative altitudes of the surface relief were well documented on the 1978 map, but accuracy of spatial positions was less precise. In contrast, the 1995 map, mainly made by SPOT images, represents a more precise positioning of each surface form, while the vertical forms such as small-scale ice-cliffs and elevations were not recognized with any accuracy, and are not represented on the map.

In order to find the morphological changes in research areas I–IV since 1978 (Iwata *et al.*, 1980; Watanabe *et al.*, 1980), each area was resurveyed in 1995. Details of the surveying method and the results are reported by Kadota *et al.* (2000).

RESULTS

Comparing the topographic maps between 1978 and 1995

The topographic sketch maps of the whole ablation area in 1978 and 1995 are presented in Fig. 1. A morphological change could be detected from the comparison of these two maps of the whole ablation area.

Upper part of the ablation area In the upper part of the ablation area, including Area IV, between 7.5 km upglacier from the terminus and Base Camp just below the icefall, the general features of the surface morphology were similar to those in 1978. A long and slender dark-coloured schistose debris-belt between the stretches of bare-ice belts with arcuate ridges or rows of ice pinnacles was found in almost the same location as in 1978, but the bare-ice surface had decreased in area by about 40%, and the debris gaps in the bare-ice belt on the right bank had moved about 0.5 km downstream (Seko *et al.*, 1998). In 1995, an apparent ridge was observed in the bare ice belt on the left bank along the dark debris band. The right bank of this part comprises a debris-covered ice-mass from Mt Lingtren and Khumbutse. This ice mass had changed significantly during the 17 years: many ponds and ice cliffs observed in 1978 had disappeared and the surface roughness had decreased.

Middle part of the ablation area This area comprises the glacier surface between 7.5 km and 2.0 km upglacier from the terminus. This mid-stream part of the ablation area changed greatly over the 17-year period. One of the authors (Iwata) carefully observed the surface features of this part from the lateral moraines in October 1995, but he could not identify the definite landforms that had been recognized in 1978.

The area between 5 and 6 km upglacier from the terminus, where Area III is located, is characterized by a deep valley on the right bank side and a line of large debris-covered cones. Most of this area had been covered with relatively thin debris, ranging from 10 to 30 cm thick, but part had been covered with debris more than 1 m thick. By 1995 more complicated landforms had appeared. For example, a large debris-covered cone had disappeared, and several circular hollows with high ice cliffs emerged; a large valley with a stream had shifted from the right bank to the centre of the glacier.

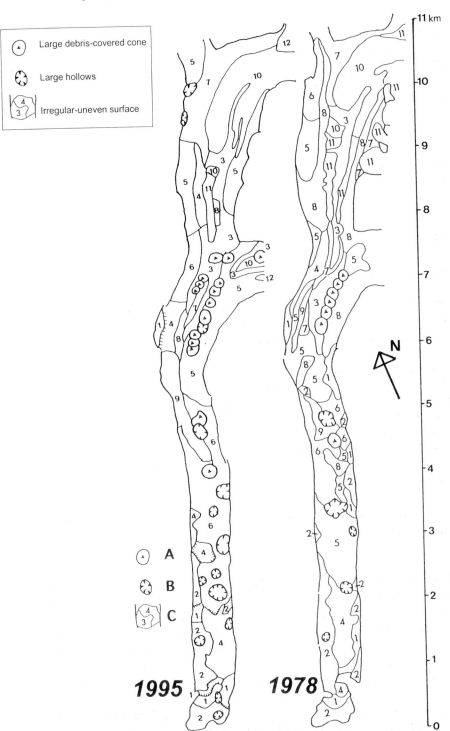

Fig. 2 Distribution of morphological units of the ablation area of Khumbu Glacier in 1978 (Iwata *et al.*, 1980) and 1995. The morphological classification was based on a combination of morphological elements: large debris-covered cones, large hollows and irregular uneven surfaces—the numbers correspond to those in Table 1.

The area between 3 and 5 km from the terminus has the largest relative height (60–80 m) from the surface of the glacier to the lateral moraine ridges. The observed rough and chaotic surface features were similar to those in 1978, but no recognizable landforms could be found, as the surface features had completely changed during the 17-year period. A notable large hollow with a nearly circular pond (0.2 m × 0.15 km) located 3.3 km from the terminus in 1978, had disappeared by 1995, but a small pond was seen near that location. In the lower part of the zone, between 2 and 3 km from the terminus, the rough topography had extended downstream. New hollows with small ponds and troughs occurred and on the right bank a low-relief area with parallel ridges had disappeared.

Lower part of the ablation area   In the area within 2 km of the terminus, including Area I near Lobuche, many landforms such as gentle ridges and several small lakes observed in 1978 were still there in 1995. Notably, partially vegetated parallel ridges on the right-bank side which had been observed in 1978 were nearly the same in 1995. On the other hand, the left-bank side margin had changed to more or less rough topography. Some subsidence features such as small hollows and a trough appeared in some places at the lowest end of the glacier.

Evolution of morphological units

Glacier karst landforms in the ablation area of Khumbu Glacier (Fig. 1) were so complicated that Iwata *et al.* (1980) had made a morphological classification map (Fig. 2) based on a combination of the morphological features shown in the 1978 topographical sketch map. The surface topography of the ablation area was first classified into three remarkable morphological units as follows: large debris-covered cones, large hollows, and irregular uneven surfaces. The irregular uneven surfaces were then classified into 11 units given in Table 1.

In 1995 the glacier surface was similarly classified, and a map was made based on the 1995 topographical sketch map and our field observation (Fig. 2). A comparison of these two maps shown in Fig. 2 reveals a morphological evolution of the debris-covered glacier surface between 1978 and 1995, and reveals three significant changes:

Table 1 Classification of the irregular uneven surfaces.

Surface relief	Relative height (m)	Directional feature	Debris-cover (thickness)	Exposure of glacier ice	Pond	Stream	Number of units
Small	0–10	Nil	Thin	Large part	A few	Many	7
Small	0–10	Nil	Thin	Small part	Nil	Nil	3
Small	0–10	Exist	Thick	Nil	Rare	Nil	2
Small	0–15	Nil	Thick	Nil	Rare	Nil	1
Small	0–15	Exist	Nil	Whole	Rare	Rare	10
Medium	10–30	Nil	Nil	Whole	Rare	Rare	11
Medium	10–30	Nil	Medium	Large part	A few	Many	8
Medium	10–30	Nil	Medium	Large part	Many	Nil	5
Medium	10–30	Nil	Medium	Very small part	Nil	Nil	4
Large	20–40	Nil	Medium	Large part	Many	Nil	6
Large	20–40	Nil	Medium	Large part	A few	Many	9

- Several new large hollows had appeared in the middle and lower parts of the ablation area.
- The distribution of irregular uneven surfaces with large relative relief (units 6 and 9) had extended downstream in the middle part of the ablation area. This implies that the surface relief in the lower part of the ablation area had increased from medium (10–30 m in height) to large (20–40 m) between 2 and 3.5 km from the terminus.
- Large relief feature (units 9 and 6) emerged on the right-side bank in the upper middle part (4.5–5.5 km from the terminus) and the lower upper part (6.5–7.5 km) of the ablation area. On the right side in the upper part of the ablation area (9.5–10.5 km) where a tributary from Lingtren and Khumbtse joins the main glacier, two large hollows appeared and the surface units changed from units 5 and 6 to unit 7, indicating a decrease in surface relief which suggests a rapid decline of this thin ice mass.

DISCUSSION

Watanabe *et al.* (1986) schematically illustrated the morphogenetic processes on the glacier surface along the longitudinal section of the ablation area, based on detailed field observations in research areas I–IV on Khumbu Glacier. It was suggested that important factors in morphogenetic processes are the discharge of glacier (ice flow), sub-aerial and sub-debris ablation rates controlled by debris thickness, and surface and subsurface water which erodes the ice directly. Recently, Nakawo *et al.* (1999) estimated the ablation rates on the surface and beneath the debris layer and the ice flow rates along the longitudinal section of the ablation area of Khumbu Glacier. This estimation was conducted using a heat-budget approach derived from analysis of satellite data. Kadota *et al.* (2000) reports a lowering of the surface in the four research

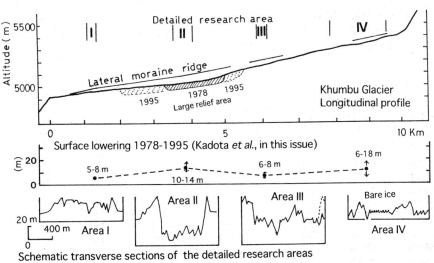

Fig. 3 Longitudinal profile of Khumbu Glacier ablation area showing expansion of large relief area, surface lowering, and transverse profiles.

areas between 1978 and 1995. This is illustrated in Fig. 3 which shows the morphological features of sections across the four research areas. The morphological evolution indicated by the detail mapping of the glacier surface in 1978 and 1995 reveals:

Upper part of the ablation area In and around Area IV, the surface features and distribution of bare and debris surfaces are mostly unchanged in the median part of the glacier. Kadota *et al.* (2000), however, found that the glacier surface had lowered by more than 10 m and that distinct longitudinal ridges had occurred in the areas of schistose debris on both sides of the band of bare ice. This nearly uniform lowering seems to be due to the thin dark-coloured debris cover (unit 3) and to the compression zone below the icefall. Although a relatively rapid ice flow was estimated in the area by Nakawo *et al.* (1999), this significant surface lowering suggests a recent rapid decrease of ice supply from upglacier.

Middle part of the ablation area In the area between 5 and 6 km from the terminus, the surface lowering is relatively small compared with the upglacier and downglacier areas (Nakawo *et al.*, 1999; Kadota *et al.*, 2000). It is probable that the morphological change including the shift of the valley is related to the decline of tributary glaciers from Lingtren and Khumbutse, and from Nuptse. This is likely to be related to the increase in the debris thickness.

The complete change in the rough and chaotic features from 3 to 5 km above the terminus is due to the large ablation rates (Inoue & Yoshida, 1980; Sakai *et al.*, 1998; Nakawo *et al.*, 1999) on the exposed ice cliffs which are eroded by running water in streams and still water in ponds. As the ice cliffs retreat by ablation and the debris-covered slopes evolve through stream erosion, the debris on the ice is redistributed to make an irregular debris cover with some nearly exposed ice surfaces. Apparent positive feedback relationships exist between high ablation rates, water erosion, exposed ice, and debris redistribution. As a consequence, irregular uneven surfaces appears and high surface lowering occurs in the area.

Lower part of the ablation area Fossil or stagnant ice in the lowermost 2 km from the terminus is covered with such thick debris that the ablation at the surface may be negligibly small (Inoue & Yoshida, 1980; Nakawo *et al.*, 1999). In spite of the occurrence of some subsidence features, the surface morphology and vegetation in this part have remained almost the same since 1978. Kadota *et al.* (2000) reports, however, that on the right bank side of Area I, the surface has lowered by 5–8 m since 1978. This suggests that the surface lowering is mainly due to subglacial and englacial meltwater, because many surface meltwater streams observed in the median part of the glacier are hidden in the lower end of the ablation area and this hidden water suddenly gushes out at the terminus.

The most important morphological change is that the area of large relief features in the middle part of the ablation area has expanded both the upglacier and downglacier. This means that since 1978 the areas of high ablation associated with large hollows, ice cliffs, and ponds and streams have spread. In ablation areas with a thick debris cover such as Khumbu Glacier, a glacial decline has occurred associated with the increase of the surface relief as well as the relative height. It thus follows that the existence of exposed ice cliffs and surface water is an important controlling factor for the morphological evolution of glaciers covered with a thick layer of debris.

Acknowledgements We express our appreciation to Department of Hydrology and Meteorology, Ministry of Science and Technology, His Majesty's Government of Nepal for their cooperation in our research in Nepal. This study was financially supported by Grant-in-Aid for Scientific Research (no. 06041051 and no. 09490018) from the Ministry of Education, Science, Sports and Culture, Japanese Government.

REFERENCES

Fushimi, H. (1981) Glacial history in the Khumbu region, Nepal Himalayas, in relation to upheavals of the Great Himalayas. In: *Glaciological and Ecological Studies of Qinghai-Xizang Plateau* (ed. by D.-S. Liu) (Proc. Beijing Symp.), vol. 2, 1641–1648. Science Press, Beijing.

Fushimi, H., Yoshida, M., Watanabe, O. & Upadhyay, B. P. (1980) Distributions and grain sizes of supraglacial debris in the Khumbu Glacier, Khumbu region. *J. Japan. Soc. Snow Ice (Seppyo)* **41**, special issue, 18–25.

Inoue, J. & Yoshida, M. (1980) Ablation and heat exchange over the Khumbu Glacier. *J. Japan. Soc. Snow Ice (Seppyo)* **41**, special issue, 26–33.

Iwata, S. (1976) Late Pleistocene and Holocene moraines in the Sagarmatha (Everest) region. *J. Japan. Soc. Snow Ice (Seppyo)* **38**, special issue, 105–114.

Iwata, S., Watanabe, O. & Fushimi, H. (1980) Surface morphology in the ablation area of the Khumbu Glacier. *J. Japan. Soc. Snow Ice (Seppyo)* **41**, special issue, 9–17.

Kadota, T., Seko, K., Aoki, T., Iwata, S. & Yamaguchi, S. (2000) Shrinkage of the Khumbu Glacier, east Nepal from 1978 to 1995. In: *Debris-Covered Glaciers* (ed. by M. Nakawo & C. F. Raymond & A. Fountain) (Proc. Seattle Workshop, September 2000). IAHS Publ. no. 264 (this volume).

Nakawo, M., Iwata, S., Watanabe, O. & Yoshida, M. (1986) Processes which distribute supraglacial debris on the Khumbu Glacier, Nepal Himalaya. *Ann. Glaciol.* **8**, 129–131.

Nakawo, M., Yabuki, H. & Sakai, A. (1999) Characteristic of Khumbu Glacier, Nepal Himalaya: recent change in the debris-covered area. *Ann. Glaciol.* **28**, 118–122.

Röthlisberger, F. (1986) *10 000 Jahre Gletschergeschichte der Erde*. Verlag Sauerländer, Aarau, Switzerland.

Sakai, A., Nakawo, M. & Fujita, K. (1998) Melt rate of ice cliffs on the Lirung Glacier, Nepal Himalayas, 1996. *Bull. Glacier Res.* **16**, 57–66.

Seko, K., Yabuki, H., Nakawo, M., Sakai, A., Kadota, T. & Yamada, Y. (1998) Changing surface features of Khumbu Glacier, Nepal Himalaya revealed by SPOT images. *Bull. Glacier Res.* **16**, 33–41.

Watanabe, O., Fushimi, H., Ikegami, K., Tanaka, Y., Yoshida, M., Iwata, S., Inoue, J. & Upadhyay, B. P. (1980) Outline of studies on supraglacial debris of Khumbu Glacier, Khumbu region. *J. Japan. Soc. Snow Ice (Seppyo)* **41**, special issue, 5–8.

Watanabe, O., Iwata, S. & Fushimi, H. (1986) Topographic characteristic in the ablation area of the Khumbu Glacier, Nepal Himalaya. *Ann. Glaciol.* **8**, 177–180.

Debris-Covered Glaciers (Proceedings of a workshop held at Seattle, Washington, USA, September 2000). IAHS Publ. no. 264, 2000.

Radio echo-sounding through supraglacial debris on Lirung and Khumbu Glaciers, Nepal Himalayas

A. GADES, H. CONWAY, N. NERESON

University of Washington, Geophysics Program, Box 351650, Seattle, Washington 98195-1650, USA

e-mail: tgades@geophys.washington.edu

N. NAITO

Institute for Hydrospheric–Atmospheric Sciences, Nagoya University, Furo-cho, Chikusa-ku, Nagoya 464-8601, Japan

T. KADOTA

Frontier Observational Research System for Global Change, Sumitomo Hamamatsu-cho Building 4F, 1-8-16 Hamamatsu-cho, Minato-ku, Tokyo 105-0013, Japan

Abstract We have used ground-based radio echo-sounding (RES) to measure the ice thickness of debris-covered Lirung and Khumbu glaciers in the Nepal Himalayas in pre-monsoon season, 1999. Successful ice thickness measurements of ice up to 450 m on Khumbu and 160 m on Lirung Glacier were made using a portable lightweight (<5 kg) RES system at elevations up to 5400 m a.s.l., through supraglacial debris up to 3 m thick. These measurements provide valuable data for glacier climate response modelling and demonstrate the suitability of RES for making ice thickness measurements on a wide variety of debris-covered glaciers.

INTRODUCTION

Glaciers in the Himalayas are very sensitive to summer warming because both accumulation and ablation occur primarily during the summer monsoon season (e.g. Ageta *et al.*, 1980). Small increases in summer temperature increase the rain/snow fraction of precipitation, as well as increasing the ablation. The ablation regions of most of the large Himalayan glaciers are covered with rock debris. Understanding the response of glaciers to climate change requires knowledge of the ice volume. Here we report measurements of ice thickness made on two debris-covered glaciers in Nepal Himalayas. We have chosen radio echo-sounding (RES) over alternative methods for measuring ice thickness distribution (e.g. seismic reflection, gravity measurements) because it is faster, provides better resolution, uses easily portable instrumentation, and does not require explosives.

The use of RES for determining ice thickness has long been common in polar and temperate regions, but few successful thickness measurements have been made on debris-covered glaciers. Three main obstacles hamper the use of RES on temperate debris-covered glaciers. First, the supraglacial debris attenuates the amount of energy transmitted into and out of the underlying ice. Second, englacial rock and water inclusions cause much of the transmitted energy to be lost to scattering. Third, the rugged surface terrain on many of these glaciers reflects some energy, which complicates the interpretation of the bed reflection.

STUDY SITE

Field measurements were made during May and June 1999 at two locations (Fig. 1):
–   The ablation region of Lirung Glacier in the Langtang Valley is separated from the accumulation area by a steep ice-free rock wall. The ablation area is 4 km long, 0.4–0.6 km wide, and ranges in elevation from 4000–4400 m a.s.l. The ablation area of Lirung Glacier is covered by rock debris that increases in thickness from about 0.5 m immediately below the rock wall to about 3 m near the terminus.
–   The ablation region of Khumbu Glacier ranges in elevation from 5400 m a.s.l. immediately below the icefall to 4900 m a.s.l. at the terminus. This section of the glacier is about 9 km long and 0.7–1 km wide. The debris cover on Khumbu Glacier varies from generally less than 0.10 m below the icefall to more than 2 m near the terminus (Nakawo *et al.*, 1986). Both Lirung and Khumbu Glaciers have significant surface undulations that we estimate to have wavelengths of 10–100 m and amplitudes up to 10 m.

Fig. 1 Location of the two study sites in the Nepal Himalayas: Lirung Glacier in the Langtang region and Khumbu Glacier in the Everest region.

INSTRUMENTS AND METHODS

We assembled a RES system with the specific goal of making it lightweight and constructing it with the best available portable instrumentation technology. The transmitter used for these measurements was a lightweight (<0.25 kg) mono-pulse unit described by Jones *et al.* (1989). A Tektronix THS 720A (100 MHz, 500×10^6 samples s^{-1}, 12-V input digital oscilloscope (1.5 kg) was used to receive and stack 256 measurements (at 10 Hz) at each location. A Hewlett Packard 200 LX palmtop computer (3 V, 0.25 kg) was used to control the oscilloscope and to store the stacked records. Power for the transmitter and the oscilloscope was supplied by separate 12-V, 2 Ampere-hour batteries that last for about 100 records. Batteries were recharged using two 10-W flexible solar panels (United Solar Systems: USF-11). Weighted dipole antennae (ϕ = 300 Ω) (Watts & Wright, 1981), threaded inside climbing webbing for protection, with centre frequencies of 5, 7, 10 or 20 MHz, were used depending on the ice thickness and debris cover. Thicker ice and/or debris cover required the use of lower frequencies. One and a half full dipole antennae lengths separated the transmitter and receiver. Because of rough surface topography, a geodetic survey measurement was made at the centre of the transmitter–receiver pair at each of the RES measurement points to record the horizontal and vertical location.

Because of the difficulty in unambiguously interpreting individual isolated spot RES measurements, ice thickness was determined from a series of contiguous measurements that were typically spaced 10 m apart. Such a profile is necessary in order to interpret individual measurements of ice thickness in context with the adjacent measurements. Over short distances, the bed reflection is spatially consistent and appears in each record, but interfering reflections (from rock or water inclusions) generally appear at different depths in each record. An example of a single measurement and then that measurement with the surrounding measurements is shown in Fig. 2. It is not possible to identify the bed reflection of the single measurement (Fig. 2, *left* panel) but it can be determined when considered in context with the surrounding measurements (Fig. 2, *right* panel).

Ice thickness measurements were made by first determining the highest frequency that allowed us to detect a bed reflection. When a bed reflection was not observed, we used a lower frequency; the lowest used was 5 MHz. Longer wavelength (lower frequency) increases the amount of energy that passes through the surface debris layer and decreases the amount of energy scattered from within the ice. However, longer wavelengths also decrease the resolution and the longer antennae associated with lower frequencies are more difficult to move in rough terrain.

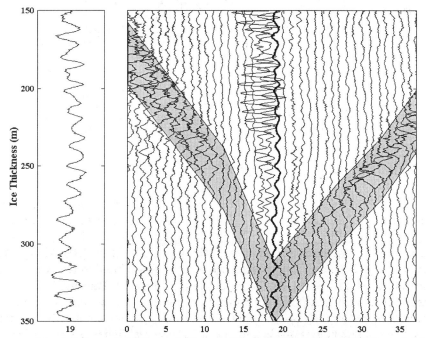

Fig. 2 *Left* panel: Example single record from Khumbu Glacier. *Right* panel: The record on the left (#19) is now drawn as a heavy black line, and is shown with the adjacent records of the profile that span the glacier. The grey band shows the region of the bed reflection.

Once the optimal frequency was determined, a profile of measurements was recorded by laying out the antennae, connecting the transmitter and receiver, making the measurement, surveying the centre point, turning off (to conserve power) and disconnecting the instruments and moving the RES system to the next location (generally 10 m between records). Having four people made moving the system over the rough surface terrain efficient (Fig. 3). Two additional people surveyed the location of each measurement—one person surveyed from a known benchmark and the other travelled with the RES system with a corner reflector; that person also assisted in moving the system. Care was necessary to ensure RES measurements were not made at the same time as hand-held radio communication between the two surveyors because the hand-held radio transmissions interfered with the RES record. In addition, we found that RES profiles along the flattest surface path (avoiding paths along ridges) and profiles that avoided large supraglacial lakes gave the best results.

When all the equipment was working properly and the surface terrain was not very difficult, we were able to complete a measurement cycle every 10–15 min, of which approximately 2 min were required for the receiver to stack and save the record. Most complete profiles done on Lirung and Khumbu Glaciers consisted of between 20 and 50 records.

Fig. 3 Radio echo-sounding the BC line on debris-covered Khumbu Glacier.

DATA AND ERROR ANALYSIS

For each profile, all records were first bandpass filtered. The records were then adjusted vertically relative to one another using the surveyed surface elevation. These data were then migrated using the maximum convexity technique outlined in Robinson & Treitel (1980). Where the amplitude of the surface topography is of the order of the ice thickness, it is necessary to adjust the records for surface elevation before migrating to accurately determine the ice thickness.

Errors in our RES measurements arise from three main sources:
– from the migration,
– from our inability to select the precise bed reflection location from the migrated records and
– from uncertainty in the radio wave velocity within the glacier.

Errors in migrating the data could result from incorrectly using the input parameters but it is quite stable for reasonable estimates. Errors in selecting the bed location from the migrated record depends on signal frequency and strength of the bed reflection and generally results in constant uncertainty for all measurements in a profile. Errors in wave velocity results in uncertainty that increases with ice thickness. For these measurements, the uncertainty in selecting the bed reflection was between 5 and 20 m. Wave propagation speed was assumed to be 167 ± 4 m μs^{-1}. Additional uncertainty that is related to the maximum potential resolution for a given transmitted wavelength is small compared to the other uncertainties in these data.

SUMMARY OF RESULTS

The profile (G2 line) shown in Fig. 4 was measured 3 km downglacier from the icefall, and is typical of the results from Khumbu Glacier. The results of profiles that could be interpreted from Khumbu and Lirung Glaciers are summarized separately.

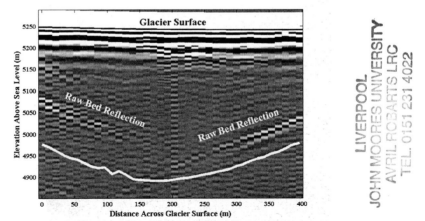

Fig. 4 Figure 2 RES profile (G2 line) from Khumbu Glacier 3 km downglacier from the icefall. The heavy white line shows the bed after migration. Accounting for the geometry of the transmitter–receiver pair results in a greater ice thickness as is seen at the centre of the subglacial trough. The glacier surface and unmigrated bed reflection is shown with text.

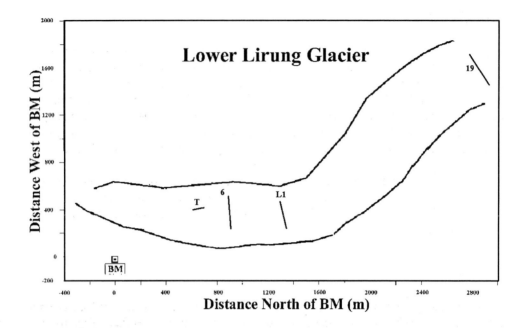

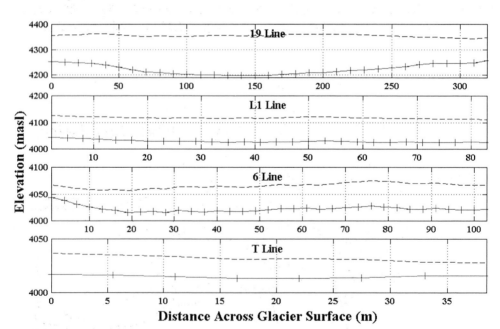

Fig. 5 *Upper* panel: Location map of Lirung Glacier, Nepal Himalaya, showing successful RES profiles using the coordinate system in Aoki & Asahi (1998). *Lower* panel: Summary of surface (dashed lines) and bed topography measurements (solid line with + at each measurement) on Lirung Glacier, May 1999. Note that the vertical and horizontal axes are different in each panel. Uncertainty in the surface elevation is less than 0.5 m and in the bed elevation it is less than 15 m. We list the start and end points (x, y, z) of each profile rounded to the nearest metre. 19 line: (2929, 1465, 4357), (2795, 1683, 4347); L1 line: (1345, 240, 4125), (1293, 462, 4111); 6 line: (912, 241, 4067), (888, 519, 4067); T line: (666, 415, 4037), (632, 409, 4028).

Lirung Glacier

Eight profiles were recorded on Lirung Glacier but only five produced interpretable bed reflections. Uninterpretable profiles resulted from either profiling near supraglacial lakes, which produced interference; profiling along supraglacial ridges, which produced multiple reflectors; or from using a frequency that was too high to detect the bed. The locations of the four longest, successful profiles are shown in Fig. 5 (*upper* panel) and the analysed results are summarized in the *lower* panel. Ice thickness varied from 157 ± 10 m about 1 km below the icefall (Fig. 5, 19 line) to 20 ± 5 m near the terminus (Fig. 5, T line).

These measurement are comparable to the estimates of Naito *et al.* (1998) who used measurements of surface velocities and laminar flow theory for ice to estimate ice thickness of 100 m or more in the upper section of the ablation region of Lirung Glacier and about 50 m on the L1 line.

Khumbu Glacier

Over a 12-day period, we measured eight transverse profiles on Khumbu Glacier with 10 m spacing between measurements and 1–2 km between profiles (Fig. 6). Ice thickness varied from 440 ± 20 m about 0.5 km below the icefall (Fig. 7, BC line) to less than 20 m about 2 km up from the terminus (Fig. 7, L3 line). Only the final profile

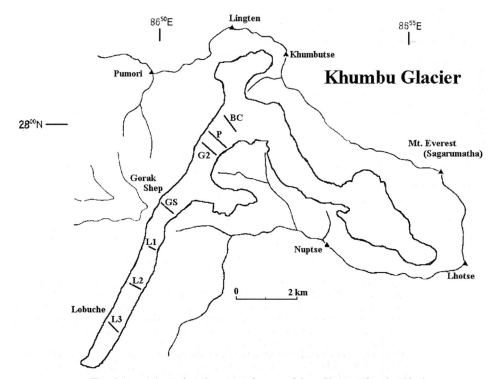

Fig. 6 Approximate location map of successful profiles on Khumbu Glacier.

near the glacier terminus did not produce interpretable results because either the ice thickness was less than 20 m or because the thick surface debris (>3 m) prevented sufficient energy transmission into the underlying ice. Previous measurements of Khumbu ice thickness include those by Moribayashi (1978) who estimated thickness based on gravity measurements. These estimates were somewhat thinner on BC line, but thicker on P line than the present measurements but the reason for this discrepancy is unknown. Kodama & Mae (1976) estimated the thickness of Khumbu from surface flow speed through laminar flow theory, similar to methods Naito et al. (1998) used for Lirung, and calculated ice thickness to be thinner than the present direct

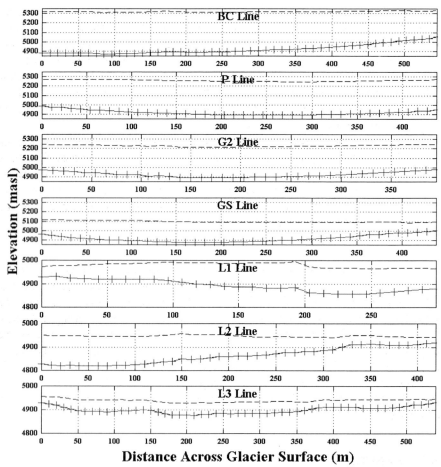

Distance Across Glacier Surface (m)

Fig. 7 Summary of surface (dashed lines) and bed topography measurements (solid line with + at each measurement) on Khumbu Glacier May–June 1999. Note that the vertical and horizontal axes are different in each panel. Uncertainty in the surface elevation is less than 0.5 m and in bed elevation is less than 20 m. We list the start and end points (x, y, z) of each profile rounded to the nearest metre using the coordinate system in Watanabe et al. (1980). BC line: (2866, 12 120, 5319), (2821, 12 624, 5332); P line: (2288, 11 300, 5270), (2037, 11 643, 5276); G2 line: (2866, 12 120, 5319), (2821, 12 624, 5332); GS line: (571, 9304, 5117), (275, 9518, 5097); L1 line: (−229, 7645, 4972), (−302, 7623, 4966); L2 line: (−815, 6607, 4951), (−453, 6492, 4943); L3 line: (−176, −1002, 4957), (−369, −583, 4946).

measurements. This is likely due to the assumption of laminar flow and if the calculations of Naito *et al.* (1998) and Kodama & Mae (1976) had accounted for lateral drag, the estimates should have been thicker. Higuchi *et al.* (1977) estimated the thickness based on the relation between surface slope, flow speed and the thickness, given in Budd & Allison (1975). These estimates appear to give ice thicknesses closest to our direct measurements, though direct comparison is not possible due to the difficulties of co-registration.

CONCLUSIONS

Successful ice thickness measurements were obtained using a combination of relatively low frequencies and by measuring a series of records that helped locate ambiguous bed reflectors. In addition, though none of the commercial instrumentation used was rated for use above 3000 m a.s.l., all of the equipment performed well at elevations up to 5400 m a.s.l. The success of these ice thickness measurements at relatively extreme conditions of high elevation and thick supraglacial debris cover demonstrates the potential of such a RES system for measuring ice thickness in a wide variety of conditions.

The direct measurements of ice thickness on Lirung and Khumbu Glaciers generally resulted in greater ice thicknesses than previous studies that have used surface velocity measurements together with laminar flow theory to estimate ice thickness. As a result, we feel that ice thickness estimates using laminar flow theory can be concluded to be underestimated for both Lirung and Khumbu due in part to neglecting the effects of lateral drag.

Acknowledgements This collaborative research was supported by the US National Science Foundation through Grant ATM 9530691 and US–Japan Cooperative Science Grant INT-9726704 as well as Japan–US Cooperative Science Program from the Japanese Society for the Promotion of Science and Japanese Government Grant-in-Aid for Scientific Research (no. 09041103) from the Ministry of Education, Science, Sports and Culture. We thank the Department of Hydrology and Meteorology of Nepal, and Ang J. P. Lama, Ang Pasang Lama, Ang Pasang Sherpa, Man Bahadur, and Pan Bahadur, who provided logistical support. We especially wish to thank L. Blank for her help in the field and M. Nakawo, and C. Raymond for their valuable contributions.

REFERENCES

Ageta, Y., Ohata, T., Tanaka, Y., Ikegami, K. & Higuchi, K. (1980) Mass balance of Glacier AX010 in Shorong Himal, east Nepal during the summer monsoon season. *J. Japan. Soc. Snow Ice (Seppyo)* **41**, 34–41.

Aoki, T. & Asahi, K. (1998) Topographical map of the ablation area of the Lirung Glacier in the Langtang Valley, Nepal Himalaya. *Bull. Glacier Res.* **16**, 19–31.

Budd, W. F. & Allison, I. F. (1975) An empirical scheme for estimating the dynamics of unmeasured glaciers. In: *Snow and Ice* (Proc. Moscow Symp., August 1971), 246–256. IAHS Publ. no. 104.

Higuchi, K., Mae, S. & Kodama, H. (1977) Thickness of the Khumbu Glacier flowing from Mt Everest, east Nepal. In: *Data of Glaciological Studies Chronicle, Discussion*, 107–112 (in Russian with figures and references) and 171–175 (in English with tables). Academy of Sciences of the USSR Publ. no. 33.

Jones, F., Narod, B. & Clarke, G. K. C. (1989) Design and operation of a portable, digital impulse radar. *J. Glaciol.* **35**(119), 143–148.

Kodama, H. & Mae, S. (1976) The flow of glaciers in the Khumbu region. *J. Japan. Soc. Snow Ice (Seppyo)* **38**, 31–36.

Moribayashi, S. (1978) Transverse profiles of Khumbu Glacier obtained by gravity observation. *J. Japan. Soc. Snow Ice (Seppyo)* **40**, 21–25.

Naito, N., Nakawo, M., Aoki, T., Asahi, K., Fujita, K., Sakai, A., Kadota, T., Shiraiwa, T. & Seko, K. (1998) Surface flow on the ablation area of the Lirung Glacier in the Langtang Valley, Nepal Himalaya. *Bull. Glacier Res.* **16**, 67–73.

Nakawo, M., Iwata, S., Watanabe, O. & Yoshida, M. (1986) Processes which distribute supraglacial debris on the Khumbu Glacier, Nepal Himalaya. *Ann. Glaciol.* **8**, 129–131.

Robinson, E. A. & Treitel, S. (1980) *Geophysical Signal Analysis.* Prentice-Hall. Englewood Cliffs, New Jersey.

Watanabe, O., Fushimi, H., Inoue, J., Iwata, S., Ikegami, K., Tanaka, Y., Yoshida, M. & Upadhyay, B. P. (1980) Outline of debris cover project in Khumbu Glacier. *J. Japan. Soc. Snow Ice (Seppyo)* **41**, special issue, 5–8.

Watts, R. D. & Wright, D. L. (1981) Systems for measuring thickness of temperate and polar ice from the ground or from the air. *J. Glaciol.* **27**(97), 459–469.

2 Mass and Energy Balance

Debris-Covered Glaciers (Proceedings of a workshop held at Seattle, Washington, USA, September 2000). IAHS Publ. no. 264, 2000.

The influence of a debris cover on the mid-summer discharge of Dome Glacier, Canadian Rocky Mountains

LEIF ERIC MATTSON

Department of Geography, Nipissing University, North Bay, Ontario P1B 8L7, Canada
e-mail: ericm@unipissing.ca

Abstract Meltwater discharge patterns of two glacierized mountain basins in the Canadian Rocky Mountains are compared over the same 25-day period in 1994 and 1995. The glaciers under study are the Dome and Athabasca; both situated in the Columbia Icefield. The two glaciers lie adjacent to one another and are similar in size, orientation, and range in elevation. They differ however, in their surficial characteristics. While the ablation zone of the Athabasca Glacier is mostly debris free, the ablation zone of the Dome Glacier displays an extensive debris cover. It is postulated that this debris cover significantly influences the diurnal discharge patterns of the Dome Glacier's meltwater stream producing different discharge patterns to those observed in the Athabasca Glacier meltwater stream. Results indicate that the debris cover on the Dome Glacier acts as a regulator of streamflow producing annual variances of volumetric discharge of only 1.0% between 1994 and 1995 as compared with 24% for the debris-free Athabasca Glacier.

INTRODUCTION

It has long been known that significant portions of the world's glaciers carry either a partial or complete debris cover that masks their ablation zones. It is hypothesized that this debris cover significantly influences the discharge characteristics of the meltwater streams emerging from these glaciers through the alteration of surficial energy fluxes. The purpose of this paper is to test this hypothesis by comparing and contrasting the meltwater discharge characteristics of a debris-free glacier and a debris-covered glacier over two contrasting field seasons.

REVIEW

During the summer of 1989, a 14% difference in meltwater discharge between the Dome and Athabasca Glaciers was measured (in favour of the Athabasca), despite their similarities in size (Mattson, 1990). It was postulated that this difference could possibly be attributed to the debris on the Dome Glacier. Mattson *et al.* (1993) illustrated that a debris cover can significantly influence the surficial ablation process where, after a threshold thickness of approximately 0.02 m, ablation rates decreased in comparison to "clean" glacier surfaces. They found that the greatest mean ablation rate occurred beneath a debris cover of about 0.01 m. Those areas with less than 0.01 m of debris exhibited relatively lower ablation rates. Similar results had been obtained for other debris-covered glaciers through out the world, (e.g. Østrem, 1959; Loomis, 1970; Nakawo & Takahashi, 1982; Khan, 1989). This hyperbolic relationship occurs because a thin layer of debris, rather than insulating the underlying ice, decreases albedo, thereby increasing absorbed shortwave radiation which in a thin debris cover is transmitted to the ice interface contributing to rapid ablation (Mattson & Gardner, 1989).

The thermal properties of thick debris covers (>0.03 m) are of critical importance in determining the rate of heat transfer to the debris/ice interface. Mattson & Gardner (1989) found a three-fold increase in the percentage of absorbed surface energy reaching the debris/ice interface of the Rakhiot Glacier when the debris cover was moistened by rainfall. This occurs because of an increase in thermal conductivity. With the continuous fluctuation of the temperature gradient within the debris profile resulting from the variability of the net rate of heat exchange at the surface, the phase and condition of water located within the profile will alter. As a result, the debris cover will not display a continuous conductivity but rather, a series of conductivity's depending on the moisture conditions (Mattson, 1986).

STUDY SITES

The two basins chosen for this study are the Athabasca (52°11′N, 117°15′W) and the Dome (52°12′N 117°17′W), both of which are located in the Columbia Icefield (Fig. 1). These adjacent basins contain the streams that form the headwaters of the Sunwapta River which, in turn, flows via the Athabasca, Slave, and Mackenzie Rivers to the Arctic Ocean. The factors considered in the selection of the basins relate to the degree of similarity between them as well as the relatively easy access to the sites.

The Athabasca basin displays a general northeast orientation. It covers an area of roughly 28 km^2. Of this area about 65% or 18 km^2 is covered by glacial ice. There are four glaciers situated within this basin, three of which are relatively small cirque glaciers: the Sunwapta, the AA, and the Andromeda. In total these three glaciers cover an area of 3.7 km^2. The Athabasca Glacier accounts for the remaining 14.3 km^2 of ice cover.

The drainage divide for the Athabasca basin is defined by a series of peaks and connecting ridges that encompass it. Along the southeast perimeter Mount Athabasca (3491 m) and Mount Andromeda (3445 m) form the divide. The southern perimeter of the basin is difficult to define because it is located in the greater Icefield. Mount Snow Dome (3456 m) and Little Dome (2750 m) define the northwest perimeter. The mouth of the basin is located along its northeast end. The Sunwapta River emerges from the toe of the glacier and it is from this stream that discharge measurements were derived.

The Dome basin also displays a general northeast orientation. In total, the basin covers an area of about 15 km^2 and of this about 68% or 10 km^2 is ice. There is a single cirque glacier associated with the Dome basin; it is situated on the divide between the two basins. This small glacier, known as the Saddle Dome, covers an area of 0.25 km^2 and is thought to contribute an insignificant amount of meltwater to the basin due to its small size and high elevation. The Dome Glacier accounts for the remaining 9.75 km^2 of ice cover.

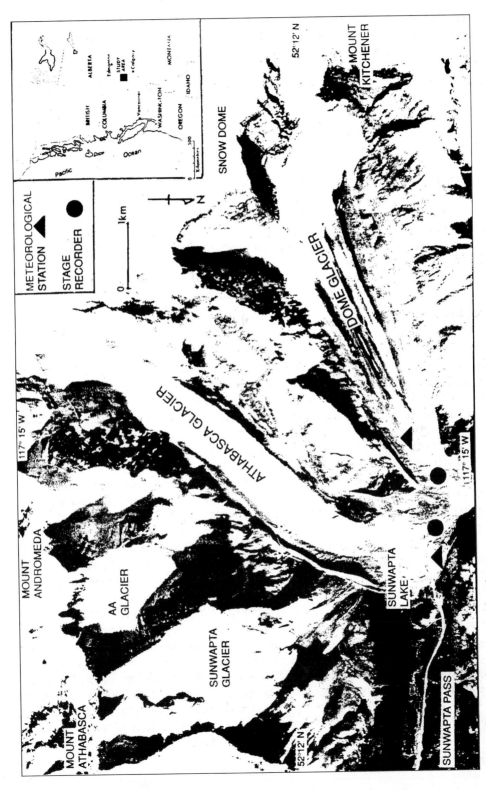

Fig. 1 Study site and measurement locations.

The drainage divide for the Dome basin is also defined by a series of peaks and the ridges. Little Dome marks the southeast perimeter, Mount Snow Dome marks the southern perimeter, and Mount Kitchener (3490 m) marks the northwestern perimeter. The mouth of the basin is located at the northeast end. There is a single meltwater channel, the Dome River, which flows out of the basin and into the Sunwapta River, 1.5 km below the terminus of the Dome Glacier.

The Dome and Athabasca basins are composed predominantly of sedimentary rock from the Palaeozoic era. These rocks have been disturbed and contorted by folding and faulting in response to tectonic activity. The lithologies present are mainly fine-grained mudstone, limestone and dolomite. Green conglomerate, quartzite and shale are also present. It is unknown if either basin is watertight with respect to the subsurface exiting of groundwater.

A list of the morphometric, morphologic and dynamic characteristics of the Dome and Athabasca Glaciers is presented in Table 1. It indicates that the two glaciers are very similar with regards to all physical attributes. The extensive debris cover is the most evident characteristic that differentiates the Dome from the Athabasca Glacier. Debris thickness were interpolated for the surface from a series of spot depth measurements, including manually dug pits where thickness could not be visually estimated. The debris cover extends completely over the glacier surface from the terminus to a distance of 625 m upglacier. From this point on, to a distance of 3.5 km from the terminus, the debris cover dominates the surface of the glacier with only a thin strip of "clean" ice extending up the centre. There is a general tendency for the debris-cover thickness to decrease from the lateral margins to the centre axis of the glacier. The debris is up to 0.5 m thick along the margins of the glacier. Summer field observations since 1984 indicate that debris sources include: snow and ice avalanches off the north face of Mount Snow Dome (as many as 21 per day), high-frequency low-magnitude rockfalls from adjacent slopes (as many as 100 per day), and the emergence of englacial debris derived from subglacial erosion.

Table 1 Morphologic, morphometric, and dynamic characteristics of the Dome and Athabasca Glaciers.

Physical attributes	Dome	Athabasca
Glacier length (m)	8.5	5.4
Maximum elevation (m a.s.l.)	3460	3460
Terminus elevation (m a.s.l.)	2000	2000
Altitudinal range (m)	1460	1460
Average gradient	1:6	1:4
Firn line elevation (m a.s.l.)	2500	2500
Area of accumulation zone (km^2)	8.3	4.9
Area of ablation zone (km^2)	6.0	5.5
Ice thickness at base of icefall (m)*	300	-
Velocity at base of icefall (m year^{-1})†	75	35
Year of maximum Holocene extent‡	1843	1846
Rate of retreat (1721–1953) (m year^{-1})§	4.7	4.7
Rate of retreat (1738–1960) (m year^{-1})	28	19

* Cited in Kite & Reid (1977).
† Cited in Paterson & Savage (1963).
‡ Cited in Luckman (1988).
§ Cited in Deaton (1975).

DATA COLLECTION

Meltwater discharge was monitored for both years from 11 July to 9 August for the Dome Glacier basin. Discharge data derived from this basin include both instantaneous stream discharge, calculated on the basis of measurements of water velocity (using an Ott model 10-152 current meter) and cross-sectional area and continuous stage records which have been translated to hourly readings of discharge through a rating curve. The rationale for employing this technique, though not recommended for streams displaying unstable hydraulic conditions, was to maintain consistency with the data set collected by the Federal Government for the Sunwapta River. Discharge measurements were taken over a 12-h period (06:00–18:00 h) at 15-min intervals resulting in 48 readings. Regression analysis between stage and discharge revealed an r^2 value of 0.98 and 0.97 for 1994 and 1995, respectively. Discharge data for the Sunwapta River (Athabasca basin) were obtained from Inland Waters of Environment Canada and are stated to contain less than 5.0% error. Figure 1 indicates the location of the Sunwapta and Dome River stage recorders.

Meteorological measurements were collected from a standard meteorological station situated near the confluence of the two basins at an elevation of 1950 m (Fig. 1). Specific variables measured included relative humidity, air and surface temperature, precipitation as well as incident solar and net radiation. Readings were recorded at 5-min intervals through the employment of a Squirrel data logger. These values were then averaged over hourly periods resulting in a record of over 5000 readings per field season. Additional meteorological information was obtained from the Columbia Icefield Information Centre operated by Parks Canada.

OBSERVATIONS

Because of the high contrast in meteorological conditions, the 1994 and 1995 field seasons turned out to be ideal for this study. The 1994 field season was predominantly warm, with clear skies and air temperatures averaging 12.1°C. The maximum and minimum temperatures recorded were 22.5°C and 2.5°C, respectively. Cloud cover, measured three times a day, ranged from 0 to 10 tenths but averaged 3 and rain only occurred on 7 days resulting in a total of 30.5 mm.

Conversely, the 1995 field season was characterized by cool, wet conditions. The mean air temperature averaged 9.5°C, a difference of 2.6°C from the previous year. The maximum and minimum temperatures recorded were 18.8°C and 1.3°C, respectively. Cloud cover ranged from 0 to 10 tenths but averaged 9 and rain occurred on all but 2 days resulting in a total of 60.9 mm.

The 1994 and 1995 hydrographs of the Sunwapta and Dome Rivers (Figs 2 and 3, respectively) were characterized by a series of oscillating waves typical of most proglacial streams described in the literature. This basic pattern consists of a diurnal cycle of rising and falling limbs superimposed over a more consistent baseflow. The baseflow is derived primarily from a combination of groundwater and subglacial melt however the percent contribution of each is unknown to the author. The superimposed daily pattern is primarily controlled by the individual components of the diurnal energy

Athabasca Glacier, 1994 / 95 Discharge

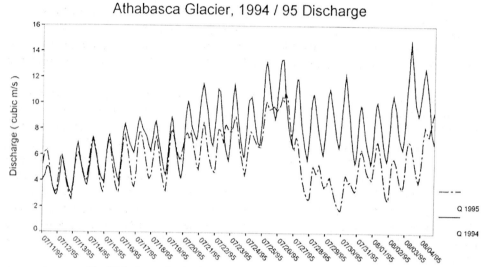

Fig. 2 Discharge for the Sunwapta River from 11 July to 5 August 1994 and 1995.

Dome Glacier, 1994 / 95 Discharge

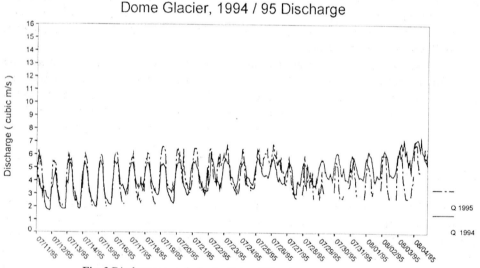

Fig. 3 Discharge records for the Dome River from 11 July to 5 August 1994 and 1995.

exchange that exists between the atmospheric boundary layer and the surface of the glacier. The energy exchange includes the turbulent fluxes of latent and sensible heat, net radiation, conductive heat flux and precipitation heat transfer. This energy exchange controls the amount of surficial ablation which, in turn, determines the amount of meltwater production from the surface of the glacier.

It is evident that the quantities of water released by both basins are of the same order of magnitude. However, a significant difference does exist. The mean discharge for the Sunwapta River during the 1994 field season was 7.79 m^3 s^{-1} resulting in an average runoff of 0.28 m^3 s^{-1} km^{-2} for the Athabasca basin. The total volume of meltwater produced over the sampling period was 16.74×10^6 m^3. The mean seasonal discharge for the Dome River for the same period was only 4.40 m^3 s^{-1} resulting in an average runoff of 0.29 m^3 s^{-1} km^{-2} for the Dome basin. The total volume of meltwater produced over the sampling period was 9.45×10^6 m^3; 7.28×10^6 m^3 less than that of the Athabasca basin.

The 1995 discharge pattern of the Dome River was similar to that experienced for the same sampling period in 1994 with the exception of an obvious increase in the amount of "noise" experienced. An examination of the meteorological record reveals that these minor spikes in the discharge record correspond with rainfall events. A lag of approximately 1 h exists between the initiation of rainfall and an abrupt increase in discharge indicating the time in which it takes for water to travel through the glacial system. The reason for the absence of the same phenomenon on the discharge record for the Athabasca basin is due to the fact that Sunwapta Lake, a small proglacial lake (Fig. 1) lies between the glacier and the stage recorder. The lake acts as a buffer to these events which results in a much smoother hydrograph. Discharges greater than the 1994 maximum were also due to rainfall events.

The mean discharge of the Dome basin in 1995 was approximately 4.41 m^3 s^{-1} resulting in an average runoff of 0.29 m^3 s^{-1} km^{-2}. The total volume of water produced from the basin was 9.48×10^6 m^3. The 1995 mean seasonal discharge for the Sunwapta River was 5.84 m^3 s^{-1} resulting in an average runoff of 0.21 m^3 s^{-1} km^{-2}. The total volume of water produced from the basin was 12.55×10^6 m^3; 3.08×10^6 m^3 more than for the Dome over the same period.

In comparing the basins on an individual basis over the two years one can see that large differences exist. Volumetric discharge derived from the Dome Glacier between the 1994 and 1995 field seasons varied by 0.002×10^6 m^3 which translates to a difference of less than 1.0%. On the other hand, the volumetric discharge derived from the Athabasca Glacier for the same period differed by 4.18×10^6 m^3 or 24%.

DISCUSSION

Lower volumes of meltwater derived from the Dome basin, when compared to the Athabasca basin, can be easily explained by the fact that it is smaller in size and contains less ice cover. More specifically, the Dome basin is smaller by 13 km^2 and contains 8 km^2 less ice cover. When the areas of each basin are taken into consideration, and specific discharge or runoff is calculated for each, the two almost equate. This is not surprising considering the fact that the basins lie adjacent to each other and experience the same meteorological conditions.

What is of greater interest is the large variation in discharge for the Athabasca basin between the two field seasons compared to that for the Dome basin which varied little. One possible explanation for this could be due to the absence or presence of a debris cover. In the case of the Athabasca Glacier, which displays primarily a debris-free surface, all of the energy being absorbed through the latent, sensible, and radiative heat fluxes is used directly to melt the exposed ice. No energy is lost through the conductive heat flux into the glacier due to the fact that the ice is at its pressure melting point. During the 1994 field season, which was characterized by warm, clear sky conditions, ample energy was available to promote ablation which, in turn, led to the production of large quantities of meltwater. However, during the 1995 field season, which was characterized by cool, overcast conditions, less energy was available to promote ablation leading to significantly less runoff.

In the case of a relatively thick debris cover, such as that found on the Dome Glacier, the situation is quite different. During the 1994 field season the debris cover became very dry and much of the energy being absorbed at the debris surface could not reach the underlying ice. A large portion of the energy was expended in increasing the surface and subsurface temperature of the debris cover. This energy was then lost back to the atmospheric boundary layer through the emission of longwave radiation and sensible heat. Only a fraction of the absorbed energy could be transferred to the debris/ice interface because of the low conductivity associated with the dry debris. The wet conditions associated with the 1995 field season exerted a tremendous influence on the physical properties of the debris cover by increasing its thermal conductivity. Although less energy was being absorbed at the atmosphere/debris interface a greater proportion of it was being transferred to the underlying ice to promote ablation. The two-fold increase in precipitation would also add to the volume of water leaving the Dome and Athabasca basins over the 1995 field season but would not account for the differences in variation between the two.

CONCLUSIONS

This study indicates, by way of presenting volumetric discharge data, that a debris cover may play a significant role in glacier hydrology. Results suggest that the debris cover on the Dome Glacier acts as a regulator of streamflow producing annual variances of volumetric discharge of only 1.0% between 1994 and 1995 as compared with 24% for the debris-free Athabasca Glacier. This most likely occurs because of the changes of moisture content within the debris cover between field seasons. When atmospheric conditions are warm and dry, and ample energy is available for melt, the debris cover retards the transfer of energy to the ice because of its low thermal conductivity. When atmospheric conditions are cool and wet, and little energy is available for melt, the debris cover promotes the transfer of energy to the ice because of its increased thermal conductivity. This implies that a debris-covered glacier may not be as sensitive to changes in climate as would be a debris-free glacier, however, further research is required in order to substantiate this claim.

REFERENCES

Deaton, G. H. (1975) Glaciers of the Canadian Rocky Mountains. In: *Mountain Glaciers of the Northern Hemisphere* (ed. by W. O. Field). CRREL, Bangor, Maine, USA.

Khan, M. (1989) Ablation on Barpu Glacier, Karakoram Himalaya, Pakistan: a study of melt processes on a faceted, debris-covered ice surface. Unpublished Master's Thesis, Wilfrid Laurier University, Waterloo, Canada.

Kite, G. W. & Reid, L. A. (1977) Volumetric change of the Athabasca Glacier over the last 100 years. In: *J. Hydrol.* **32**, 279–294.

Loomis, S. R. (1970) Morphology and Structure of an Ice-cored Medial Moraine, Kaskawulsh Glacier, Yukon. In: *Studies of Morphology and Stream Action on Ablating Ice* (ed. by S. R. Loomis, J. Dozier & K. J. Ewing), 1–56. Res. Paper no. 57, Arctic Inst. North America, Calgary, Ontario, Canada.

Luckman, B. H. (1988) Dating the moraines and recession of Athabasca and Dome Glacier, Alberta, Canada. *Arctic Alpine Res.* **20**(1), 40–54.

Mattson, L. E. (1986) The formation and degradation of recently developed ice-cored lateral moraines, Boundary Glacier, Canadian Rocky Mountains. Unpublished Master's Thesis, University of Waterloo, Canada.

Mattson, L. E. (1990) The role of debris covers on glacial meltwater discharge, Canadian Rocky Mountains. In: *47th Eastern Snow Conference Annual Proceedings* (ed. by M. Ferrick) (Bangor, Maine), 237–242. CRREL Special Report 90-44, Bangor, Maine, USA.

Mattson, L. E. & Gardner, J. S. (1989) Energy exchanges and ablation rates on the debris covered Rakhiot Glacier, Pakistan. *Z. Gletscherk. und Glazialgeol.* **25**(1), 17–32.

Mattson, L. E., Gardner, J. S. & Young, G. J. (1993) Ablation on debris covered glaciers: an example from the Rakhiot Glacier, Punjab, Himalaya. In: *Snow and Glacier Hydrology* (ed. by G. J. Young) (Proc. Kathmandu Symp., November 1992), 289–296. IAHS Publ. no. 218.

Nakawo, M. & Takahashi, S. (1982) A simplified model for estimating glacier ablation under a debris layer. In: *Hydrological Aspects of Alpine and High-Mountain Areas* (ed. by J. W. Glen) (Proc. Exeter Symp., July 1982), 137–145. IAHS Publ. no. 138.

Østrem, G. (1959) Ice melting under a thin layer of moraine, and the existence of ice cores in moraine ridges. *Geogr. Ann.* **41**, 228–230.

Paterson, N. S. B. & Savage, J. C. (1963) Geometry and movement of the Athabasca Glacier. *J. Geophys. Res.* **68**, 4513–4520.

Debris-Covered Glaciers (Proceedings of a workshop held at Seattle, Washington, USA, September 2000).
IAHS Publ. no. 264, 2000.

Mass balance of adjacent debris-covered and clean glacier ice in the North Cascades, Washington

MAURI S. PELTO

Nichols College, Dudley, Massachusetts 01571, USA
e-mail: peltoms@nichols.edu

Abstract As part of the ongoing annual mass balance measurements on Lyman Glacier and Columbia Glacier, North Cascades, Washington, measurements were completed from 1986–1998 on adjacent clean and debris-covered sections of each glacier. On Columbia Glacier annual ice ablation is 3.3 m water equivalent for clean glacier ice and 2.3 m water equivalent for debris-covered areas. On Lyman Glacier from 1986 to 1999, average annual ablation on the clean glacier ice is 3.4 m and under the debris cover average annual ablation is 2.6 m water equivalent. On both glaciers annual ablation is significantly reduced (25–30%) under the debris cover. Late-summer ablation, after both the clean glacier ice and debris-covered ice have lost all snow cover, is reduced 30–40% under the debris cover. The debris cover on Columbia Glacier has reduced ablation more substantially. The debris cover on Columbia Glacier is a complete cover (100%) and is a relatively fine-grained clay–sand mixture. The Lyman Glacier debris cover is not a complete cover (85%), and is comprised of sand–boulder size particles. In the North Cascades temperate-maritime climate finer grain size debris cover provides a better insulation from ablation conditions.

INTRODUCTION

From 1984 to 1999 the North Cascade Glacier Climate Project has measured the annual mass balance of nine North Cascade glaciers (Pelto, 1996). None of these glaciers is primarily debris covered; however, the Lyman Glacier and Columbia Glacier both have small, but significant debris-covered areas near their termini. To accurately determine mass balance ablation stakes were placed in both the debris covered and adjacent clean ice areas of the glacier. Previous researchers have noted the ablation rate of adjacent clean and debris-covered areas of a glacier (Nakawo & Young, 1981; Sturm *et al.*, 1986; Rogerson *et al.*, 1986); however, this study provides a long-term record of comparison of the influence of two different types of debris cover on ablation.

COLUMBIA GLACIER

Both glaciers have retreated continuously during the twentieth century (Pelto, 1993). Columbia Glacier retreated 70 m from 1975 to 1998. On both glaciers the thinning rate has been prominent in the terminus region since 1984. the debris-covered areas has developed notable increased vertical relief from the general glacier surface, since measurements began in 1984 on Columbia Glacier.

Table 1 provides the basic geographical characteristics of each glacier. Columbia Glacier is a south facing cirque glacier with a comparatively low slope for a North Cascade Glacier. The glacier has the lowest mean elevation (1600 m) of any glacier over 0.5 km^2 in the North Cascades. This low mean elevation despite its southern exposure is due to the tremendous avalanching off of the 800 m high cirque walls on the east and west sides of the glacier and the radiational shading the cirque walls provide. The avalanches yield a surprisingly limited amount of debris for the glacier surface. Seldom is more than 10% of the surface of the glacier in the ablation zone adjacent to two of the large avalanche fans, covered by debris. Debris on the surface snowpack each year is limited to typically only a few rocks in each avalanche fan.

Table 1 Geographic characteristics of Columbia Glacier and Lyman Glacier.

Glacier	Orientation	Length	Area	Slope	Terminus elevation	Top elevation	Mean elevation
Columbia	South	1400 m	0.9 km^2	0.18	1460 m	1720 m	1600 m
Lyman	North	800 m	0.5 km^2	0.25	1800 m	2100 m	1920 m

Description of debris cover

The debris cover of interest on Columbia Glacier is in the terminus region and contrasts sharply with the large angular fragments of the avalanche debris. The debris cover is a fine-grained clay–sand mixture and covers the underlying glacier ice completely. The

Fig. 1 Terminus area of Columbia Glacier in 1986. The debris cover is on the right-hand side of the image, just protruding from the snowpack.

Fig. 2 Terminus area of Columbia Glacier from the same vantage point in 1998. The debris cover is now the prominent knob in the centre of the image.

extent of the debris cover is 250 m^2. The average thickness of the debris cover has been measured in 1985, 1990 and 1998. In 1985 and 1990 the mean thickness was 0.20–0.25 m. By 1998 the mean thickness had increased slightly to 0.22–0.27 m. More than 80% of the debris cover has a grain-size diameter between 1 and 6 phi.

In 1985 and 1996 deposition of some of this debris was observed from englacial and/or subglacial streams that emerged at the glacier surface near the terminus. The stream at that time yielded a sand–clay slurry that quickly covered the glacier surface to a depth of 5–15 cm over an area of 50 m^2. The origin of the larger existing debris-covered area is postulated to be from similar supraglacial discharges, since the grain-size composition is the same. When first observed in 1984 the debris-covered areas of the glacier had a 1–2 m of vertical relief from the adjacent clean glacier ice (Fig. 1). Glacier ice was observed with active crevassing on both sides of the debris cover. Since 1984, the debris cover has become largely detached from the glacier with rapid terminus and marginal retreat. The debris-covered ice in 1998 is separating from the main glacier due to downwasting and retreat and has a relief of 10–12 m from the adjacent clean glacier ice (Fig. 2). The debris-covered area at first glance today looks like a well-developed ice cored terminal moraine; however, it was observed to have developed on the glacier itself not at the margin of the glacier.

LYMAN GLACIER

Lyman Glacier has retreated continuously during this century. From 1950 to 1998 Lyman Glacier retreated 512 m. In the 1930s, a large rockfall fell from Chiwawa Peak

Fig. 3 Lyman Glacier in 1986, the debris cover is just reaching the terminus on the right.

onto the upper portion of Lyman Glacier. This rockfall is evident in photographs of the glacier in 1940 by J. B. Richardson and in 1944 by W. A. Long both of the US Forest Service. The rockfall progression down glacier is visible in photographs of the glacier from 1958–1999 taken by the US Geological Survey. In 1986 the debris-covered area of the glacier began to reach the glacier front (Fig. 3). In 1999 the debris-covered area still dominates the southern half of the terminus, and has noticeably reduced the retreat rate on this side of the glacier (Fig. 4). The rockfall travelled a distance of 430 m between the 1930s and 1986, an average velocity of 6–7 m year^{-1}. In 1986 the rockfall debris covered an area of 1200 m^2. By 1999, the debris-covered area had been reduced, by calving into a lake at the terminus, to 700 m^2.

The Lyman Glacier debris-covered area developed no distinctive profile from the general glacier surface through 1967, during this interval the rockfall was in the accumulation zone. From 1967 to 1986 the debris-covered area moved into the ablation zone and developed 8–12 m of surface prominence from the clean glacier ice. The debris cover averages 0.15–0.25 m in thickness, but varies widely. The debris consists mainly of coarse gravel and small iron-stained gneissic boulders. The debris cover is 85% complete with clean glacier ice exposed in particular around the larger boulders.

ABLATION MEASUREMENT

On each glacier several ablation stakes have been emplaced in adjacent clean glacier ice and debris-covered glacier ice for 15 years (1984–1998) on Columbia Glacier and

Fig. 4 Lyman Glacier in 1994, the debris cover is now at the calving front of the terminus (photograph from Austin Post).

13 years (1986–1998) on Lyman Glacier. Ablation is measured on each glacier in early summer, mid-summer and again at the end of the ablation season. Ablation stakes are typically redrilled during each field visits. Table 2 documents the observed annual ablation at stakes in adjacent clean glacier ice and debris-covered glacier ice. On Columbia Glacier there are two stakes in the clean glacier ice and two in the debris-covered area forming a 15-m-wide square. On Lyman Glacier there are two stakes in the clean glacier ice and two stakes in the debris-covered ice again forming a 15-m-wide square.

Surface relief of the debris-covered area on Columbia Glacier has increased from 1–2 m in 1984 to 10–12 m by 1998. This indicates that during the intervening 14 years cumulative ablation totalled approximately 10 m more for the clean glacier ice area.

From 1967 to 1986 the debris-covered area of Lyman Glacier developed 8–12 m of surface prominence from the clean glacier ice, indicating less than 0.5 m+ of reduced ablation annually under the debris cover.

Average winter accumulation is considerably less on the debris-covered area because of their vertical prominence. On Columbia Glacier the debris-covered area is typically exposed by early July, and clean glacier ice not until middle to late July. On Lyman Glacier, the debris-covered area is exposed by mid-July, and the clean glacier ice by late July.

Ablation measurements from the initial visit in late July to the end of the summer indicate that the debris cover reduces ablation by 30–40% on both glaciers (Table 3). The annual ablation reduction is less significant because of the longer period of exposure at the surface.

Table 2 Observed annual ablation in m water equivalent, on Columbia Glacier and Lyman Glacier, for adjacent clean glacier ice and debris-covered glacier ice.

Year	Columbia Glacier: Clean	Debris	Lyman Glacier: Clean	Debris
1984	−2.8 m	−1.9 m		
1985	−3.7	−2.7		
1986	−3.2	−2.2	−3.2 m	−2.5 m
1987	−3.9	−2.8	−3.7	−2.9
1988	−3.2	−2.1	−3.2	−2.6
1989	−3.0	−2.0	−3.2	−2.5
1990	−3.5	−2.4	−3.4	−2.8
1991	−1.7	−1.4	−2.1	−1.7
1992	−4.0	−3.0	−4.2	−3.1
1993	−3.5	−2.6	−3.8	−2.9
1994	−3.6	−2.6	−3.6	−2.5
1995	−3.2	−2.2	−3.4	−2.5
1996	−3.4	−2.1	−3.2	−2.3
1997	−2.6	−1.9	−2.6	−2.0
1998	−4.1	−3.0	−4.2	−3.2
Mean	−3.3	−2.3	−3.4	−2.6

Table 3 Late July–late September ablation on Columbia and Lyman Glacier (in m water equivalent), under a debris cover and for adjacent clean glacier ice.

Year	Clean	Debris	Clean	Debris
1986	−2.9	−1.6	−3.0	−2.2
1988	−3.1	−1.7	−3.1	−1.7
1990	−2.8	−1.9	−2.6	−2.4
1992	−3.0	−1.9	−3.3	−2.0
1994	−2.8	−1.6	−2.8	−1.8
1998	−3.2	−2.1	−3.0	−2.3
Mean	−3.0	−1.8	−3.0	−2.1

The observed reduction in ablation is less than that observed by Rogerson et al. (1986) in the Torngat Mountains, Labrador, Canada, where ablation under the debris cover was reduced 65% compared to clean-ice ablation. The thickness of the debris cover on these two North Cascade glaciers is also moderate. On the Piedmont terminus section of the Drift Glacier, Alaska, an observed 1 m+ fine-grained debris cover eliminated ablation in an area that had previously experienced 5 m year^{-1} of ablation (Sturm et al., 1986).

IMPACT ON TERMINUS BEHAVIOUR

The impact on terminus behaviour is limited by the small areal extent of the debris cover on Lyman and Columbia Glaciers. In both cases the debris cover is limited to one side of the terminus. In neither case has that side of the glacier had a substantially different rate of retreat, despite the reduced rate of thinning. There are other glaciers in

Fig. 5 The terminus debris cover on Mazama Glacier, Mt Baker, covering stagnant ice remaining from the more advanced Little Ice Age period.

the region where extensive debris cover has noticeably influenced terminus behaviour. Mazama Glacier (Fig. 5) has a complete debris cover at the terminus. This has prevented complete melting of the stagnant ice beyond the active terminus, remaining from the more advanced position of the Little Ice Age. All of the other glaciers on Mt Baker have lost this stagnant ice zone that was observed on each glacier by Austin Post in the 1940s. Total retreat from the Little Ice Age maximum is less on Mazama Glacier than on any other Mt Baker glacier.

Carbon Glacier on Mt Rainier, Washington, retreated 900 m in the nineteenth century compared to more than 1600 m for all other Mt Rainier glaciers (Driedger, 1986). Carbon Glacier was also the last glacier on Mt Rainier to begin to recede after the 1950–1980 period of glacier advance (Driedger, 1986). The comparatively slow and smaller retreat, is in part due to the extensive debris cover on the terminus of the Carbon Glacier. The headwall of the Carbon Glacier experienced a major rockfall in 1916, which is the source of much of the surface rock cover on the glacier (Driedger, 1986).

CONCLUSIONS

In the North Cascades it is evident that a complete debris cover in excess of 0.20 m in thickness reduces mid-late summer ablation rates by 30–40%, however, such regions have a longer ablation season and overall annual ablation is reduced 25–30%. Based on our observations the finer-grained debris cover on Columbia Glacier has a greater insulating capacity for the underlying ice. On both glaciers the debris cover is small enough so that it cannot play a substantial role in altering glacier behaviour.

Long-term measurement of ablation on adjacent clean and debris-covered glacier ice in the North Cascades indicates a reduction in observed annual ablation of 0.8–1.0 m of water equivalent per year. The mass balance impact of debris cover is substantial and quantifies the potential impact on glaciers in the area that have a more substantial debris cover. This is the case on the Mazama Glacier, Mt Baker, and Carbon Glacier, Mt Rainier.

REFERENCES

Driedger, C. L. (1986) *A Visitor's Guide to Mount Rainier Glaciers*. Pacific Northwest Parks and Forests Association, Longmire, Washington, USA.

Nakawo, M. & Young, G. J. (1981) Field experiments to determine the effect of a debris layer on ablation of glacier ice. *Ann. Glaciol.* **2**, 85–91.

Pelto, M. S. (1993) Current behavior of glaciers in the North Cascades and effect on regional water supplies. *Washington Geol.* **21**(2), 3–10.

Pelto, M. S. (1996) Annual net balance of North Cascade glaciers, 1984–1994. *J. Glaciol.* **42**, 3–9.

Rogerson, R. J., Olson, M. E. & Branson, D. (1986) Medial moraine and surface melt on glaciers of the Torngat Mountains, Northern Labrador. *J. Glaciol.* **32**, 350–354.

Sturm, M., Benson, C. & MacKeith, P. (1986) Effects of the 1966–68 eruptions of Mount Redoubt on the flow of Drift Glacier, Alaska, USA. *J. Glaciol.* **32**, 355–362.

Debris-Covered Glaciers (Proceedings of a workshop held at Seattle, Washington, USA, September 2000).
IAHS Publ. no. 264, 2000.

Dust influence on the melting process of glacier ice: experimental results from Lirung Glacier, Nepal Himalayas

SUNIL ADHIKARY

Department of Earth Science, Nagoya University, Furo-cho, Chikusa-ku, Nagoya 464-02, Japan
e-mail: sunil@eps.nagoya-u.ac.jp

MASAYOSHI NAKAWO, KATSUMOTO SEKO*

Institute for Hydrospheric–Atmospheric Sciences, Nagoya University, Furo-cho, Chikusa-ku, Nagoya 464-01, Japan

BINOD SHAKYA

Central Department of Meteorology, Tribhuvan University, Kathmandu, Nepal

Abstract Ablation of natural ice under a dust cover was investigated at Lirung Glacier, Nepal Himalayas. Total ablation of a relatively flat ice surface was increased to a maximum of about 4 to 5 fold when the initial dust concentration increased from 0 to 0.112 kg m^{-2}. Ablation decreased from the maximum rate when the dust concentration exceeded 0.112 kg m^{-2}. The most effective dust concentration (0.112 kg m^{-2}) for ice ablation did not depend on weather conditions, and was larger by a factor of 1.4 compared to that for snow (0.08 kg m^{-2}) found in previous research. With the initial application of dust concentration in the range 0–0.112 kg m^{-2}, the ice surface albedo was reduced to values of 0.15–0.22 that were substantially lower than the albedo of the bare ice (average 0.39). Dust particles on melting ice were usually washed away depending on the surface slope and the amount of meltwater. Migration of locally-applied dust particles on the melting surface caused an evolution of the spatial pattern of albedo that spreads the albedo reduction to adjacent cleaner ice surfaces. During our observations the influence of dust on ice melting was relatively large on a cliff compared to a flat surface.

INTRODUCTION

The presence of surface debris consisting of dust, silts, sands, gravel, cobbles and boulders is a common feature of Himalayan glaciers. Moribayashi & Higuchi (1977) classified Himalayan glaciers into two categories: (a) clean type (C type) without rock debris and (b) debris-covered type (D type) covered with rock debris. However, contrary to their name, C type glaciers are not truly clean but are actually covered with fine dust (Kohshima *et al.*, 1993). The dust concentration at the surface is particularly visible during the summer season when significant melting of the glaciers takes place. Although the Lirung Glacier is a typical example of the D type glacier with heavy debris cover, there are still many ice cliffs that are usually covered with a thin layer of scattered particles (hereafter referred to as TS dust). Ablation at such cliffs in D type glaciers plays a very important role in the total ablation (Inoue & Yoshida, 1980). Examples of TS dust on cliffs are shown in Fig. 1 for two different slopes and orientations. For

* *Present address not known.*

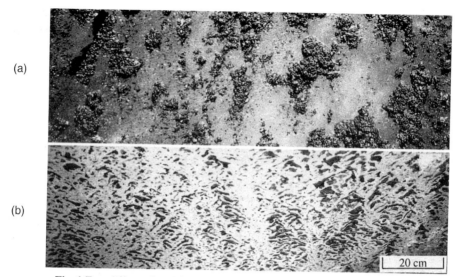

Fig. 1 Two different ice cliffs at Lirung Glacier (30 May 1996). (a) Mean slope: 45°; orientation: southeast. (b) Mean slope: 60°; orientation: Northwest.

Lirung Glacier the average melting rate is 10 times larger at ice cliffs than on the less steep debris-covered area (Private communication; A. Sakai, December 1999). This result indicates that TS dust is important for ablation even on D type glaciers.

The melting of the Himalayan glaciers is dominated by the radiation balance at the surface. In particular, the surface albedo affects the absorption of solar radiation (Ohata & Higuchi, 1980). For a TS dust covered surface, the effect on albedo is more important than insulation by the debris. According to Warren & Wiscombe (1980), ice is very weakly absorptive in the visible region of solar radiation, and even a trace amount of dust can strongly reduce the albedo of an ice surface.

Unlike a heavy debris cover (e.g. cobble or boulder size), TS dust of relatively fine particles (e.g. dust or silt) has a tendency to redistribute on melting snow or ice surfaces causing the effect on albedo to be dynamic and complicated (Adhikary *et al.*, 1997). Consequently in order to understand the full effect of dust, it is essential to monitor the albedo in space and time. Adhikary *et al.* (1997) showed that the albedo of melting snow surfaces with distributed dust, increases with time due to gradual aggregation of dust particles. However, the behaviour of dust on a melting ice surface could be different from that of the snow. Observations have consistently shown that the ablation rate of the underlying snow or ice can be accelerated if the debris thickness is relatively thin (order of a few centimetres) (e.g. Østrem, 1959; Fujii, 1977; Nakawo & Young, 1981). However, studies on TS dust-covered surfaces have received considerably less attention than heavily debris-covered surfaces, particularly because of uncertainties about redistribution of the particles. Experimental data on TS dust layers are crucial for realistic modelling studies, for which it is important to consider albedo as a spatial and temporal variable influenced by melting and dependent on slope orientation and magnitude.

In this study we report experimental data illuminating the behaviour of dust particles on melting ice and the consequent quantitative changes in albedo and melting rate. Two dissimilar surface types, one relatively flat and one on a slope, are examined to investigate the effect of gravity driven flow of meltwater on the particles.

EXPERIMENTAL PROCEDURES

Field experiments were carried out during daytime (11:00–14:00 NST) on 28, 29 and 30 May 1996 at Lirung Glacier, Langtang region, Nepal Himalayas, as a part of the GEN project (Nakawo *et al.*, 1997). The weather conditions during each set of the experiments are summarized in Table 1.

Table 1 A summary of major meteorological parameters for the 3-h period of each set of experiments evaluated from recorded 5-min mean values.

Parameter	28 May:			29 May:			30 May:		
	min.	mean	max.	min.	mean	max.	min.	mean	max.
Air temperature (°C)	10.7	15.7	17.8	9.4	12.3	14.6	13.0	13.9	15.2
Incoming solar radiation (W m^{-2})	43.8	184.4	825.4	272.7	684.8	1093.3	717.7	829.0	985.6
Relative humidity (%)	30.7	45.5	64.1	41.1	50.8	62.6	38.6	46.0	54.4
Wind speed (m s^{-1})	5.4	6.2	7.5	5.1	5.9	6.9	5.1	6.1	7.3
Average cloud cover (in tenths)	9/10			8/10			7/10		

Experiment on a relatively flat surface

On the 28 and 29 May a 5 m × 2 m plot at elevation 4400 m a.s.l. (Site F, Fig. 2) was cleaned free of debris and smoothed with a shovel. Remaining scattered dust or sand was removed with water. The flatness of the surface was verified with the help of a spirit level. Each day the prepared bare ice surface was manually dusted using a known dust material (black soil containing a large amount of organic matter, albedo 0.08 and 0.06 for dry and wet conditions respectively, particle size $0.35 \geq \phi > 0.15$ mm, bulk density 450 kg m^{-3}) on seven sub-plots P1 to P7 (25 cm × 25 cm) with varying concentrations (Table 2). Besides the seven dusted plots, an approximate area of 40 cm × 40 cm of the prepared ice surface about 1 m away from the nearest dusted plot was monitored as an undusted reference plot (P8). Measurements of albedo and surface lowering (ablation)

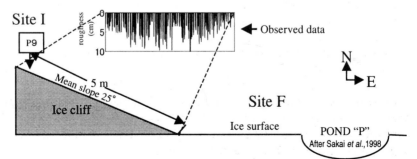

Fig. 2 A schematic drawing showing the experimental setting, where Sites I and F refer to the ice cliff and the relatively flat surface respectively. The observed roughness (expressed by the amplitude of the surface undulation) of the ice cliff surface prepared for the experiment is also shown. P9 is the dusted plot.

Table 2 Comparative statistics between initial and final conditions of dust concentrations, surface albedos, and ablation.

Initial dust concentration (kg m^{-2}) (11:00)	Initial thick-ness (mm)	Initial albedo (11:00):		Final dust concentration (kg m^{-2}) (14:00):		Final albedo (14:00):		Total (3 h) ablation (cm, ice):	
		28 May	29 May	28 May	29 May	28 May	29 May	28 May	29 May
P1	0.056	0.13	0.16	0.22	0.050	0.047	0.24	0.28	0.85	1.18
P2	0.080	0.18	0.16	0.21	0.067	0.062	0.19	0.27	1.32	1.69
P3	0.112	0.25	0.15	0.17	0.092	0.088	0.17	0.18	1.45	1.86
P4	0.160	0.36	0.15	0.14	0.136	0.130	0.17	0.15	1.12	1.45
P5	0.224	0.50	0.13	0.13	0.201	0.188	0.15	0.15	0.60	1.04
P6	0.448	1.00	0.11	0.11	0.413	0.402	0.14	0.11	0.33	0.75
P7	0.896	2.00	0.10	0.11	0.842	0.808	0.11	0.09	0.24	0.58
P8	Bare ice	-	0.38	0.39	-	-	0.37	0.40	0.28	0.51

on each plot were made. The instrumentation and the methods of observation employed for all sets of experiments are the same as those described in Adhikary et al. (1997).

Experiment on an ice cliff

On the 30 May an ice cliff with an average surface gradient of 25° sloping towards the east, length 15 m and width 5 m was chosen for the experiment. Existing scattered debris on the lower portion of the cliff (~6 m) was removed as described for the flat surface. The average surface roughness (expressed here as the amplitude of the surface undulation) on the lower portion of the cliff along three longitudinal profiles was of the order of several centimetres, which was larger than that of the natural bare surface (Site I, Fig. 2). A trench was dug immediately above the debris cleared portion of the cliff, so that the experimental area would not be affected by water or debris flow from the upper portion (~9 m) of the cliff. An area approximately 25 cm × 25 cm on the uppermost part of the cleared portion of the cliff was artificially contaminated with 3.5 g (or 0.056 kg m^{-2}) dust (P9). Also, an area approximate 40 cm × 40 cm with the same slope as the cleared section of the cliff (i.e. 25°), was isolated as a reference, undusted surface (P10) by digging another trench.

Quantitative measurements of dust flow on melting surfaces

Since dust particles on melting ice surfaces are often transported by meltwater, we measured the net dust loss from each dusted plot during the experiments. The average slope of P1, P2 and P3 were also measured by an inclinometer at the end of the experiments on 28 and 29 May. They were small (approximately 0.2° southward in all the cases). It was not practical to measure the slope of the remaining plots due to the soft surface of the dust layer. At the end of each experiment, the remaining dust from each area of the plot was drawn off together with the underlying ice samples to a depth of about 1 cm. The ice was melted and filtered through Millipore filters with a pore size of 0.45 μm in order to measure the dust content. Next, ice samples were collected at the lower zone of the cliff down from P9. The method of sampling and measuring the dust inclusion was the same as for the flat surfaces.

RESULTS AND DISCUSSION

Ablation observations

Figure 3(a) and Table 2 show ablation (3 h total) on 28 and 29 May for different initial dust concentrations. The thickness for each concentration was calculated based on given mass and observed bulk density assuming that the dust material was distributed

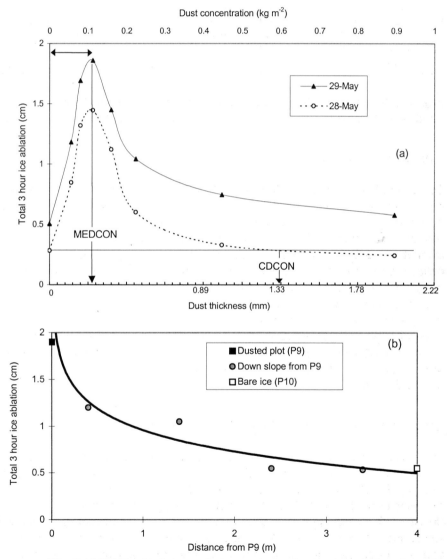

Fig. 3 (a) Relationship between dust concentration (or dust layer thickness) and the total ice ablation during the experimental periods. MEDCON and CDCON stand for most effective dust concentration and critical dust concentration respectively. The horizontal bar with double arrows shows the range of dust concentration of special interest. (b) Total ablation on the ice cliff for P9, P10, and various points down-slope from P9. The exponential curve is the best fit to the observed data.

uniformly. Total ice ablation increased with increasing dust concentration (thickness) from 0 to 0.112 kg m^{-2}. There was a decreasing trend for concentrations larger than 0.112 kg m^{-2} (0.25 mm). The critical dust concentration, beyond which the ablation was smaller than for clean (bare) glacier ice was approximately 0.6 kg m^{-2} (1.33 mm) on 28 May. Total ablation was generally larger on 29 than on 28 May. It was larger under the most densely dusted surface (0.896 kg m^{-2}) than for bare ice. The most effective dust concentration (hereafter abbreviated as MEDCON) for the ablation was the same (0.112 kg m^{-2}) on both days. The total ablation under the MEDCON on 28 (1.45 cm) and 29 (1.86 cm) May was about 5 and 4 times larger than for bare ice. These results are qualitatively similar to those observed by previous researchers since Østrem (1959) did his pioneering work.

Adhikary *et al.* (1997) found 0.08 kg m^{-2} MEDCON for snow ablation. Although the physical properties of the dust used by Adhikary *et al.* (1997) that used in the present experiment are very similar, a larger initial concentration by a factor of 1.4 is required for maximum ablation for ice compared to snow. This difference suggests that similar dust material work differently on snow and ice surfaces. Dust particles on a melting ice surface are vulnerable to transport by meltwater and migrate as the melt progresses. Consequently the spatial pattern of melting changes with time due to the alteration of the rate of solar energy absorption caused by the redistribution of dust particles. A short horizontal line with double arrows in Fig. 3(a) illustrates the range of concentration 0 to MEDCON of special interest for the following discussion.

Figure 3(b) shows the results for differential ice ablation on the experimental ice cliff on 30 May. During the observation period the total amount of ice ablation measured on P9 was 1.9 cm compared to 0.5 cm on P10. The meltwater from the cliff did not accumulate on the surface but flowed down the steep slope (25°). Some of the dust particles were observed to be sliding down the cliff moving along with the meltwater. The scattered bold dots on Fig. 3(b) indicate our ablation measurements along the moving path of the particles on a longitudinal profile down-slope from P9. The data show that total ice ablation decreased as the distance from P9 increases. The trend is approximately exponential.

In spite of the equal initial dust concentration (0.056 kg m^{-2}), total ablation on P9 (1.9 cm) was about 2 times greater than on P1 (1 cm, average from 28 and 29 May). Ablation rates on P9 (cliff) and P1 (flat surface) relative to respective bare ice were about 4 and 2.5 times greater respectively (see Table 2 and Fig. 3(b)). Other than the difference in absolute values of ablation, which depend on the prevailing weather conditions and exposure angle to the sun, ablation under a dust cover relative to bare ice was greater on the sloping cliff surface than on the flat surfaces. Reasons for the difference in ablation between the cliff and the flat surfaces may be that:
–   each dust particle absorbs more solar radiation on the sloping cliff surface because the radiation intensity on a slope is higher than on a flat surface;
–   each moving particle leaves a track of surface disturbance that absorbs solar radiation.

The former can be explained in terms of the effect of dust on albedo that leads to greater ablation on a cliff than on a flat surface. For Lirung Glacier, sloping surfaces, in particular those facing east generally receive greater solar radiation (Sakai *et al.*, 1998). Our experimental cliff was facing the east which might have exposed it to greater solar radiation during the early part of the experiment when the sky was relatively clear. Dust particles on the cliff were more scattered than on the flat surfaces, so that the shadow of one particle on an adjacent particle was insignificant. This situation allows each particle to absorb maximum radiation.

The latter relates to the action of each individual particle moving on the ice surface. Dust particles on a sloping cliff surface are more dynamic than on a flat surface due to the gravity driven flow of meltwater. As pointed out by Kotlyakov & Dolgushin (1972), dust particles not only absorb the solar energy and release it for melting, but also form pits in the ice surface where they are placed that collect meltwater. Such surface morphology leads to an additional decrease of surface albedo and increase in melting. The additional decrease in albedo is caused by trapping of a certain amount of the incident total solar radiation due to multiple reflection inside the pit and absorption in the water. However, if a particle is in a pit, its effectiveness for absorbing radiation will decrease. Formation of such pits by a particle would be greater on the cliff than on a flat ice surface since the gravity-driven flow of meltwater would usually displace a particle from a pit, allowing the particle to form successive pits on its way down the surface. However, the preceding pits do not last long as the melt progresses. The principle difference of surface morphology between the cliff and the flat surface caused by the actions of individual particles may account for the relatively large ablation on the cliff compared to the flat surface during our observations.

Albedo observations

Table 2 shows albedos of dusted surfaces on 28 and 29 May at the beginning and end of each experiment. The data indicate that the albedo of the ice surfaces covered with dust decreased with increasing concentration and approached the albedo of dust itself when the underlying surface was fully covered by the dust. A comparison of the albedos at the beginning and end indicates that the albedo increased dramatically with time particularly on more lightly dusted surfaces. This shows that the albedo of the TS dust-covered surface is variable with time during conditions of melt.

Figure 4 shows the time variation of albedo on dirty and clean areas of the ice cliff. Albedo was measured at 10-min intervals. With the initial application of dust, the albedo of the cliff surface dropped from 0.45 (bare ice) to 0.22 (P9), then increased monotonically with time until reaching a value of about 0.36. After that there were small variations around a mean of 0.36. Observations at areas below P9 show that the albedo decreased over time at a slow rate broken by frequent small fluctuations. The lowering of albedos at locations close to P9 was particularly evident. The albedo of P10, however, remained nearly constant.

Behaviour of dust on melting surfaces

Figure 5(a) shows the amount of dust lost from the flat dusted surfaces during the melting of the ice surface on 28 and 29 May. The data indicate that dust loss increased sharply with increasing initial concentration up to the MEDCON, which resembles the rising portions of the ablation curves (Fig. 3(a)). Unlike a snow surface, which is generally porous, an ice surface is usually relatively impermeable. Thus, meltwater remains on the surface instead of percolating into the ice. However, for a sloping surface, meltwater flows down the slope and gravitational force coupled with water-layer lubrication enhance the rate of dust loss. Although absolute values of dust loss are high for the high initial concentrations, the trend of increasing loss declines beyond the MEDCON. Visual observation in the field showed that the high absolute values were due to the considerable erosion from the edges of the higher dust concentration plots. Although the correlation coefficient for both the curves ((i) and (ii) in Fig. 5(a)) is high (above 0.90), there are significant errors above the MEDCON. Contrary to the snow surface, where the aggregation of dust particles was clearly observed (Adhikary *et al.*, 1997), the aggregation of dust particles was not evident on the flat melting ice surfaces. Lack of aggregation was probably due to the short duration of the experiments and impermeability of the ice surface, which favours the export of the particles out of the plot together with the local meltwater derived from intense melting. However, clumps of particles forming interesting patterns that were seen on frozen cliffs (Fig. 1) presumably testify the earlier actions of gravity driven channels of meltwater.

Figure 5(b) shows the distribution of dust concentrations on the ice cliff at the beginning and the end of the experiment. The lowermost portion of the cliff was initially dirtier than the upper part. The figure also shows the dust concentration increase (final minus initial) due to P9 upslope on the cliff. The concentration increase decreased toward the lower part of the cliff with down-slope distance from P9. The result gives direct verification that the dust particles moving downward with meltwater caused the decrease in surface albedo shown in Fig. 4.

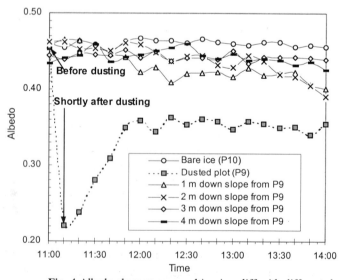

Fig. 4 Albedo changes on a melting ice cliff with different dust concentrations. The dust was distributed shortly after 11:00 (30 May).

The experimental results presented in this paper are basically restricted to a few short periods on TS dust-covered surfaces that indeed constitute the most difficult range of debris concentration for estimation of ablation underneath. Most of the

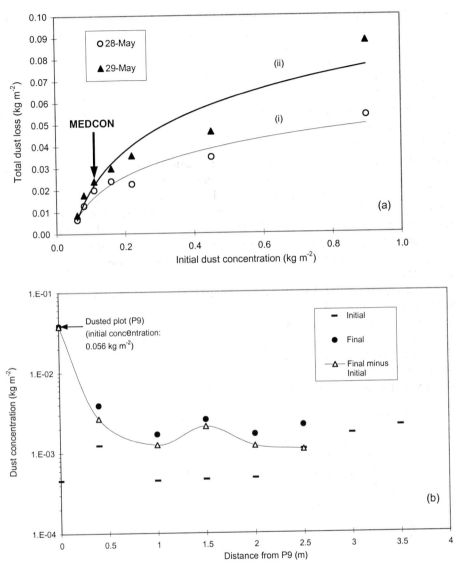

Fig. 5 (a) Dust loss from dusted surfaces due to horizontal migration of particles with meltwater. Curves (i) and (ii) are the best fits to the data for 28 and 29 May respectively. MEDCON is the most effective dust concentration for ice ablation. (b) Dust concentration on the ice cliff at the beginning (initial) and end (final) of the experiment.

previous studies found maximum ice ablation under a debris layer (MEDCON) a few centimetres thick, while our results show that maximum ice ablation can be attained under a very thin dust layer (0.25 mm or 0.112 kg m^{-2}). This striking difference of MEDCON may indicate the effect of the size of particles upon glacier ice melting. The uniqueness of our study lies in the examination of glacier ice ablation under fine particles covering a wide range in albedo. Even in remote areas, for example the Himalayas, glacier surfaces have been found to be contaminated by atmospherically derived fine particles (aerosol). The presence of such dust can lower glacier surface albedo significantly, with an increase in ablation. Moreover, such fine particles can be easily moved by surface meltwater thereby reducing albedo on adjacent cleaner ice surfaces. The total consequences on the glacier surface melting would be even higher as a result of redistribution of particles that changes surface morphology as noted earlier. Our study suggested that for a TS dust covered glacier surface, the behaviour of the particles must be considered an important factor in modelling surface melting. We believe that the present study will support realistic modelling work, but, further studies on TS dust layers are necessary.

Acknowledgements We thank Mr Chetan Sherpa, Mr Tek Bahadur Chhetri and Mr Maya Prakesh Bhatt for field assistance and Dr Birbal Rana for his cooperation and help in the laboratory. We are grateful to Dr Yashushi Yamaguchi and Prof. Katsuro Ogawa for valuable suggestions. We also thank Prof. Charles F. Raymond (scientific editor of this paper) and two anonymous referees for important comments and suggestions. This work was supported in part by a Grant-in-Aid for the International Scientific Research Programme (no. 06041051) from the Ministry of Education, Science, Sports and Culture, Japanese Government.

REFERENCES

Adhikary, S., Seko, K., Nakawo, M., Ageta, Y. & Miyazaki, N. (1997) Effect of surface dust on snow melt. *Bull. Glacier Res.* 15, 85–92.

Fujii, Y. (1977) Field experiment on glacier ablation under a layer of debris cover. *J. Japan. Soc. Snow Ice (Seppyo)* 39, special issue, 20–21.

Inoue, J. & Yoshida, M. (1980) Ablation and heat exchange over the Khumbu Glacier. *J. Japan. Soc. Snow Ice (Seppyo)* 41, special issue, 26–33.

Kohshima, S., Seko, K. & Yoshimura, Y. (1993) Biotic acceleration of glacier melting in Yala Glacier, Langtang region, Nepal Himalaya. in: *Snow and Glacier Hydrology* (ed. by G. J. Young) (Proc. Kathmandu Symp., November 1992), 309–316. IAHS Publ. no. 218.

Kotlyakov, V. M. & Dolgushin, L. D. (1972) Possibility of artificial augmentation of melting by surface dusting of glaciers. In: *Role of Snow and Ice in Hydrology* (Proc. Banff Symp., September 1972), 1421–1426. IAHS Publ. no. 107.

Moribayashi, S. & Higuchi, K. (1977) Characteristics of glaciers in the Khumbu region and their recent variations. *J. Japan. Soc. Snow Ice (Seppyo)* 39, special issue, 3–6.

Nakawo, M. & Young, G. J. (1981) Field experiments to determine the effect of a debris layer on ablation of glacier ice. *Ann. Glaciol.* 2, 85–91.

Nakawo, M., Fujita, K., Ageta, Y., Shankar, K., Pokhrel, A. & Yao, T. (1997) Basic studies for assessing the impacts of the global warming on the Himalayan cryosphere, 1994–1996. *Bull. Glacier Res.* 16, 53–58.

Ohata, T. & Higuchi, K. (1980) Heat balance study on glacier AX010 in Shorong Himal, East Nepal. *J. Japan. Soc. Snow Ice (Seppyo)* 41, special issue, 42–47.

Østrem, G. (1959) Ice melting under a thin layer of moraine, and the existence of ice cores in moraine ridges. *Geogr. Ann.* 41, 228–230.

Sakai, A., Nakawo, M. & Fujita, K. (1998) Melt rate of ice cliffs on the Lirung Glacier, Nepal Himalayas, 1996. *Bull. Glacier Res.* 16, 57–66.

Warren, S. G. & Wiscombe, W. J. (1980) A model for the spectral albedo of snow. II: Snow containing atmospheric aerosols. *J. Atmos. Sci.* 37, 2734–2745.

Debris-Covered Glaciers (Proceedings of a workshop held at Seattle, Washington, USA, September 2000).
IAHS Publ. no. 264, 2000.

Characteristics of ablation and heat balance in debris-free and debris-covered areas on Khumbu Glacier, Nepal Himalayas, in the pre-monsoon season

YUKARI TAKEUCHI*

The Research Institute for Hazards in Snowy Areas, Niigata University, Igarashi, Niigata 950-2181, Japan

e-mail: y-take@pwri.go.jp

RIJAN BHAKTA KAYASTHA & MASAYOSHI NAKAWO

Institute for Hydrospheric–Atmospheric Sciences, Nagoya University, Furo-cho, Chikusa-ku, Nagoya 464-8601, Japan

Abstract Ablation and heat balance were measured in debris-covered and debris-free areas of the ablation zone of Khumbu Glacier from 22 May to 1 June 1999. On the debris-free ice, the ablation rates ranged from 1.4 to 4.7 cm day^{-1} and were inversely correlated with the albedo. The contribution of turbulent heat flux to melting was very small, so net radiation accounted for about 98% of the incoming heat. Melting under debris decreased sharply with increasing thickness. Debris with thickness of 10 cm slowed melting to about 40% of that of bare ice with the same low albedo. The primary cause of melt reduction was the insulating effect of the debris. The heat stored in the debris layer during daytime was released to the atmosphere during night-time and warmed the air rather than being conducted downward to melt ice.

INTRODUCTION

Most of the glacier ice in the Nepal Himalayas is covered by debris (Moribayashi, 1974; Moribayashi & Higuchi, 1977; Fujii & Higuchi, 1977). Effects from the debris on ablation processes probably dominate recent glacier changes in the Nepal Himalayas (Nakawo *et al.*, 1997).

Ablation processes were examined by Kraus (1975) and Inoue & Yoshida (1980) on Khumbu and other debris-covered glaciers. Inoue & Yoshida (1980) made heat balance observations at two areas covered with different types of debris on Khumbu Glacier for several days. They reported that solar radiation was the main heat source for ablation and that a thin layer of schistose debris with low albedo enhanced ablation. Nakawo & Young (1982) showed that the surface temperature of the debris layer can be used for estimating the thermal resistance and consequently the ablation under the layer. This model was simplified for its practical use in the field by Nakawo & Takahashi (1982). Moreover Nakawo *et al.* (1993) proposed that a model could be used to estimate the melt rate of a debris-covered glacier by using surface temperature data derived from thermal infrared satellite images. Recently, Sakai *et al.* (1998) showed that the ablation of ice cliffs can contribute significantly to the total ablation in a debris-covered area.

---

* *Now at*: Niigata Experimental Laboratory, Public Works Research Institute, Arai 944-0051, Japan.

No simultaneous meteorological observations in both debris-covered and debris-free areas on the same glacier had been made prior to the present study. This paper compares heat balance characteristics on debris-covered and debris-free areas at Khumbu Glacier under the same meteorological conditions. It also examines how the different surface characteristics affect the local micrometeorology.

METHODS

Observation methods

Heat balance observations were carried out near the Everest Base Camp (27°59′N, 86°51′E, 5350 m a.s.l.) on the upper ablation zone of Khumbu Glacier from 22 May to 1 June 1999 just before the monsoon season. Meteorological stations were established both in the debris-free and debris-covered areas (Fig. 1). The two stations were about 200 m apart and at nearly the same altitude. Measurements on the debris-free ice included net radiation, air temperature, relative humidity, wind speed and direction. Solar radiation, air temperature, relative humidity, wind speed and surface temperature of the debris were measured over the 10-cm-thick debris. Observations were made continuously and recorded with portable data loggers. Ablation in the debris-free area was measured once or twice a day at seven stakes. Albedo of the ice surface at each stake was measured at 11:00–12:00 h on sunny days. The ablation rate under various thicknesses of debris (2, 5, 10, 20, 30 and 40 cm) was measured four times (8:00,

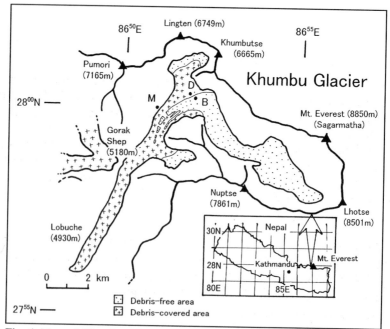

Fig. 1 Map of Khumbu Glacier, Nepal Himalayas and observation sites. B: the observation site on the debris-free ice. D: the observation site in the debris-covered area. M: the observation site on the lateral moraine.

11:00, 14:00 and 17:00 h) a day. The surface temperature and albedo of the debris layers were also measured at those times. Air temperature was measured continuously on the lateral moraine close to the glacier margin (Fig. 1). Details of measurement methods are reported by Kayastha *et al.* (2000) and Takeuchi *et al.* (2001).

Heat balance computations

The heat balance equation at a melting bare ice surface and upper surface of debris can be written as follows:

$$R + S + L + M = 0 \qquad \text{(bare ice)}$$

and
(1)

$$R + S + L + C = 0 \qquad \text{(debris layer)}$$

where positive indicates toward the surface for all components. R is the all-wave net radiation. S is the sensible heat flux. L is the latent heat flux. M is the heat for ice melting. C is the conductive heat flux through debris layer. M and C were calculated as residual of equation (1). R was measured directly by an all-wave net radiometer on the bare ice. On the debris, it was calculated by the radiative balance equation using data for solar radiation, albedo, surface temperature measured on the debris layer and net radiation measured on the bare ice (Takeuchi *et al.*, 2001). It is assumed that heat conduction in the ice is negligible.

The turbulent heat fluxes (S and L) were calculated using a bulk aerodynamic approach following Stull (1988). The formulae are:

$$S = \rho_a C_p D_H (T_z - T_0)$$
(2)

and

$$L = \rho_a L_e D_E (0.622/P_a)(e_z - e_0)$$
(3)

where ρ_a is the air density; C_p is the specific heat of air at constant pressure; T_z is the air temperature at height z; T_0 is the surface temperature; L_e is the specific latent heat of vaporization of water; P_a is the atmospheric pressure; e_z and e_0 are the vapour pressure at height z and at the surface; D_H is the bulk exchange coefficient for heat. D_E is the bulk exchange coefficient for water vapour. The temperature and vapour pressure at the melting ice surface are taken as 0°C and 6.11 hPa, respectively.

Under neutral conditions, D_H and D_E are assumed to be equal to the momentum exchange coefficient given by:

$$D_0 = k^2 U_z [\ln(z/z_0)]^{-2}$$
(4)

k is the von Karman constant (= 0.4); U_z is the wind speed at height z; z_0 is the roughness length for momentum. The values of z were 1.06 m and 1.52 m at debris-free and debris-covered sites, respectively. z_0 was calculated from wind speeds at two heights assuming neutral conditions using the equation:

$$z_0 = \exp[(U_2 \ln z_1 - U_1 \ln z_2)/(U_2 - U_1)]$$
(5)

In this measurement, z_1 and z_2 were 0.52 m and 1.52 m, respectively. The value of z_0 for the debris-covered surface was found to be 6.3 mm. This is similar to the value

(3.5 mm) obtained by Inoue & Yoshida (1980). The wind speed profile could not be measured well for the bare ice surface where wind speed was very small. The value of z_0 for the bare ice surface was taken to be the same as for the debris surface. This assumption is reasonable because the bare ice surface was very rough due to differential melting by the strong solar radiation.

The measured ablation amount h_i is related to the heat for melting (M'), by:

$$M' = \rho_i L_i h_i \tag{6}$$

where ρ_i is the density of glacier ice (900 kg m^{-3}) and L_i is the specific latent heat of melting.

RESULTS

Ablation characteristics

Mean daily ablation rate measured with seven stakes and the mean albedo for the seven debris-free sites are shown in Fig. 2. The ablation rates ranged from 1.4 to 4.7 cm day^{-1} and were inversely correlated with the albedo for the reason discussed below.

The mean ablation rate under the debris depended on the thickness of the debris (Kayastha *et al.*, 2000). The highest rate occurred under debris with thickness of about 0.3 cm. For greater thicknesses, the ablation rate decreased with increasing thickness. The thickness at which the ablation rate was the same as for bare ice was about 5 cm.

The cumulative ablation on bare ice (S1 and S4) and under 10 cm of debris are compared in Fig. 3. Values of albedo were 0.44 and 0.21 for the bare ice sites, and 0.21 for the debris layer. The 10-cm debris layer slowed ice melting to about 40% of that of bare ice with the same low albedo (S4). It was also smaller than that of bare ice (S1), which had the highest albedo among the seven measurement sites.

Heat balance characteristics

The heat for ice melting calculated as a residual of the heat balance (M in equation (1)) is compared with that obtained from measured ablation (M' in equation (6)) in Fig. 4. During the first half of the observation period, the values from heat balance are

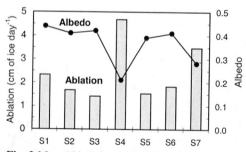

Fig. 2 Mean ablation rates and mean albedo over 10 days at the seven stakes (S1 to S7) on the bare ice.

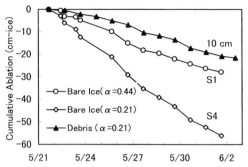

Fig. 3 Cumulative ablation on bare ice and under a 10-cm debris layer during the observation period

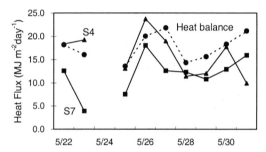

Fig. 4 Comparison of heat for ice melting on bare ice (albedo 0.26) obtained from the heat balance method (dashed) and measurement of ablation at S4 (albedo 0.21) and S7 (albedo 0.28).

between those from melting at S4 and S7. This result is reasonable because the albedo of the meteorological station on bare ice (0.26) was between the albedos at S4 and S7 (0.21 and 0.28, respectively). During the second half of the observation period, the trends agree, but heat for melting calculated from heat balance is slightly larger than that found from ablation. The causes are not well understood at present.

The conductive heat flux C was calculated as a residual of equation (1) for a 10-cm thickness of debris. Because the actual vapour pressure of the debris surface was not known, two limiting cases were considered: saturated with maximum latent heat flux and dry with no latent heat flux. These estimates of C are compared with the heat for ice melting under the same thickness obtained from measured ablation (Fig. 5). Most of the measured values are between the two limiting cases and this result is considered to be reasonable. Accordingly, the characteristics of the contribution of the heat balance components to ice melting in both debris-free and debris-covered areas can be calculated by the heat balance method.

Mean daily values of the heat balance components on the bare ice and the 10-cm debris layer are compared in Fig. 6. For the debris layer, the maximum latent heat flux is shown. On the bare ice, the sensible and latent heat fluxes were very small because the wind speed was very small (see also Takeuchi *et al.*, 2001), and almost all heat for melting came from net radiation.

The net radiation was similar in value on both surfaces. On the debris cover, increased shortwave absorption due to lower albedo is balanced by higher outgoing longwave radiation from the higher surface temperature (Takeuchi *et al.*, 2001). On the

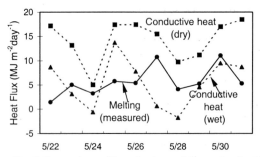

Fig. 5 Comparison of heat for ice melting under the 10-cm debris layer obtained from measurement of ablation and conductive heat flux calculated from the heat balance.

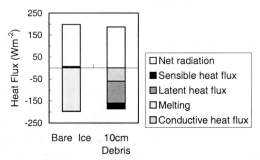

Fig. 6 Comparison of heat balance components on the bare ice and the 10-cm-thick debris layer assuming saturation over the debris.

bare ice, almost all the absorbed energy by net radiation and sensible heat flux was used directly for ice melting. Under the debris layer, the energy source for icemelt was the conductive heat flux through the warmed debris layer. The negative sensible and latent heat fluxes and oscillating storage of heat in the upper part of the debris layer should result in less ablation under the debris layer.

DISCUSSION AND CONCLUSION

The reason that the ablation rate for bare ice is related to albedo can be understood from the heat balance data. Generally, the energy source for the melting of bare ice consists of not only net radiation but also turbulent heat fluxes. On Khumbu Glacier, the contribution of turbulent heat flux to melting was very small, so net radiation accounted for about 98% of the heat income. The mean ablation was largest at S4, where the albedo was lowest, even though the turbulent heat flux was smallest. Since only S4 was on a flat area, the turbulent heat flux may have been smaller than at the other six stakes which were on a ridge on the glacier surface.

The relationships between the debris thickness, the heat for melting and the total incoming heat at the upper surface of the debris during the daytime are shown in Fig. 7. In the calculations, the hourly daytime surface temperature at each debris site was estimated from three-hourly measurements interpolated using the hourly values at the 10-cm site assuming linear relationships. Albedo and surface temperature varied at

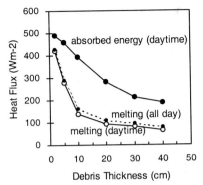

Fig. 7 Relationships between debris thickness and the heat for melting and net absorbed energy by net radiation and sensible heat flux.

the sites, but meteorological variables such as air temperature, wind speed, solar radiation and atmospheric radiation were assumed to be equal at all the sites.

Melting under a debris layer decreased with increasing thickness of debris, as found by many previous workers (e.g. Fujii, 1977; Mattson *et al.*, 1993). One reason is that the absorbed energy was less for larger debris thickness (Fig. 7). At thickness larger than 2 cm, the absorbed solar radiation decreased with increasing debris thickness because the surface of a thicker debris layer was easy to dry and had higher albedo. However, outgoing longwave radiation increased with debris thickness because the surface temperature became higher. Moreover the outgoing sensible heat flux also increased for the same reason. Furthermore, heat stored in the debris layer in the daytime increases with debris thickness. Melting decreased sharply under thin debris (less than 10 cm) but gradually under thick debris, in spite of the absorbed energy decreased linearly. This implied that the insulating effect of the debris had a more significant effect on the smaller melting than the decrease of absorbed energy.

Over the observation period, changes in the heat stored in the debris from day to day integrate approximately to zero. However, there are diurnal variations in the amount of heat stored. It increases in the daytime and decreases at night. Some heat stored in the daytime could be used for melting during the night-time, but the mean night-time ablation rate (the difference between melting in the daytime and all day in

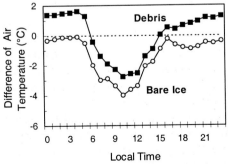

Fig. 8 Mean daily variations of air temperature difference (temperature on the bare ice and the debris minus that on the moraine).

Fig. 7) was very little for any debris thickness. Accordingly, it is likely that most stored heat was used to keep the debris surface temperature higher and was released back to the atmosphere at night.

Diurnal variations of air temperature over the bare ice and the debris layer were compared with those on the lateral moraine, under which there is no glacier ice (Fig. 8). In the daytime, the air temperature over both the bare ice and the debris layer were lower than that on the moraine, but it was higher at night over the debris layer. This night-time warming over the debris was probably caused by the release of heat stored in it during the daytime as described above. Release of stored heat at night by the same process did not happen on the moraine probably because of the thermal characteristics of the moraine surface (e.g. conductivity and capacity). Many glaciers in the Himalayas are considered very vulnerable to the recent global warming (Nakawo *et al.*, 1997). The changes in glacier debris-free and debris-covered areas and changes in debris thickness may affect the local climate through the surface–atmosphere interaction. Differences between the thermal characteristics of supraglacial debris layers and moraine may play a role and need investigation.

Acknowledgements The authors would like to express their sincere gratitude to the Department of Hydrology and Meteorology, His Majesty's Government of Nepal. They are also grateful to the following support for this study. Field assistance was provided by Dr T. Kadota and Dr N. Naito of the Institute for Hydrospheric–Atmospheric Sciences (IHAS), Nagoya University, and all members who joined the project. Prof. Y. Ageta and Dr K. Fujita of IHAS, and Prof. S. Kobayashi and Dr K. Izumi of Niigata University cooperated in this study. The Nagaoka Institute of Snow and Ice Studies generously loaned the instruments for the observations. This is a joint study of IHAS, Nagoya University and was supported by a Grant-in-Aid for Scientific Research (no. 09041103: principal investigator, Y. Ageta) of the Ministry of Education, Science, Sports and Culture of Japan.

REFERENCES

Fujii, Y. (1977) Field experiment on glacier ablation under a layer of debris cover. *J. Japan. Soc. Snow Ice (Seppyo)* **39**, special issue, 20–21.

Fujii, Y. & Higuchi, K. (1977) Statistical analyses of the forms of the glaciers in the Khumbu Himal. *J. Japan. Soc. Snow Ice (Seppyo)* **39**, special issue, 7–14.

Inoue, J. & Yoshida, M. (1980) Ablation and heat exchange over the Khumbu Glacier. *J. Japan. Soc. Snow Ice (Seppyo)* **41**, special issue, 26–33.

Kayastha, R. B., Takeuchi, Y., Nakawo, M. & Ageta, Y. (2000) Practical prediction of ice melting beneath various thickness of debris cover on Khumbu Glacier, Nepal, using a positive degree-day factor. In: *Debris-Covered Glaciers* (ed. by M. Nakawo, C. F. Raymond & A. Fountain) (Proc. Seattle Workshop, September 2000). IAHS Publ. no. 264 (this volume).

Kraus, H. (1975) An energy balance model for ablation in mountainous areas. In: *Snow and Ice* (Proc. Moscow Symp., August 1971), 74–82. IAHS Publ. no. 104.

Mattson, L. E., Gardner, J. S. & Young, G. J. (1993) Ablation on debris covered glaciers: an example from the Rakhiot Glacier, Panjab, Himalaya. In: *Snow and Glacier Hydrology* (ed. by G. J. Young) (Proc. Kathmandu Symp., November 1992), 289–296. IAHS Publ. no. 218.

Moribayashi, S. (1974) On the characteristics of Nepal Himalayan Glaciers and their recent variation (in Japanese with English abstract). *J. Japan. Soc. Snow Ice (Seppyo)* **36**, 11–21.

Moribayashi, S. & Higuchi, K. (1977) Characteristics of glaciers in the Khumbu region and their recent variations. *J. Japan. Soc. Snow Ice (Seppyo)* **39**, special issue, 3–6.

Nakawo, M., Fujita, K., Ageta, Y., Shankar, K., Pokhrel, P. A. & Tandong, Y. (1997) Basic studies for assessing the impacts of the global warming on the Himalayan cryosphere, 1994–1996. *Bull. Glacier Res.* **15**, 53–58.

Nakawo, M., Moroboshi, T. & Uehara, S. (1993) Satellite data utilization for estimating ablation of debris covered glaciers. In: *Snow and Glacier Hydrology* (ed. by G. J. Young) (Proc. Kathmandu Symp., November 1992), 75–83. IAHS Publ. no. 218.

Nakawo, M. & Takahashi, S. (1982) A simplified model for estimating glacier ablation under a debris layer. In: *Hydrological Aspects of Alpine and High-Mountain Areas* (ed. by J. W. Glen) (Proc. Exeter Symp., July 1882), 137–145. IAHS Publ. no. 138.

Nakawo, M. & Young, G. J. (1982) Estimate of glacier ablation under a debris layer from surface temperature and meteorological variables. *J. Glaciol.* **28**(98), 29–34.

Sakai, A., Nakawo, M. & Fujita, K. (1998) Melt rate of ice cliffs on the Lirung Glacier, Nepal Himalayas, 1996. *Bull. Glacier Res.* **16**, 57–66.

Stull, R. B. (1988) *An Introduction to Boundary Layer Meteorology.* Kluwer, Dordrecht, The Netherlands.

Takeuchi, Y., Kayastha, R. B., Naito, N., Kadota, T. & Izumi, K. (2001) Comparison of meteorological features in the debris-free and debris-covered areas at the Khumbu Glacier, Nepal Himalayas, in the premonsoon season, 1999. Submitted to: *Bull. Glaciological Res.* **19**.

Debris-Covered Glaciers (Proceedings of a workshop held at Seattle, Washington, USA, September 2000).
IAHS Publ. no. 264, 2000.

Influence of a fine debris layer on the melting of snow and ice on a Himalayan glacier

PRATAP SINGH, NARESH KUMAR, K. S. RAMASASTRI & YATVEER SINGH

National Institute of Hydrology, Roorkee 247667, Uttar Pradesh, India
e-mail: pratap@cc.nih.ernet.in

Abstract The effect of a thin layer of fine debris on the melting of snow and ice was investigated over Dokriani Glacier at an altitude of about 4000 m in the Garhwal Himalayas (31°49 –31 52 N, 78 47 –78 51 E). Such investigations were made during summer 1995, 1997 and 1998. The average melt rate with respect to unit temperature or degree-day factor for clean and dusted snow was computed to be 5.8 and 6.4 mm $°C^{-1}$ day^{-1}, whereas for clean ice and debris-covered ice the value of this factor was 7.3 and 8.0 mm $°C^{-1}$ day^{-1}, respectively. Melt rate of clean ice was about 1.26 times greater than that for clean snow under similar weather conditions. The effect of debris layer on the melt rate of snow was more prominent than that for ice. The presence of debris on the ice increased the melt rate by about 8.5%, whereas for snow it increased by about 11.6%. Information on such factors is useful for runoff modelling of glacierized drainage basins.

INTRODUCTION

An appreciable quantity of the flow of Himalayan rivers is derived from the snow and glacier melt runoff (Singh *et al.*, 1995; Singh *et al.*, 1997). One of the most common characteristics of Himalayan and Trans-Himalayan glaciers is the presence of debris covering a large portion of their ablation zone (Fujii & Higuchi, 1977; Nakawo & Young, 1982; Singh & Ramasastri, 1999). Østrem (1959) and Fujii & Higuchi (1977) found that ablation is accelerated under a thin layer of debris and retarded under a thick layer. Nakawo *et al.* (1993) attempted to estimate the melt rate of a debris-covered area of glaciers using satellite data. Mattson *et al.* (1993) reported direct ablation measurements by drilling wooden stakes into a glacier at different locations with different depths of debris cover. They found a large increase in ablation with debris cover thickness increasing from 0 to 10 mm followed by a reduction in ablation with debris-cover thickness increasing beyond 10 mm. They observed that 30-mm thickness of debris cover as a critical thickness indicating that at thickness greater than 30 mm ablation is suppressed compared with that expected from debris-free ice. Rana *et al.* (1996) measured ablation under debris thickness varying from 0 to 130 mm in the Nepal Himalayas. Similar to other findings, they also found that ablation increased as debris thickness increased up to a certain thickness and then decreased as debris thickness increased further. The maximum ablation was observed for a debris thickness of 26 mm. Evaluation of snowmelt and icemelt under debris cover is important for runoff modelling of glacierized drainage basins.

The quantity of meltwater produced depends on the prevailing weather conditions and the physical characteristics of surface. The degree-day factor representing the meltrate from snow and ice with respect to unit temperature is the most important parameter because of its practical importance in estimating ablation using temperature data. This parameter is used to convert degree-days to snowmelt or icemelt expressed in units of depth of water. In most mountainous basins, only temperature data are available in high altitude regions. However, most stations are located along the valley bottoms. Temperature data at higher elevations can be easily extrapolated using data from the stations located at lower altitudes. In the Himalayan region almost all snowmelt and glacier-melt studies are carried out using this temperature index approach. The first application of degree-day approach was made by Finsterwalder & Schunk (1887) in the Alps. Since then, this approach has been used all over the world for the estimation of snowmelt and icemelt runoff. The melt rate or degree-day factor can be determined from:

$$D = M/(T_a - T_o)$$

where M = depth of meltwater (mm day^{-1}), T_a = mean air temperature (°C); T_o = base temperature (usually, 0°C); and D = degree-day factor (mm °C^{-1} day^{-1}). It is possible to compute the degree-day factor at a point by measuring temperature and meltwater from the snow or ice block. The number of degree-days for one day is obtained by averaging positive air temperatures.

In spite of the importance of degree-day factors for snow and ice for computation of melting from snow- and ice-covered areas, only limited studies have been carried out to determine these factors in the Himalayan region (Singh & Kumar, 1996). No study has been carried out to estimate degree-day factor for ice. In the present study degree-day factors for both snow and ice, including the effect of a thin debris layer on these factors, are determined at the Dokriani Glacier located in Garhwal Himalayas in India. A large portion of the ablation area of this glacier is covered by debris which varies in thickness from a few millimetres to a few metres.

MELTING FROM CLEAN AND DUSTED SNOW AND ICE

The dusting or blackening of snow and ice surfaces by any dark material tends to a reduction in the albedo. This results in higher absorption of solar radiation which, in turn, leads to accelerated melt and higher meltwater yield. Few studies pertain to increased melting of a snowpack due to dusting (Avsiuk, 1953, 1962; Kotlyakov & Dolgushin, 1972; Singh & Kumar, 1996). A review of the values of degree-day factors reported by various investigators for clean snow varied between 3.0 and 5.7 mm °C^{-1} day^{-1}, whereas for clean ice it varied between 5 and 7.7 mm °C^{-1} day^{-1} (Braithwaite, 1995).

EXPERIMENTS ON DOKRIANI GLACIER

In the present study, two pairs of snow and ice blocks (each 30 cm × 30 cm × 30 cm) were extracted from the glacier snowpack and ice body at an altitude of about 4000 m without disturbing their structure. The density of the snow and ice was measured and found to be 600 and 900 kg m^{-3}, respectively. Each block was wrapped in a plastic sheet, except for their top, and replaced in the snowpack, so that the top was at the same level as the surrounding area. One of the pairs of snow and ice blocks was kept clean while the other was covered with a 2-mm layer of fine debris naturally available on the glacier surface. The major source of such fine debris deposited over different parts of the glacier is landslides, rockslides from the surrounding valley walls and the reworking of old moraines. The density of the fine debris used in the present study was observed to be about 1800 kg m^{-3} and thus the weight of debris over unit area is computed to be about 0.36 gm cm^{-2}. The plastic sheet prevented any infiltration, percolation or lateral movement of the meltwater from the surrounding snowpack.

Observations were made continuously for 24 h on the days of the experiments. Experiments were carried out under fair weather conditions. All the study plots were adjacent to each other so that melting from each block may take place under similar weather conditions. Temperature was observed only at 15-min intervals at 2-m height above the snow surface at a single location in the centre of each plot. These were then averaged for each hour. For all study plots the surface temperature was 0°C because of the snow surface.

The meltwater from each block was collected in separate buckets at a frequency of 1 h and the volume was measured using standard beakers. On 5, 6 June 1995 only snow blocks were studied, while on 29 May 1997 and 24, 25 June and 22 July 1998 both snow and ice blocks were studied. Runoff from the study blocks along with observed air temperature are shown in Fig. 1(a)–(f). Computed degree-day factors for clean and debris-covered snow and ice are given in Table 1.

RESULTS AND DISCUSSIONS

The degree-day factor for the clean snow and debris-covered snow was determined to be 5.8 and 6.4 mm °C^{-1} day^{-1}, respectively, whereas for the clean ice and dusted ice it was observed to be 7.3 and 8.0 mm °C^{-1} day^{-1}. A comparison of degree-day factors for clean snow and ice with the values reported in the literature (for clean snow 3.0–5.7 mm °C^{-1} day^{-1} and for clean ice 5.0–7.7 mm °C^{-1} day^{-1}) at different locations worldwide shows that degree-day factors computed for the Himalayan glacier both for clean snow and ice are close to the upper range of the reported values. These large values are explained by large solar radiation in the low latitude area. Takahashi *et al.* (1981) and Sato *et al.* (1984) examined the dependency of sensible heat, latent heat and longwave radiation on temperature and showed that degree-day factor increases with absorbed shortwave radiation. According to this estimation, the degree-day factor would be large due to large shortwave radiation in the low latitude area. Because diurnal variation in snowmelt factor is controlled by the distribution of temperature, therefore, time of maximum value of the hourly melt factor also follows the time of maximum temperature. Usually, maximum value of the hourly snowmelt and icemelt factors occurred at about 12:00–13:00 h for both clean and dusted blocks. The average maximum hourly snowmelt factor for clean and dusted snow was 0.74 and 0.85 mm °C^{-1} h^{-1}, respectively. For clean and dusted ice, the average maximum hourly icemelt factor was 0.92 and 1.11 mm °C^{-1} h^{-1}.

Pratap Singh et al.

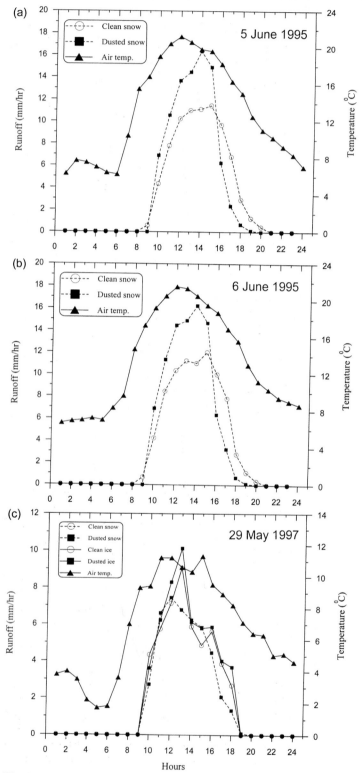

Fig. 1 Melt runoff from clean and dusted snow blocks along with air temperature.

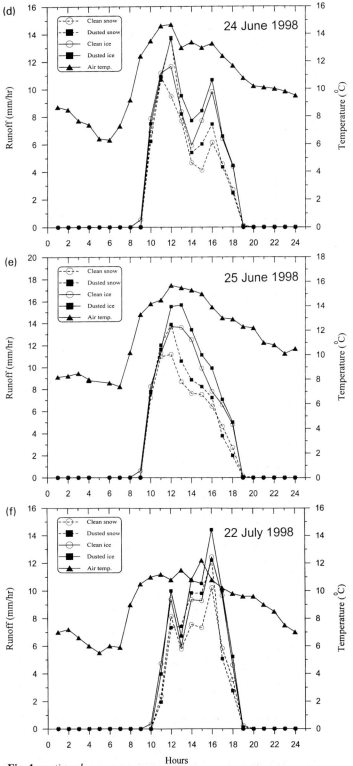

Fig. 1 *continued.*

Table 1 Degree-day factors for clean and dusted snow and ice (mm °C⁻¹ day⁻¹). Daily average temperature was obtained from the mean of hourly (0000–2400 h) temperature data. The degree-day factor of clean ice was larger than that of clean snow and it was increased by the existence of debris cover.

Date	Degree-day factor for snow:			Degree-day factor for ice:		
	Clean snow	Debris-covered snow	Increase due to debris layer (%)	Clean ice	Debris-covered ice	Increase due to debris layer (%)
5 June 1995	5.9	6.6	11.9	-	-	-
6 June 1995	6.0	6.7	11.7	-	-	-
29 May 1997	5.8	6.4	10.3	7.3	7.9	8.2
24 June 1998	5.4	6.1	13.0	7.0	7.5	7.1
25 June 1998	5.8	6.4	10.3	7.7	8.4	9.1
22 July 1998	5.7	6.4	12.3	7.4	8.1	9.5
Average	5.8	6.4	11.6	7.3	8.0	8.5

Our observations indicate that the degree-day factor for ice is higher than the degree-day factor for snow. On an average, degree-day factor for ice was about 26% higher than that for snow. Such an increase in the degree-day factor for ice is possible because the lower albedo of the ice results in a greater absorbed radiation at the ice surface compared with a snow surface (Sato *et al.*, 1984).

The introduction of a debris layer on the ice increased the degree-day factor by about 8.5%, whereas for snow it was increased by 11.6% due to presence of debris. Generally a thin debris layer promotes ablation and causes a large degree-day factor, while a thick debris layer suppresses ablation and yields a small degree-day factor. In the present study a 2-mm-thick debris layer is a thin layer which therefore increased the ablation. The reason why its influence was larger on snow than ice was that the albedo change was larger on snow because the original albedo of snow was higher than that of ice. The degree-day factors established in the present study through field investigations can be used for the estimation of melting from snow- and ice-covered areas using only temperature and snow/ice covered area information.

Acknowledgement The authors are grateful to the Department of Science and Technology, Government of India, for providing funds to carry out the study.

REFERENCES

Avsiuk, G. A. (1953) Artificial augmentation of snow and ice melting of mountain glaciers. In: *Proc. Inst. Geogr., Acad. Nauk SSSR* **56**. Moscow.

Avsiuk, G. A. (1962) *Artificial Augmentation of Melting of Mountain Glaciers to Increase the Runoff of Rivers in Soviet Central Asia.* Acad. Nauk Series, Geography, no. 5, Moscow.

Braithwaite, R. J. (1995) Positive degree-day factors for ablation on the Greenland ice sheet studied by energy-balance modelling. *J. Glaciol.* **41**, 153–160.

Finsterwalder, S. & Schunk, H. (1887) Der Suldenferner. *Z. Deutsch. Österreich. Alpenvereins* **18**, 72–89.

Fujii, Y. & Higuchi, K. (1977) Statistical analysis of the forms of glaciers in Khumbu region. *J. Japan. Soc. Snow Ice (Seppyo)* **39**, special issue, 7–14.

Kotlyakov, V. M. & Dolgushin, L. D. (1972) Possibility of artificial augmentation of melting by surface dusting of glaciers (results of Soviet investigations). In: *Role of Snow and Ice in Hydrology* (Proc. Banff Symp., September 1972), vol. 2, 1421–1426. IAHS Publ. no. 107.

Mattson, L. E., Gardner, J. S. & Young, G. J. (1993) Ablation on debris-covered glaciers: an example from Rakhiot Glacier, Punjab Himalayas. In: *Snow and Glacier Hydrology* (ed. by G. J. Young) (Proc. Kathmandu Symp., November 1992), 289–296. IAHS Publ. no. 218.

Nakawo, M., Morohoshi, T. & Uehara, S. (1993) Satellite data utilization for estimating ablation of debris covered glaciers. In: *Snow and Glacier Hydrology* (ed. by G. J. Young) (Proc. Kathmandu Symp., November 1992), 75– 83. IAHS Publ. no. 218.

Nakawo, M. & Young, G. J. (1982) Estimate of glacier ablation under a debris layer from surface temperature and meteorological variables. *J. Glaciol.* **28**, 29–34.

Østrem, G. (1959) Ice melting under a thin layer of moraine and existence of ice cores in moraine ridges. *Geogr. Ann.* **41**, 686–694.

Rana, B., Nakawo, M., Ageta, Y. & Seko, K. (1996) Glacier ablation under debris cover: field observations on Lirung Glacier, Nepal Himalayas. In: *Proc. International Conference on Ecohydrology of High Mountain Areas* (24–28 March, Kathmandu), 393–403. International Centre for Integerated Mountain Development, Kathmandu, Nepal.

Sato, A., Takahasi, S., Naruse, R. & Wakahama, G. (1984) Ablation and heat balance of the Yukikabe snow patch in the Daisetsu mountains, Hokkaido, Japan. *Ann. Glaciol.* **5**, 122–126.

Takahashi, S., Sato, A. & Naruse, R. (1981) A study of heat balance on Yukikabe snow patch in the Daisetsu mountains. *J. Japan. Soc. Snow Ice (Seppyo)* **43**, 147–154.

Singh, P. & Kumar, N. (1996) Determination of snowmelt factor in the Himalayan region. *Hydrol. Sci. J.* **41**(3), 301–310.

Singh, P. & Ramasastri, K. S. (1999) *Temporal Distribution of Dokriani Glacier Melt Runoff and its Relationship with Meteorological Parameters*. Project Report, National Institute of Hydrology, Roorkee, India.

Singh, P., Jain, S. K. & Kumar, N. (1997) Snow and glacier melt runoff contribution in the Chenab River at Akhnoor. *Mountain Res. Develop.* **17**, 49–56.

Singh P., Ramasastri, K. S., Singh, U. K., Gergan, J. T. & Dobhal, D. P. (1995) Hydrological characteristics of the Dokriani Glacier in the Garhwal Himalayas. *Hydrol. Sci. J.* **40**(2), 243–257.

Debris-Covered Glaciers (Proceedings of a workshop held at Seattle, Washington, USA, September 2000).
IAHS Publ. no. 264, 2000.

Practical prediction of ice melting beneath various thickness of debris cover on Khumbu Glacier, Nepal, using a positive degree-day factor

RIJAN BHAKTA KAYASTHA

*Institute for Hydrospheric–Atmospheric Sciences, Nagoya University, Furo-cho, Chikusa-ku,
Nagoya 464-8601, Japan*
e-mail: rijan@ihas.nagoya-u.ac.jp

YUKARI TAKEUCHI*

*The Research Institute for Hazards in Snowy Areas, Niigata University, Igarashi,
Niigata 950-2181, Japan*

MASAYOSHI NAKAWO & YUTAKA AGETA

*Institute for Hydrospheric–Atmospheric Sciences, Nagoya University, Furo-cho, Chikusa-ku,
Nagoya 464-8601, Japan*

Abstract Ice ablation on bare ice and under various thickness of debris was
measured on Khumbu Glacier from 21 May to 1 June 1999 in order to study
how debris affects the relationship between positive degree-day factor and
ablation rate. Results for a debris cover ranging in thickness from 0 to 5 cm
show that ice ablation is enhanced by a maximum at 0.3 cm. Debris thicker
than 5 cm retards ablation. Although meteorological measurements show that
the main energy source for ablation is net radiation (about 96% of total energy
available for ablation on bare ice) the positive degree-day factor is
nevertheless a successful predictor. For ice ablation on bare ice it is 16.9 mm
day^{-1} °C^{-1}. Under 10- and 40-cm-thick debris layers, the factors are 11.1 and
5.3 mm day^{-1} °C^{-1}, respectively. The data required to predict ice ablation under
a debris layer are ablation rate on bare ice, ratio of degree-day factor for debris
cover to bare ice based on thermal resistance for the critical debris thickness
and effective thermal resistance of the debris cover.

INTRODUCTION

The means to predict ablation on glaciers in the Himalayas is important in order to
predict the long-term availability of water resources and assess glacier response to
climate change. The use of an energy balance model to calculate ablation on a remote
Himalayan glacier is difficult due to limited input data. Furthermore, the ablation areas
of many glaciers in the Himalayas are covered by debris. Debris has a strong influence
on the surface energy balance and melting of the underlying ice. The thermal
conductivity (or thermal resistance) and albedo are the main physical characteristics of
a debris layer that control heat conduction to the ice–debris interface. This barrier to
heat transfer causes the rate of ablation to decrease with increasing debris thickness
once a critical thickness is exceeded (Østrem, 1959; Loomis, 1970; Fujii, 1977;
Mattson & Gardner, 1989; Rana *et al.*, 1997). A critical debris thickness is defined as

* *Now at*: Niigata Experimental Laboratory, Public Works Research Institute, Arai 944-0051, Japan.

the thickness at which the ablation rate for debris-covered glacier ice is the same as for debris-free ice. A simple model by Nakawo & Young (1981) showed that the ablation under a given debris layer can be estimated from meteorological variables when the thermal resistance of the debris layer is known. Nakawo & Takahashi (1982) proposed a model to overcome the difficulty of determining heat flux components from meteorological variables. The model used positive degree-day factor as input data. However, the proposed model needs meteorological data, thermal resistance, radiation and albedo data, which are difficult to determine for a remote glacier.

Many studies have been carried out using positive degree-day factors for glacier ablation on a debris-free ice surface. Kayastha *et al.* (2000) studied the positive degree-day method on debris-free Glacier AX010 in the Nepalese Himalayas and compared their results with other glaciers. Since the positive degree-day method can give a good estimate of ablation on debris free-ice without radiative and turbulent heat flux data, there is good reason to investigate whether it could be effective where there is a debris cover. This paper describes the degree-day factors for ablation under various thickness of debris cover characterized by their thermal resistance on Khumbu Glacier. A practical relationship between degree-day factor and effective thermal resistance is established so that the degree-day factor can be predicted from the thermal resistance of a debris layer. In addition, different energy balance components are calculated using meteorological data to establish their relative importance for ablation. The energy balance method is tested by comparing the calculated and measured values for ice ablation. Variations of ice ablation and positive degree-day factors on different debris-covered glaciers are studied by comparing measured ice ablation and calculated degree-day factors on two other glaciers.

OBSERVATION SITE AND DATA COLLECTION

Observations were made on the uppermost part of the ablation area of Khumbu Glacier near the Everest Base Camp (5350 m a.s.l.). Ablation measurements were carried out from 21 May to 1 June 1999. Seven plots were prepared ranging from bare ice to debris cover up to 40 cm thick (Fig. 1). The length of each plot ranges from about 0.5 m to 1 m with breath about 0.5 m. The plots were prepared by first removing all the debris and then rearranging the debris with different thickness of 2 cm, 5 cm, 10 cm, 20 cm, 30 cm and 40 cm. The debris consisted of mainly angular, loosely packed wet cobbles up to 3 cm in diameter. The dominant debris lithology was light coloured granitic rocks. A string was tied tightly to two poles that were drilled and frozen solidly into the ice to about 1.5 m depth at the extreme end of the plots. The vertical distance from the string to the bare ice or debris surface was measured at fixed points over each plot four times (08:00, 11:00, 14:00 and 17:00) a day. The change in height with time was taken as a measure of ice ablation. In addition, stake measurements were carried out between 26 May to 1 June 1999 near the plots on a clean ice surface with a thin debris layer (average thickness 0.3 cm) prepared by spreading fine debris onto the bare ice.

The surface temperature and albedo of the bare ice and different debris surfaces were measured at the four observation times using an infrared thermometer and a

Fig. 1 Experimental site on Khumbu Glacier, Nepal, showing plots of debris thickness ranging from 0 to 40 cm.

photodiode. The albedo measured by the photodiode was calibrated with an albedometer (by Eiko-seiki). The cloud amount and type were also observed at the four observation times. Meteorological variables such as dry and wet bulb temperature, incoming shortwave radiation, wind speed, and surface temperature on a debris thickness of 10 cm were recorded at 10 minute intervals at another plot near the measured plots. The types of instruments used in the field were described in detail in Takeuchi *et al.* (2000).

METEOROLOGICAL CONDITIONS

The observation period was just before the onset of the monsoon, and weather was dominated by high pressure. There were only two precipitation events, one on 24 May (1.9 mm) and another on 27 May (2.5 mm). The following means for the full observation period were recorded: air temperature 1.5°C, incoming shortwave radiation 310 W m^{-2}, relative humidity 91%, wind speed 0.7 m s^{-1}, and cloud cover 7/10. The most common cloud type was stratus with a few cases of cumulus. Variations of air temperature, incoming shortwave radiation, wind speed, relative humidity, cloud cover, albedo for bare ice and 10-cm thick debris cover, and surface temperature on a 10-cm thick debris cover are shown in Fig. 2. The hourly values of daytime albedo and cloud cover are obtained by linearly interpolating between measurements at 3-h intervals from 8:00 to 17:00. Similarly, the hourly cloud cover during night-time was obtained by interpolating the data from 17:00 and 8:00 with the addition of 1/10 to take account of climatological information that more precipitation occurs during night-time than daytime in the valleys of the Nepalese Himalayas (Ageta, 1976).

Rijan Bhakta Kayastha et al.

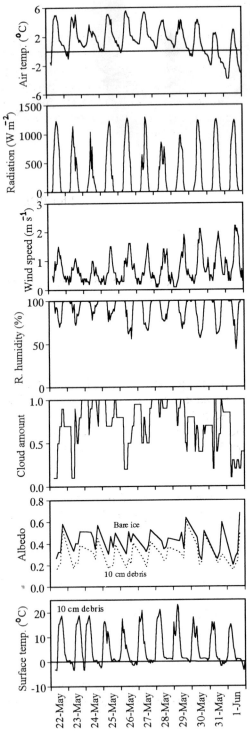

Fig. 2 Variations of meteorological parameters on Khumbu Glacier during the observation period in 1999.

POSITIVE DEGREE-DAY FACTOR

The positive degree-day method assumes that the amount of snow or ice melt during any particular period is proportional to the sum of daily mean temperatures above the melting point during that period. This sum is called the positive degree-day sum (*PDD*). The factor linking ablation to *PDD* is the positive degree-day factor (*k*). The factor *k* involves a simplification of complex processes that are properly described by the energy balance of the glacier surface and overlaying atmospheric boundary layer (Braithwaite, 1995). By definition *k* is calculated as:

$$k = \frac{\Sigma a}{PDD} \tag{1}$$

where Σa is total ablation during the same period as the period for *PDD*.

ENERGY BALANCE CALCULATION

The energy balance equation on a melting bare ice surface can be expressed as:

$$Q_M = Q_R + Q_H + Q_E \tag{2}$$

On top of a debris layer it is

$$Q_C = Q_R + Q_H + Q_E \tag{3}$$

where Q_M, Q_C, Q_R, Q_H, and Q_E are energy used for ablation on bare ice, conductive heat flux through the debris, net radiation flux, sensible heat flux, and latent heat flux, respectively. All the fluxes are taken to be positive downward.

The net radiation flux is the sum of net shortwave (*K**) and longwave radiation (*L**) fluxes. The net shortwave radiation flux can be calculated as:

$$K^* = G(1 - \alpha) \tag{4}$$

where *G* is the global radiation and α is the albedo of the surface.

The longwave radiation emitted from the surface, $L_\uparrow$, can be calculated from the Stephan-Boltzmann law:

$$L_\uparrow = \sigma(T_S + 273K)^4 \tag{5}$$

where σ is Stephan-Boltzmann constant (5.67×10^{-8} W m^{-2} K^{-4}) and T_S is surface temperature (°C).

The downward longwave radiation under clear-sky, $L_\downarrow$, is calculated from the equation by Kuz'min (1961):

$$L_\downarrow = \sigma(T_a + 273)^4(0.62 + 0.005\sqrt{e_a}) \tag{6}$$

where T_a is air temperature (°C), and e_a is vapour pressure of the air (Pa).

According to Oke (1987), the net longwave radiation under a cloudy sky (mostly stratus cloud) is given by:

$$L^* = (L_\downarrow - L_\uparrow)(1 - 0.96c^2) \tag{7}$$

where c is the cloud amount as a fraction.

The convective energy fluxes Q_H and Q_E are estimated using the bulk aerodynamic method:

$$Q_H = \beta u (T_a - T_s) \tag{8}$$

$$Q_E = \beta u L_e \frac{0.622}{Pc_p} (e_a - e_s) \tag{9}$$

where β is the bulk transfer coefficient (4.9 J m^{-3} K^{-1}, Naruse *et al.*, 1970); u is wind speed (m s^{-1}); L_e is the latent heat of evaporation (2.5 × 10^6 J kg^{-1}); P is atmospheric pressure (hPa); c_p is the specific heat of air at constant pressure (1005 J kg^{-1} °C^{-1}); e_a is vapour pressure of the air (hPa); e_s is saturation vapour pressure at the surface (hPa). Since the debris was wet at the beginning and only the top few millimetres of debris ever dried out, it is assumed that the vapour pressure at the debris surface was saturated.

A linear variation of temperature is assumed in the debris layer so that:

$$Q_C = \frac{T_s}{R} \tag{10}$$

where T_s is the debris surface temperature relative to melting (0°C) and R (m^2 °C W^{-1}) is the effective thermal resistance of the debris layer.

The energy used for ice ablation Q_M or Q_C is calculated from:

$$Q_M \text{ or } Q_C = L_f \rho_i r \tag{11}$$

where L_f is the latent heat of phase change of ice (334 × 10^3 J kg^{-1}), ρ_i is density of the ice (900 kg m^{-3}) and r is ablation rate in ice thickness (m s^{-1}).

RESULTS

Ice ablation and energy balance

Measured mean daily ablation rates on bare ice and under 10- and 40-cm-thick debris layers during the observation period are about 3.1, 2 and 1 cm day^{-1}, respectively

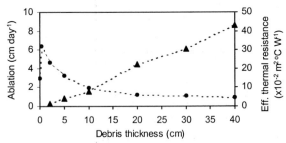

Fig. 3 Variation of measured mean daily ice ablation (dotted line with solid dots) and calculated thermal resistance (dotted line with solid triangles) with respect to debris thickness.

Table 1 Measured ice ablation and daily mean air temperature, calculated positive degree-day factors (k) and effective thermal resistances (R) for different thickness of debris cover.

Date	Air temp. (°C)	Daily ice ablation (cm) under a debris layer of thickness:							
		0 cm	0.3 cm	2 cm	5 cm	10 cm	20 cm	30 cm	40 cm
21 May	0.6	1.3	-	4.5	2.4	1.5	0.6	0.7	0.6
22 May	1.9	4.6	-	5.4	3.6	1.4	1.0	1.9	0.7
23 May	2.3	1.7	-	4.2	2.7	1.8	1.6	1.6	1.2
24 May	1.6	1.4	-	3.4	1.2	1.2	0.8	0.8	0.5
25 May	2.4	2.6	6.7	5.0	3.2	2.0	1.5	1.5	1.1
26 May	2.6	4.2	8.3	6.6	4.0	2.8	1.6	1.1	1.0
27 May	2.6	3.9	6.3	4.7	4.3	1.9	1.6	1.3	0.9
28 May	2.2	3.1	5.2	4.2	2.6	1.7	0.8	0.7	0.8
29 May	1.6	2.7	5.1	4.1	4.1	3.3	1.0	0.9	1.5
30 May	1.0	3.4	6.5	4.7	3.9	2.0	2.8	1.1	0.9
31 May	−0.9	3.6	6.5	5.1	3.5	2.1	1.6	1.8	1.6
1 June	−1.4	2.7	6.5	4.2	2.9	1.5	0.6	0.4	0.3
Mean	1.5	3.1	6.4	4.7	3.3	2.0	1.4	1.2	1.0
k (mm day^{-1} °C^{-1})		16.9	37.2	26.9	18.4	11.1	7.4	6.6	5.3
R ($\times 10^{-2}$ m^2 °C W^{-1})				1.4	4.0	8.1	22.3	30.6	43.0

(Fig. 3 and Table 1). It is found that the largest mean daily ablation rate (6.4 cm day^{-1}) during the observation period occurred beneath a debris layer of about 0.3 cm. The ablation rate under a debris cover thicker than about 5 cm is less than that for clean ice. Ablation becomes negligible for a debris thickness greater than about 1 m.

We first examine now how well the energy balance method explains this pattern. The energy balance components are calculated only for bare ice and a 10-cm debris layer, since continuous surface temperature is available only for the 10-cm debris layer. The

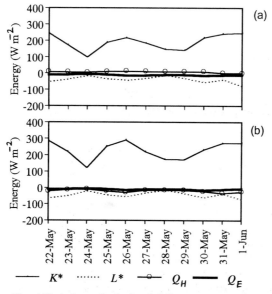

Fig. 4 Variations of calculated daily mean energy balance components on (a) bare ice and (b) a 10-cm-thick debris layer.

surface temperature of bare ice is assumed to be always 0°C. The variations of energy balance components are shown in Fig. 4. Figure 4 shows that the main energy source is the net shortwave radiation, which contributes about 96% of total energy available for ablation on bare ice and near 100% under the 10-cm debris layer. Sensible heat makes only a little contribution (4%) on bare ice. All energy balance components are negative except shortwave radiation on the 10-cm debris surface mainly due to higher surface temperature and evaporation from the wet debris. The very low values of the net shortwave radiation on 24 May and 28–29 May are due to rainfall and the presence of high cloud cover, respectively.

Figure 5 shows calculated and measured variations of daily ice ablation on bare ice and under the 10-cm debris layer. The calculated ice ablation is always greater than the measured value and the difference is especially large in the case of the 10-cm debris. The overestimated energy on bare ice and the 10-cm debris layer are about 45 W m^{-2} and 80 W m^{-2}, respectively, during the observation period. In general, the difference is higher on clear days than cloudy days (e.g. 24, 28 and 29 May). The main cause for this systematic difference may be the parameterization of elements in different energy balance equations. In any case there is uncertainty in the standard application of the energy balance method.

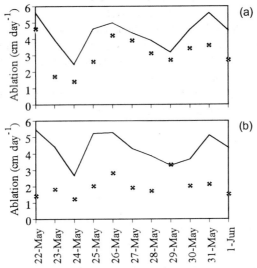

Fig. 5 Comparison of measured and calculated daily ice ablation (a) on bare ice and (b) under a 10-cm-thick debris layer. Crosses and lines indicate the measured and calculated ice ablation, respectively.

Thermal resistance and positive degree-day factor

Effective thermal resistances of different debris layers are calculated from the measured ice ablation and surface temperature using equation (10) during daytime (from 06:00 to 18:00), but full day averages are used for the 10-cm debris layer. The effective thermal resistance increases as the debris thickness increases (Fig. 3 and Table 1).

Positive degree-day factors for ablation on bare ice and different thickness of debris cover are calculated from 21 May to 1 June 1999, except for the 0.3-cm-thick debris layer where measurements did not start until 25 May 1999. Since the air temperature is the same in all cases, the calculated positive degree-day factor increases as the ablation increases. Therefore, the positive degree-day factor for ablation is highest at 37.2 mm day^{-1} °C^{-1} for a 0.3-cm-thick debris layer and the lowest at 5.3 mm day^{-1} °C^{-1} for a 40-cm-thick debris layer. The positive degree-day factor for ablation on bare ice is 16.9 mm day^{-1} °C^{-1}.

The positive degree-day factor for bare ice k_b is probably controlled by meteorological conditions and the degree-day factor for ice ablation under a debris cover k_d is affected by both the debris properties and the meteorological conditions. Therefore, we seek a relationship between k_d and these two kinds of variables in simplified form given by

$$\frac{k_d}{k_b} = F\left(\frac{R}{R_c}\right)$$
(12)

This assumes that the meteorological information is expressed entirely in k_b and that the characteristics of the debris are given by the function F. F should depend primarily on the thermal resistance R of the debris. However, to account for effects from debris albedo and possibly other secondary variables, we define F to be a function of R/R_c, where R_c is thermal resistance for critical debris thickness. R_c is calculated as the ratio of critical debris thickness to the thermal conductivity of debris cover. In this experiment an average found for thickness 2–40 cm was used. Figure 6 shows the function F as defined by our measurements. This relationship should be transferable to other glaciers with debris with possibly different thermal characteristics. So, if R/R_c is known, k_d/k_b and ice ablation under the debris layer can be estimated.

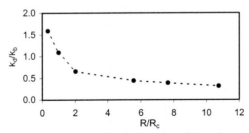

Fig. 6 Ratio of k_d to k_b (k_d: degree-day factor for given debris thickness, k_b degree-day factor for bare ice) *vs* ratio of R to R_c (R: effective thermal resistance of debris and R_c: thermal resistance for critical debris thickness).

Comparison of the results with other similar experimental results

The present results are compared with results of similar experiments on two other glaciers in the Himalayas. An experiment on Lirung Glacier (4350 m a.s.l.) showed a maximum ablation rate (4.5 cm day^{-1}) for a 2.6-cm-thick debris layer and the critical thickness of about 9 cm (Rana *et al.*, 1997). Maximum ablation (12.1 cm day^{-1}) was recorded under a 1-cm-thick debris layer and the critical thickness was about 3 cm on

Rakhiot Glacier at about 3350 m a.s.l. (Mattson & Gardner, 1989). The present and the above-mentioned experiments showed that the ice ablation under a debris layer varies widely from glacier to glacier as well as from one point to another even on the same glacier.

The positive degree-day factors for ablation on bare ice and under the 10-cm-thick debris layer were recalculated for Lirung and Rakhiot Glaciers using the original data, which gave 6.6 and 5.5 mm day^{-1} °C^{-1} on Lirung Glacier and 6.6 and 3.5 mm day^{-1} °C^{-1} on Rakhiot Glacier. The degree-day factors for ablation on bare ice were similar on Lirung and Rakhiot Glaciers, although their observation periods were different. The predicted degree-day factor for ice ablation under the 10-cm-thick debris cover on Rakhiot Glacier was smaller than on Lirung Glacier. In the case of Khumbu Glacier, these values are very large as shown in Table 1 (16.9 and 11.1 mm day^{-1} °C^{-1}) due to the smaller *PDD* at higher altitudes compared to the Lirung and Rakhiot Glaciers and a strong contribution of the net radiation to ablation energy.

Very large positive degree-day factors for ablation were also found on Glacier AX010, east Nepal, in June at high altitude (15.6 mm day^{-1} °C^{-1}; Kayastha *et al.*, 2000), in Spitsbergen (13.8 mm day^{-1} °C^{-1}; Schytt, 1964), and on GIMEX profile (20.1 mm day^{-1} °C^{-1}; van de Wal, 1992). Since thermal properties of the debris were not available on the Lirung and Rakhiot Glaciers, the results could not be compared in terms of the ratio of k_d to k_b and R to R_c.

According to the present study, the data required to predict ice ablation under a debris layer are ablation rate on bare ice and k_d/k_b. The k_d/k_b ratio can be obtained from F defined in Fig. 6 if R/R_c is known. R_c can be measured for different glaciers, and it is likely that R_c will be the same for the same geological environment. Regional estimate of glacier ablation from debris-covered glaciers can be implemented with the aid of remote sensing data giving surface temperature to estimate thermal resistance R of the debris cover (Nakawo *et al.*, 1993). The most important parameter remaining is then the degree-day factor for bare ice k_b.

Acknowledgements We would like to express our thanks to the staff of the Department of Hydrology and Meteorology, Ministry of Science and Technology, His Majesty's Government of Nepal. Field assistance was provided by Drs T. Kadota and N. Naito of the Institute of Hydrospheric–Atmospheric Sciences, Nagoya University, and all members of the project. We would also like to thank Prof. C. F. Raymond, University of Washington for his valuable suggestions on the first draft of this paper. This study was supported by a Grant-in-aid for International Scientific Research and Analysis (nos 09041103 and 09490018) of the Ministry of Education, Science, Sports and Culture of Japan, and Cooperative Research under the Japan–US Cooperative Science Programme from the Japan Society for the Promotion of Science.

REFERENCES

Ageta, Y. (1976) Characteristics of the precipitation during monsoon season in Khumbu Himal. *J. Japan. Soc. Snow Ice (Seppyo)* **38**, special issue, 84–88.

Braithwaite, R. J. (1995) Positive degree-day factors for ablation on the Greenland ice sheet studied by energy-balance modelling. *J. Glaciol.* **41**(137), 153–160.

Fujii, Y. (1977) Experiment on glacier ablation under a layer of debris cover. *J. Japan. Soc. Snow Ice (Seppyo)* **39**, special issue, 20–21.

Kayastha, R. B., Ageta, Y. & Nakawo, M. (2000) Positive degree-day factors for ablation on glaciers in the Nepalese Himalayas: case study on Glacier AX010 in Shorong Himal, Nepal. *Bull. Glaciol. Res.* **17**, 1–10.

Kuz'min, P. P. (1961) *Protsess Tayaniya Shezhnogo Pokrova* (Melting of snow cover). Gidrometeorol. Izd. Leningrad (English Translation TT71-50095, Israel Program Sci. Transl., Jerusalem, 1972).

Loomis, S. R. (1970) Morphology and ablation processes on glacier ice. *Proc. Ass. Am. Geogr.* **2**, 88–92.

Mattson, L. E. & Gardner, J. S. (1989) Energy exchange and ablation rates on the debris-covered Rakhiot Glacier, Pakistan. *Z. Gletscherk. Glaziageol.* **25**(1), 17–32.

Nakawo, M. & Takahashi, S. (1982) A simplified model for estimating glacier ablation under a debris layer. In: *Hydrological Aspect of Alpine and High-Mountain Areas* (ed. by J. W. Glen) (Proc. Exeter Symp., July 1982), 137–145. IAHS Publ. no. 138.

Nakawo, M. & Young, G. J. (1981) Field experiments to determine the effect of a debris layer on ablation of glacier ice. *Ann. Glaciol.* **2**, 85–91.

Nakawo, M., Morohoshi, T. & Uehara, S. (1993) Satellite data utilization for estimating ablation of debris covered glaciers. In: *Snow and Glacier Hydrology* (ed. by G. J. Young) (Proc. Kathmandu Symp., November 1992), 75–83. IAHS Publ. no. 218.

Naruse, R., Oura, H. & Kojima, K. (1970) Kion-yusetsu no yagai kenkyu (Field studies on snow melt due to sensible heat transfer from the atmosphere). *Teon Kagaku: Low temperature Science*, series A (28), 191–202.

Østrem, G. (1959) Ice melting under a thin layer of moraine, and the existence of ice cores in moraine ridges. *Geogr. Ann.* **41**(4), 228–230.

Oke, T. R. (1987) *Boundary Layer Climates*, second edn. Methuen, London and New York.

Rana, B., Nakawo, M., Fukushima, Y. & Ageta, Y. (1997) Application of a conceptual precipitation–runoff model (HYCYMODEL) in a debris-covered glacierized basin in the Langtang Valley, Nepal Himalaya. *Ann. Glaciol.* **25**, 266–231.

Schytt, V. (1964) Scientific results of the Swedish Glaciological Expedition to Nordaustlander, Spitsbergen, 1957 and 1958. *Geogr. Ann.* **46**(3), 243–281.

Takeuchi, Y., Kayastha, R. B., Naito, N., Kadota, T. & Izumi, K. (2000) Meteorological features at the Khumbu Glacier, Nepal Himalayas, in the premonsoon season, 1999. Submitted to: *Bull. Glaciol. Res.* **18**.

Wal, R. van de (1992) Ice and climate. PhD Thesis, Utrecht University.

Debris-Covered Glaciers (Proceedings of a workshop held at Seattle, Washington, USA, September 2000).
IAHS Publ. no. 264, 2000.

Air temperature environment on the debris-covered area of Lirung Glacier, Langtang Valley, Nepal Himalayas

KOJI FUJITA & AKIKO SAKAI

*Institute for Hydrospheric–Atmospheric Sciences, Nagoya University, Furo-cho, Chikusa-ku,
Nagoya 464-8601, Japan*
e-mail: bri@ihas.nagoya-u.ac.jp

Abstract Meteorological observations have been carried out for different surface covers (grass, debris-free glacier and rock-covered glacier ice in Langtang Valley, Nepal Himalayas. Change in the daily mean lapse rate over debris-covered ice shows a significantly larger fluctuation compared with over debris-free ice. An analysis of the daily mean lapse rate reveals that a "low" ["high"] lapse rate appeared under dry [wet] conditions on the debris-covered area even though the opposite result was expected for the lapse rate of a free atmosphere. It is considered that less evaporation under dry condition would bring about high surface and then warm air temperatures. Diurnal changes in the lapse rate over debris-covered ice suggests that the air temperature changes less over the debris-covered ice than over grassland and debris-free ice. Perhaps heat stored in the debris layer would prevent large diurnal changes in air temperature. Both seasonal and diurnal changes in lapse rate suggest the strong effect on air temperature of the complex topography of the debris-covered area and the presence of the debris layer. This fact suggests that air temperature cannot be simply estimated by a constant lapse rate as in previous studies.

INTRODUCTION

One of the most common characteristics of glaciers in the Himalayas is the presence of a debris mantle masking a large portion of their ablation areas. Reports have consistently indicated that this debris cover exerts a tremendous influence on the ablation process itself. Several studies on the ablation process under the debris layer have been carried out in the Himalayas (e.g. Mattson & Gardner, 1989; Mattson *et al.*, 1993; Rana *et al.*, 1997; Nakawo & Rana, 1999). The meteorological environment over the debris has not been discussed in previous studies, though it has been treated as input data for the calculation. In this investigation, we present the seasonal and diurnal changes in air temperature over different surfaces such as grassland, debris-free glacier ice and debris-covered glacier ice by using the lapse rate.

OBSERVATIONS AND ANALYSIS

Meteorological observations were carried out at the grass-covered site of Base House (BH, 3878 m a.s.l.), the debris-covered site on Lirung Glacier (LR, 4153 m a.s.l.) and at a site of debris-free snow on Yala Glacier (YL, 5350 m a.s.l.) from May to October

Koji Fujita & Akiko Sakai

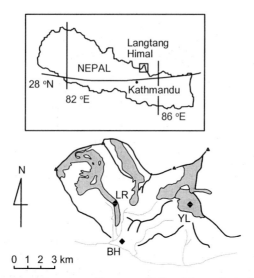

Fig. 1 Location of Langtang Valley. Meteorological observations were conducted at the grass-covered site of Base House (BH), the debris-covered site of Lirung Glacier (LR) and the debris-free snow of Yala Glacier (YL) situated in a valley.

1996. The locations of each site are shown in Fig. 1. The altitudes of each site were surveyed by a laser distance finder in 1996 (Aoki & Asahi, 1998; Fujita *et al.*, 1998). Daily mean meteorological data were summarized by Fujita *et al.* (1997).

The lapse rate (l_a, °C km^{-1}) at a certain site (subscript a) is the air temperature difference per unit elevation from a reference site (subscript r) described as:

$$l_a = \frac{(T_r - T_a)}{(h_a - h_r)} \times 1000 \tag{1}$$

where, T and h are air temperature (°C) and altitude (m a.s.l.) at each site. Air temperature was measured at a height of 1.5 m, and the sensor was shaded from solar radiation. The site BH was selected as the reference site because of the meteorological data collected there since 1985 and its location at the bottom of the main valley.

CHANGES IN DAILY MEAN LAPSE RATE

Variations in the daily mean lapse rate at LR (l_L), YL (l_Y) and BH are shown in Fig. 2. The average lapse rates at LR ($\overline{l_L}$) and at YL ($\overline{l_Y}$) were 5.1 and 5.4 (°C km^{-1}), respectively. It was reported that the lapse rate was about 10.0 (°C km^{-1}) at Chongce Glacier, which is located in the West Kunlun Mountains, on the northern side of the Tibetan Plateau, because the air mass was cooled by the glacier (Ohata *et al.*, 1989). On Yala Glacier, however, no cooling effect by the glacier can be seen in the lapse rate because its area (2.5 km^2) is considerably smaller than that of Chongce Glacier (16.4 km^2; Zhang & Jiao, 1987). Figure 2 clearly shows that the fluctuation of l_L is significantly larger than that of l_Y. Standard deviations of the lapse rate at LR (σ_L) and YL (σ_Y) are 2.1 and 0.8 (°C km^{-1}), respectively. The smaller deviation of l_Y is

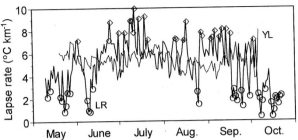

Fig. 2 Daily mean lapse rate at the debris-covered site on Lirung Glacier (LR, black line) and debris-free site on Yala Glacier (YL, grey line) compared with that for the grass-covered reference site at Base House (BH). Symbols denote "high" (rhombuses) and "low" (circles) lapse rates.

considered to be associated with the location of YL and BH. Since YL is located at the upper part of an open slope above BH, it is expected that the change in air temperatures at both sites would be that of the free atmosphere. The cold snow surface would also suppress variations and calm the atmosphere. The larger fluctuation of l_L, on the contrary, is thought to be affected by complex air flow, such as greater convection in the debris-covered area, because LR is located in the bottom of a deep valley and surrounded by heterogeneous debris topography. Figure 3 shows that at BH the wind is mainly from west-southwest toward YL (valley breeze), while the wind at YL mainly blows from north-northeast toward BH (slope wind). Although it is difficult to explain

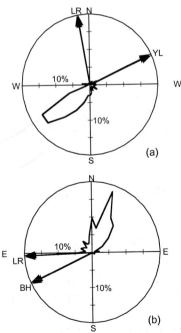

Fig. 3 Frequencies of wind direction at Base House (a) and Yala Glacier (b). Arrows denote the directions at the debris-covered site on Lirung Glacier (LR), the debris-free site on Yala Glacier (YL) and the grass-covered reference site at Base House (BH) from Base House (a) and Yala Glacier (b), respectively.

the more complex air flow at LR by the simple air flows at BH and YL, it is rare for the wind to blow from both sites toward LR. It is considered that the air temperature at LR is strongly controlled by the surface and topographical features around the site.

In order to understand which meteorological variables affect the large variation of the lapse rate at LR (l_L), three types of lapse rate were selected (Fig. 2): "high" (l_L higher than $\overline{l_L} + \sigma_L$; 26 days), "normal" ($l_L$ within $\overline{l_L} \pm \sigma_L$; 106 days) and "low" ($l_L$ lower than $\overline{l_L} - \sigma_L$; 34 days). Daily mean values of air temperature, wind speed, solar radiation, relative humidity, precipitation and surface temperature at LR and BH under each condition are summarized in Table 1. The table clearly shows that a "low" lapse rate at both sites was due to lower air temperature, higher wind speed, greater solar radiation, the smallest precipitation and the lowest relative humidity. Surface temperature at LR, on the other hand, does not seem to affect the lapse rate, while surface temperature at BH has the same effect as air temperature. The "low" lapse rate would appear under less cloudy, less precipitation and drier atmosphere conditions even though the air temperature was relatively low. Since an arid environment would bring about less evaporation, radiative fluxes absorbed at the debris surface, such as net shortwave radiation and downward longwave radiation, should be released by upward longwave radiation, sensible and ground heat fluxes except for latent heat. Because these fluxes are strongly associated with surface temperature, a higher surface temperature is expected with a dry surface, when the cooling effect on surface temperature by latent heat (evaporation) is small. As Table 1 shows, a higher surface temperature at LR appeared at a "low" lapse rate, while the air temperature was lower at LR even though both air and surface temperatures at BH were lower at a "low" lapse rate. The higher surface temperature for dry conditions would result in a relatively higher air temperature and lower lapse rate at LR. Mattson & Gardner (1989) have suggested that latent heat had an important role in the heat balance on the debris-covered glacier in the Karakoram, though it has been consistently ignored in previous studies (e.g. Rana et al., 1997; Nakawo & Rana, 1999). Figure 2 shows the occasional "low" ["high"] lapse rates during the pre- and post-monsoon [mid-monsoon] season, though a dry [wet] adiabatic lapse rate (large [small] value) is expected in the dry [wet] season. This also supports the

Table 1 Daily mean variables at the debris-covered site on Lirung Glacier (LR, upper rows) and the grass-covered reference site (BH, lower rows) for three conditions.

	Location	High	Normal	Low
Air temperature (°C)	LR	7.4	7.3	6.0
	BH	9.6	8.8	6.6
Wind speed (m s^{-1})	LR	1.0	1.2	1.4
	BH	1.3	1.7	2.1
Solar radiation (MJ m^{-2} day^{-1})	LR	12	17	25
	BH	18	20	26
Precipitation (mm water equivalent day^{-1})	LR	7.2	5.8	0.2
	BH	4.4	5.1	0.0
Relative humidity (%)	LR	98	92	74
	BH	94	89	71
Surface temperature (°C)	LR	8.7	10.5	9.4
	BH	16.1	15.7	12.4

idea that the lapse rate between LR and BH is not associated with the air temperature of the free atmosphere, but rather with the air temperature at LR, which would be strongly controlled by the local heat balance.

DIURNAL CHANGES IN LAPSE RATE

Figure 4 shows diurnal changes in hourly mean lapse rate at LR (l_L) and YL (l_Y) averaged for the period from May to October, 1996. The diurnal change in lapse rate at LR is obviously larger than that at YL. The stable l_Y suggests that the air temperature at YL and BH fluctuate synchronously. As mentioned above, the changes in air temperatures at both BH and YL would have synchronicity because of their location on an open slope and the dominant wind directions at both sites. The larger [smaller] lapse rate in daytime [night-time] at LR suggests that air temperature at LR is cooler [warmer] than at BH in daytime [night-time]. Figure 5 shows the diurnal variation of hourly mean air temperatures at BH and LR. The variation of air temperature estimated from air temperature at BH and the constant lapse rate (5.1 °C km^{-1}) is also shown in the figure. The figure suggests that the fluctuation of air temperature at LR is smaller (more stable) than at BH. Mattson & Gardner (1989) reported that 60–80% of the energy entering the debris cover was stored and used to change the temperature in the debris, and that the residual energy was used to melt ice under the debris. Their result suggests a stable fluctuation of air temperature at LR by the following process.

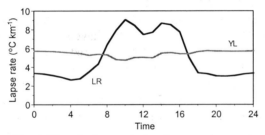

Fig. 4 Diurnal changes in hourly mean lapse rate for the debris-covered Lirung Glacier (LR, black line) and debris-free site on Yala Glacier (YL, grey line) from the grass-covered reference site at Base House.

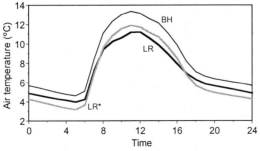

Fig. 5 Diurnal changes in hourly mean air temperature at the grass-covered reference site at Base House (BH, thin black line) and at the debris-covered site on Lirung Glacier (LR, thick black line). The grey line (LR*) denotes the diurnal change in hourly mean air temperature estimated from that at BH and the constant lapse rate (5.1 °C km^{-1}).

Increase of surface and air temperatures would be prevented in daytime by heat absorption into the debris. Then, on the following night, debris would prevent the lowering of surface and air temperatures by releasing the stored energy.

CONCLUDING REMARKS

A significant difference in seasonal and diurnal changes in air temperature in the debris-covered area is demonstrated in this study. This fact suggests that air temperature cannot be simply estimated by a constant lapse rate as in previous studies (e.g. Rana *et al.*, 1997; Nakawo *et al.*, 1999). It is considered that the large fluctuation in the lapse rate at the debris-covered site compared with the reference site are caused by the local heat balance in the complex topography of the debris-covered area. Hence, the relatively stable air temperature at the debris-covered site would be caused by the storage and release of heat in the debris layer. The heat balance for different surface conditions should be examined in further detail to find the effects on air temperature of the complex topography of the debris-covered area and the presence of the debris layer.

Acknowledgements We would like to express our thanks to the staff of the Department of Hydrology and Meteorology, Ministry of Science and Technology, His Majesty's Government of Nepal. We are much indebted to the people who assisted in this research programme in Langtang Valley. The field research and analysis were supported by a Grant-in-Aid for scientific research (project no. 06041051; 09490018) from the Ministry of Education, Science, Sports and Culture, Japanese Government, and cooperative research under the Japan–US Cooperative Science Program from the Japan Society for the Promotion of Science. We are grateful to Dr A. Fountain and anonymous reviewers for their valuable comments and suggestions on the first draft of this paper.

REFERENCES

Aoki, T. & Asahi, K. (1998) Topographical map of the ablation area of the Lirung Glacier in the Langtang Valley, Nepal Himalaya. *Bull. Glacier Res.* **16**, 19–31.
Fujita, K., Sakai, A. & Chettri, T. B. (1997) Meteorological observation in Langtang Valley, Nepal Himalayas, 1996. *Bull. Glacier Res.* **15**, 71–78.
Fujita, K., Takeuchi, N. & Seko, K. (1998) Glaciological observations of Yala Glacier in Langtang Valley, Nepal Himalayas, 1994 and 1996. *Bull. Glacier Res.* **16**, 75–81.
Mattson, L. E. & Gardner, J. S. (1989) Energy exchanges and ablation rates on the debris-covered Rakhiot Glacier, Pakistan. *Z. Gletscherk. Glazialgeol.* **25**(1), 17–32.
Mattson, L. E., Gardner, J. S. & Young, G. J. (1993) Ablation on debris covered glaciers: an example from the Rakhiot Glacier, Punjab Himalaya. In: *Snow and Glacier Hydrology* (ed. by G. J. Young) (Proc. Kathmandu Symp., November 1992), 289–296. IAHS Publ. no. 218.
Nakawo, M. & Rana, B. (1999) Estimate of ablation rate of glacier ice under a supraglacial debris layer. *Geogr. Ann.* **81A**(4), 695–701.
Nakawo, M., Yabuki, H. & Sakai, A. (1999) Characteristics of Khumbu Glacier, Nepal Himalaya: recent changes in the debris-covered area. *Ann. Glaciol.* **28**, 118–122.
Ohata, T., Takahashi, S. & Kang, X. (1989) Meteorological conditions of the West Kunlun Mountains in the summer of 1987. *Bull. Glacier Res.* **7**, 67–76.
Rana, B., Nakawo, M., Fukushima, Y. & Ageta, Y. (1997) Application of a conceptual precipitation–runoff model (HYCYMODEL) in a debris-covered glacierized basin in the Langtang Valley, Nepal Himalaya. *Ann. Glaciol.* **25**, 226–231.
Zhang, Z. & Jiao, K. (1987) Modern glaciers on the south slope of West Kunlun Mountains. *Bull. Glacier Res.* **5**, 85–91.

Debris-Covered Glaciers (Proceedings of a workshop held at Seattle, Washington, USA, September 2000).
IAHS Publ. no. 264, 2000.

Summer temperature profiles within supraglacial debris on Khumbu Glacier, Nepal

H. CONWAY & L. A. RASMUSSEN

Geophysics Program, University of Washington, Box 351650, Seattle, Washington 98195, USA
e-mail: conway@geophys.washington.edu; lar@geophys.washington.edu

Abstract Temperature measurements made during summer within supraglacial debris on Khumbu Glacier, Nepal show a strong diurnal signal that diffused downward into the debris with decreasing amplitude and increasing lag. Surface temperatures during the day were up to 35°C higher than the air temperature; energy transfer into the debris was dominated by the solar radiative flux. Temperature profiles through the debris indicate that heat flow deeper than about 0.2 m was primarily by conduction. The thermal conductivity k of the debris, estimated from a calculated thermal diffusivity and a representative volumetric heat capacity, was 0.85 ± 0.20 W m^{-1} K^{-1} at one site and 1.28 ± 0.15 W m^{-1} K^{-1} at another. At the first site the debris was 0.40 m thick and the average temperature gradient $\partial \overline{T}/\partial z = 19$ K m^{-1}; the average flux of energy through the debris was sufficient to melt 4–6 mm of ice per day. The debris was thicker (estimated to be 2.5 m) and the temperature gradient lower (4.5 K m^{-1}) at the second site, and the calculated ice-melt was less than 2 mm day^{-1}.

INTRODUCTION

Khumbu Glacier, which flows from the western cwm below Mt Everest (Fig. 1), is typical of the debris-covered glaciers of Nepal. Debris thickness increases from zero just above Everest Base Camp to more than 2 m near the terminus (Nakawo *et al.*, 1986). Ablation rates of ~30 mm day^{-1} have been measured on clean ice near Base Camp, and numerous studies have shown that ice-melt is accelerated beneath a thin layer of supraglacial debris, but inhibited by a thick layer (Fujii, 1977; Inoue & Yoshida, 1980; Kayastha *et al.*, 2000). The critical thickness at which ablation is the same as for clean ice depends on the optical and thermal properties of the debris as well as the prevailing meteorological conditions (Nakawo & Takahashi, 1982; Conway *et al.*, 1996; Adhikary *et al.*, 1997). The lithology as well as the thickness of the debris can cause variations in ice-melt; for the same thickness, ablation beneath dark-coloured schist is generally higher than beneath lighter-coloured granite because of differences in absorbed solar radiation (Inoue & Yoshida, 1980).

The energy flux through a debris layer can be modelled by the one-dimensional diffusion equation:

$$\rho c \frac{\partial T}{\partial t} = \frac{\partial}{\partial z}\left[k \frac{\partial T}{\partial z} \right] + \frac{\partial Q_N}{\partial t} \tag{1}$$

where ρ is the bulk density of the debris, t is time and z is the vertical coordinate, positive downward. Here $k\partial T/\partial z$ is the downward conductive flux, and $\partial Q_N/\partial t$

H. Conway & L. A. Rasmussen

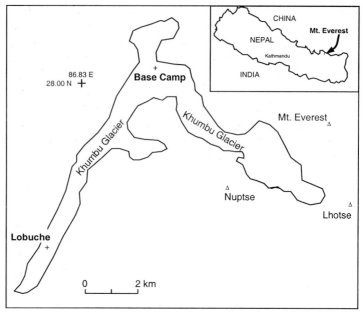

Fig. 1 Locations of study sites near Everest Base Camp (5360 m) and Lobuche (4960 m) on Khumbu Glacier, Nepal.

accounts for nonconductive processes such as convective or latent heat exchange. Thermal conductivity k and volumetric heat capacity ρc of the debris are functions of temperature T, porosity and moisture content (Hallet & Rasmussen, 1993). If the system is purely conductive ($\partial Q_N/\partial t = 0$) and k is constant with depth, then equation (1) can be written:

$$\dot{T} = \kappa T''$$
(2)

in which $\kappa = k/\rho c$ is the thermal diffusivity and the derivatives are denoted by $\dot{T} = \partial T/\partial t$ and $T'' = \partial^2 T/\partial z^2$.

The terminus position of Khumbu Glacier has been relatively stable since the last major advance about 150 years ago but lower sections of the glacier have thinned by more than 70 m (Mayewski & Jeschke, 1979). About 50 m of ice still exists beneath the debris at Lobuche (Gades *et al.*, 2000) and the glacier there is stagnant (Kodama & Mae, 1976). Here we discuss temperature profiles measured within supraglacial debris at two sites on Khumbu Glacier from 19 May to 3 June 1999. Our study is motivated by the need to improve predictions of the response of debris-covered glaciers to changes in climate.

TEMPERATURE MEASUREMENTS

Hourly temperature measurements were recorded for six days at a site near Everest Base Camp where the debris was 0.40 m thick, and four days at another site near Lobuche where the debris was more than 2 m thick. Ten thermistors were used to measure vertical temperature profiles within the supraglacial debris, and a shielded thermistor positioned 1 m above the surface recorded air temperature. Surface temperature was measured by a thermistor inserted within a few millimetres of the surface of the debris. Other thermistors were arranged at 0.05 m spacing through the debris at Base Camp, which consisted of mainly angular, loosely packed, dark-coloured, schist cobbles up to 0.1 m size. The temperature at the debris/ice interface 0.40 m below the surface was constant at 0°C. Temperature measurements at other depths (Fig. 2) show a strong diurnal signal that diffused downward into the debris with decreasing amplitude and increasing lag. The surface forcing decreased in the afternoon of day 143 because clouds reduced the incoming solar flux.

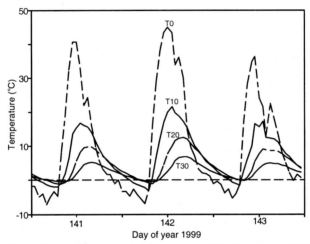

Fig. 2 Time series of selected temperatures *T0*, *T10*, *T20* and *T30* (at the surface, 0.10, 0.20, and 0.30 m below the surface), at Base Camp on days 141–143 (21–23 May 1999).

At Lobuche thermistors were spaced at 0.05 m intervals within the upper 0.15 m, and 0.1 m between 0.15 m and 0.75 m. The debris consisted of mainly coarse sand (grain size ~1 mm); scattered clumps of grass and lichen were growing within the debris. Although no quantitative measurements were made, moisture was observed in the upper 0.07 m of the profile during excavations on day 149. The excavations also indicated that the debris/ice interface was more than 1.75 m below the surface. Temperature profiles at this site also exhibit a strong diurnal signal that diffused downward into the debris with decreasing amplitude and increasing lag. The deepest thermistor (0.75 m below the surface) was above the debris/ice interface; its average temperature was 7.5°C.

Temperatures at the surface were often more than 35°C higher than the air during times of solar radiation. At night the surface was usually colder than the air, but the average surface temperature ($\overline{T0} = 10.1°C$) was warmer than the air ($\overline{T}_{air} = 2.3°C$). On average, sensible heat flowed from the debris to the air during the period of study; the flux of incoming energy was dominated by the solar component. The measurements show that high temporal resolution is necessary to fully capture the diurnal temperature cycle. Caution is needed when interpreting surface temperature from once-daily measurements.

TEMPERATURE PROFILES

The second derivative of temperature with respect to depth T'', scaled by the thermal conductivity, is the flux divergence (equation (2)). Negative curvature ($T'' < 0$) in a $T(z)$ profile represents cooling, while positive curvature represents warming. Four profiles from Base Camp (Fig. 3) show:

1.   cooling curvature throughout;
2.   warming curvature throughout;
3.   warming at the top beginning to overtake weak cooling below;
4.   cooling that has nearly overtaken weak warming at the bottom.

If the average temperature did not change over the 6-day observation period (i.e. $\dot{\bar{T}} = 0$), then for a purely conductive system with conductivity constant with depth, $\partial\bar{T}/\partial z$ should also be constant with depth (equation (1)). The measured $\partial\bar{T}/\partial z$

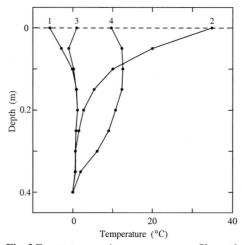

Fig. 3 Four representative temperature profiles at the Base Camp study site.

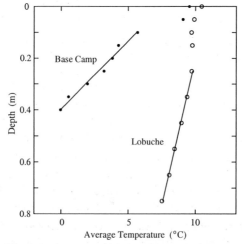

Fig. 4 Average temperature profiles at Base Camp and Lobuche.

(Fig. 4) show some departure from these conditions. Several factors could contribute to cause the deviations:

- $\dot{T}$ may not have been zero over the period of measurements.
- The system may not be purely conductive. For example, convection is likely near the surface (Harris & Pedersen, 1998), while latent heat exchange might dominate near the debris/ice interface.
- Conductivity k may not be constant with depth. For example, k increases rapidly with moisture content (Farouki, 1981; Nakawo & Young, 1981) and any variation of moisture with depth would complicate the $T(z)$ profile.
- Measurement errors. In particular, the influence of uncertainties in the vertical position (5 mm) and thermistor calibration (0.05°C) depends on $\partial\overline{T}/\partial z$ and the effective measurement error may be up to 0.15°C (Appendix).

Nevertheless, results show $\partial\overline{T}/\partial z$ was remarkably constant at depths greater than 0.1 m at Base Camp, and 0.25 m at Lobuche (Fig. 4). Extrapolation of the Lobuche profile to 0°C indicates ice ~2.5 m below the surface, consistent with our excavations that reached 1.75 m without finding ice. The average temperature gradient at Base Camp (19 K m^{-1}) was much stronger than that at Lobuche (4.5 K m^{-1}), presumably caused in part by the difference in debris thickness. On average, heat flow deeper than about 0.2 m was apparently primarily by conduction during this dry, summer period (Fig. 4). Convective processes may be more important during winter when temperatures probably increase with depth, and buoyancy forces could induce air mixing through the debris layer (Harris & Pedersen, 1998).

THERMAL PROPERTIES OF THE DEBRIS

Calculating the flux of energy available for melting ice beneath debris requires knowledge of thermal conductivity k, as well as the temperature gradient $\partial\overline{T}/\partial z$ (equation (1)). We do not have direct measurements of k but instead we estimate the depth averaged thermal diffusivity $\overline{\kappa}$ using $\dot{T}$ and T'' (equation (2)). We estimate these temperature derivatives using standard centred finite-difference expressions and distributions of $\dot{T}$ vs T'' at selected depths are shown in Fig. 5; the slope of the best fitting line through the data gives an estimate of the average diffusivity at that depth. Surprisingly, the analysis is not affected by thermistor-position and calibration errors, provided the errors do not change with time or temperature (Appendix).

The scatter about the best fitting line at 0.20 m at Base Camp (Fig. 5(a)) indicates deviations from purely conductive behaviour were relatively small at that depth. In contrast, measurements at 0.35 m (Fig. 5(b)) show that T'' was both strongly positive and negative and yet $\dot{T}$ was near zero. Examination of equation (1) indicates that a nonconductive heat source/sink (i.e. $\partial Q_N/\partial t \neq 0$) would cause such conditions—a possibility is that phase changes and associated latent heat exchange occurred at this depth. A rough calculation indicates that latent heat would dominate if only 0.02% (by mass) of water changed phase per hour. The distribution of $\dot{T}$ vs T'' is well behaved at 0.25 m at Lobuche (Fig. 5(c)); apparently heat flow there is primarily by conduction and $\kappa = 0.9$ mm^2 s^{-1}.

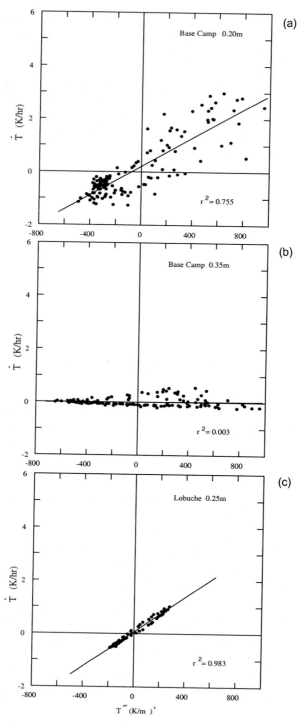

Fig. 5 Distributions of $\dot{T}$ *vs* T'' at selected depths within the supraglacial debris at study sites near Base Camp ((a) and (b)), and Lobuche (c). The slope of the best fitting line gives an estimate of κ (equation (2)).

Averaging thermal diffusivities through regions of the profile where heat flow is primarily conductive gives $\overline{\kappa} = 0.6 \pm 0.1$ mm^2 s^{-1} at Base Camp and 0.9 ± 0.1 mm^2 s^{-1} at Lobuche. Using typical values for the heat capacity (c = 750 J kg^{-1} K^{-1}) and density (ρ = 2700 kg m^{-3}) of rock (Clark, 1966), gives conductivity $k = 2.03\kappa(1 - \varphi)$ W m^{-1} K^{-1}, where φ is the porosity of the debris. The porosity of loose-packed debris is about 0.3, which yields k = 0.85 W m^{-1} K^{-1} at Base Camp, and 1.28 W m^{-1} K^{-1} at Lobuche. Assuming the estimate of $(1 - \varphi)\rho c$ has a 10% error, and that errors are uncorrelated (Bevington & Robinson, 1992), the uncertainty in k at Base Camp is 0.20 W m^{-1} K^{-1} and at Lobuche it is 0.15 W m^{-1} K^{-1}.

CALCULATED ICE-MELT

The average energy flux at the bottom of the debris layer:

$$\frac{\partial q}{\partial t} = k \frac{\partial \overline{T}}{\partial z} \qquad (3)$$

yields a melt rate in mm day^{-1} of:

$$\frac{\partial h}{\partial t} = \frac{1}{\rho_i L} \frac{\partial q}{\partial t} = 0.29 \, k \, \frac{\partial T}{\partial z} \qquad (4)$$

Here $L = 0.334$ MJ kg^{-1} is the latent heat of fusion, and ice density ρ_i = 900 kg m^{-3}. At Base Camp, where the debris is 0.4 m thick, k = 0.85 $\pm$ 0.20 W m^{-1}K^{-1} and $\partial \overline{T}/\partial z$ = 19 K m^{-1}, the daily flux of energy at the debris/ice interface would melt 4–6 mm of ice. This is slightly lower than the melt measured beneath the same thickness of debris at a nearby site during the same period, which varied from 5 to 12 mm day^{-1} (Kayastha *et al.*, 2000). At Lobuche, where the debris is about 2.5 m thick, k = 1.28 $\pm$ 0.15 W m^{-1}K^{-1} and $\partial \overline{T}/\partial z$ = 4.5 K m^{-1}, the flux of energy through the debris would melt 1–2 mm day^{-1} of ice.

We expect that monsoon rains would contribute sensible heat to the system, and would also cause k to increase. Both effects would enhance ablation during the monsoon although they might be offset by increased cloudiness that would reduce the incoming solar flux. In any event, we suspect that the melt rate was close to a maximum at the time of our measurements (a few weeks before the summer solstice and before the monsoon). For a rough estimate, we assume that ice at Lobuche melts at about half this maximum rate for half the year (i.e. a periodic cycle), which yields an ablation rate of 100–200 mm year^{-1}. Complete melting of the ice at Lobuche (about 50 m, Gades *et al.*, 2000), will take 250–500 years—longer if the debris thickness increases.

For practical purposes it is appealing to estimate ice-melt beneath supraglacial debris from remote sensing of surface temperature Ts and an effective thermal resistance of the debris R. Provided the system is purely conductive and the temperature profile through the debris is linear, the rate of ablation can be written (Nakawo & Young , 1981):

$$\frac{\partial h}{\partial t} = \frac{1}{\rho_i L} \frac{T_s}{R} \qquad (5)$$

where T_s is in °C, and the ice is at 0°C.

Results shown in Fig. 2, however, indicate that much caution is needed when estimating the surface temperature because the large diurnal variation makes it difficult to define the average surface temperature from once-daily measurements. Additional caution is needed because measurements shown in Fig. 4 indicate that the average temperature profile through the debris is typically not linear near the surface. Calculations are further complicated because deviations from linearity near the surface likely vary as convective processes become more or less active.

Deeper than about 0.2 m, however, the gradient $\partial \overline{T}/\partial z$ is more constant at both sites (Fig. 4) and heat transfer is primarily conductive. The thermal conductivity calculated through the lower portion of the debris at Base Camp (0.85 ± 0.20 W m^{-1} K^{-1}) was slightly lower than that at Lobuche (1.28 ± 0.15 W m^{-1} K^{-1}), but the average energy flux through the debris at Base Camp (~16 W m^{-2}) was much higher than at Lobuche (~5.8 W m^{-2}). Consequently, the ablation rate at Base Camp is expected to be about 3 times higher than at Lobuche.

Acknowledgements National Science Foundation supported this work through Grants ATM 9530691 and INT-9726704. We thank the Department of Hydrology and Meteorology of Nepal, and Ang Pasang Llama, Ang Pasang Sherpa, Man Bahadur, Pan Bahadur and Ang J.P. Llama who provided logistical support. We also thank L. Blank, A. Gades, T. Kadota, R. Kayastha, N. Naito, M. Nakawo, N. Nereson, C. Raymond and Y. Takeuchi for valuable contributions. Stimulating discussions with Bernard Hallet motivated this study.

REFERENCES

Adhikary, S., Seko, K., Nakawo, M., Ageta, Y. & Miyazaki, N. (1997) Effect of surface dust on snow melt. *Bull. Glacier Res.* **15**, 85–92.

Bevington, P. R. & Robinson, D. K. (1992) *Data Reduction and Error Analysis for the Physical Sciences*. McGraw-Hill, New York.

Clark, S. P. (1966) Thermal conductivity. In: *Handbook of Physical Constants: Memoir 97* (ed. by S. P. Clark), 459–482. Geological Society of America, New York.

Conway, H., Gades, A. & Raymond, C. F. (1996) Albedo of dirty snow during conditions of melt. *Wat. Resour. Res.* **32**, 1713–1718.

Farouki, O. T. (1981) Thermal properties of soils. *Tech. Report Mono, 91-1, US Army Cold Regions Research and Engineering Laboratory, Hanover, New Hampshire, USA.*

Fujii, Y. (1977) Field experiments on glacier ablation under a layer of debris cover. *J. Japan. Soc. Snow Ice (Seppyo)* **39**, 20–21.

Gades, A., Conway, H., Nereson, N., Naito, N. & Kadota, T. (2000) Radio echo-sounding through supraglacial debris on Lirung and Khumbu Glaciers, Nepal Himalayas. In: *Debris-Covered Glaciers* (ed. by M. Nakawo, C. F. Raymond & A. Fountain) (Proc. Seattle Workshop, September 2000). IAHS Publ. no. 264 (this volume).

Hallet, B. & Rasmussen, L. A. (1993) Calculation of the thermal conductivity of unsaturated frozen soil near the melting point. In: *Proc. of the Sixth Int. Conf. on Permafrost* (Beijing, China), vol. 1, 226–231. South China University of Technology Press, Wushan Guangzhou, China.

Harris, S. A. & Pedersen, D. E. (1998) Thermal regimes beneath coarse blocky materials. *Permafrost and Periglac. Processes* **9**, 107–120.

Inoue, J. & Yoshida, M. (1980) Ablation and heat exchange over the Khumbu Glacier. *J. Japan. Soc. Snow Ice (Seppyo)* **41**, 26–33.

Kayastha, R. B., Takeuchi, Y., Nakawo, M. & Ageta, Y. (2000) Practical prediction of ice melting beneath debris cover of various thickness on debris cover on Khumbu Glacier, Nepal, using a positive degree-day factor. In: *Debris-Covered Glaciers* (ed. by M. Nakawo, C. F. Raymond & A. Fountain) (Proc. Seattle Workshop, September 2000). IAHS Publ. no. 264 (this volume).

Kodama, H. & Mae, S. (1976) The flow of glaciers in the Khumbu region. *J. Japan. Soc. Snow Ice (Seppyo)* **38**, 31–36.

Mayewski, P. A. & Jeschke, P. A. (1979) Himalayan and trans-Himalayan glacier fluctuations since AD 1812. *Arctic Alpine Res.* **11**, 267–287.

Nakawo, M. & Takahashi, S. (1982) A simplified model for estimating glacier ablation under a debris layer. In: *Hydrological Aspects of Alpine and High Mountain Areas* (ed. by J. W. Glen) (Proc. Exeter Symp., July 1982), 289–296. IAHS Publ. no. 138.

Nakawo, M. & Young, G. J. (1981) Field experiments to determine the effect of a debris layer on ablation of glacier ice. *Ann. Glaciol.* **2**, 85–91.

Nakawo, M., Iwata, S., Watanabe, O. & Yoshida, M. (1986) Processes which distribute supraglacial debris on the Khumbu Glacier, Nepal Himalaya. *Ann. Glaciol.* **8**, 129–131.

APPENDIX

Measurement errors Analysis of a purely conductive, one-dimensional system with uniform diffusivity κ (equation (2)) is not hampered by measurement error δ that varies from sensor to sensor but that is constant in time t, and is therefore independent of temperature. If the measured temperature Θ differs from the true temperature T according to $T = \Theta + \delta$, when this is substituted into equation (2), it becomes:

$$\dot{\Theta} = \kappa \Theta'' + \kappa \delta'' \tag{A1}$$

The error δ has no effect on the time derivative because it is constant in time, so $\dot{T} = \dot{\Theta}$. If Θ measurements at a particular level are analysed by finding the best-fitting line,

$$\dot{\Theta} = \alpha \Theta'' + \beta \tag{A2}$$

and coefficients are equated, then $\kappa = \alpha$, and $\delta'' = \beta/\kappa = \beta/\alpha$. An example of a large δ'' detected by a linear fit of $\dot{\Theta}$ to Θ'' is at 0.20 m at Base Camp (Fig. 5(a)) where $\delta'' \sim 100$ K m^{-2}.

Although the best-fitting line does determine the value of κ at a particular level, it does not absolutely determine the sensor error δ there. The δ'' values at successive levels can be integrated twice with respect to z, however, to obtain calibration adjustments Δ that will produce values $T = \Theta + \Delta$ that satisfy equation (2), without need for a constant term, but the relation between Δ and the actual sensor error δ is not revealed.

Error ε in the depth z of a sensor corresponds to a mean error δ in its temperature that is proportional to the vertical gradient. Thus, where $\overline{T}$ is the mean temperature, the mean value is $\delta = \varepsilon \, \partial \overline{T}/\partial z$. A position error of 0.005 m at Base Camp, where $\partial \overline{T}/\partial z = 19$ K m^{-1}, corresponds to a temperature error of about 0.1°C. The same position error at Lobuche ($\partial \overline{T}/\partial z = 4.5$ K m^{-1}) corresponds to an error of only 0.02°C.

Debris-Covered Glaciers (Proceedings of a workshop held at Seattle, Washington, USA, September 2000).
IAHS Publ. no. 264, 2000.

Mass balance and runoff of the partially debris-covered Langtang Glacier, Nepal

WENDELL TANGBORN

HyMet Inc., 2366 Eastlake Avenue East, Suite 435, Seattle, Washington 98102, USA
e-mail: wendell@hymet.com

BIRBAL RANA

Department of Hydrology and Meteorology, Kathmandu, Nepal

Abstract The mass balance and runoff of the Langtang Glacier is calculated using the PTAA (precipitation–temperature–area–altitude) model. Input are meteorological observations at Kathmandu and the area–altitude distribution of the glacier. The glacier area is 75 km^2 and its altitude range is from 4500 to 7000 m. The PTAA model converts daily precipitation and temperature observations at the Kathmandu airport to snow accumulation and snow and ice ablation at each of the twenty-five 100-m altitude intervals on the glacier. The simulated annual mass balance for the period of record is –0.11 m (water equivalent) and the ELA is 5280 m. Mean summer runoff (June–September), the sum of total simulated ablation and precipitation as rain, is 14 mm per day, which is a rate similar to runoff measured for the nearby Lirung Glacier basin. Simulated ablation also agrees with ablation measurements made on the Lirung Glacier over the same time period and at approximately the same altitude.

INTRODUCTION

The mass balance of glaciers in the Himalaya is an important indicator for global climate change. These high-altitude, low-latitude glaciers are thought to be more sensitive to small temperature changes than glaciers located at lower altitudes and higher latitudes. In addition, runoff generated by the ablation of these glaciers is a major source of water for the people living in the region, therefore changes in the size of these glaciers is critical for assessing long-term water supplies (Rana *et al.*, 1997).

The Langtang Glacier, located at approximately 28°30′N latitude and 85°30′E longitude, ranges in altitude from 4500 to 7000 m and has a surface area of 75 km^2. As are many Himalayan glaciers, approximately 47% of the Langtang Glacier is covered by debris, however the debris thickness is unknown (the average thickness on the nearby Lirung Glacier at 4400 m altitude is 0.5 m (Rana *et al.*, 1996). The debris cover has a significant effect on ablation rates, and consequently on the glacier's mass balance (Østrem, 1959; Mattson & Gardener, 1989). This report describes the application of a mass balance model to the Langtang Glacier and compares ablation measured on nearby Lirung Glacier with simulated ablation on the Langtang Glacier during the same time period. Figure 1 is an oblique photo that shows the upper part of Langtang Glacier.

To produce realistic mass balance results, the model takes into account a glacier's unique area–altitude distribution, which has embedded in its surface configuration a

Fig. 1 Langtang Glacier, Nepal. Photo courtesy of Das Color Lab, Kathmandu, Nepal.

link to the past climate. A glacier's surface can be defined by a multitude of individual facets, each one with a different orientation in space (for example, the Langtang Glacier has three million if each is defined as having a surface area of 25 m^2). The area–altitude distribution is a rough approximation of these facets, which, in response to current meteorological conditions, determine the glacier's mass balance. The altitude and inclination of each facet are determined by erosion of the underlying bedrock throughout geologic time and thus has recorded the link between mass balance and the climate that prevailed during this period. The energy (by solar radiation and by the turbulent transfer of heat from the surrounding air) and mass (mostly as snow) received by each individual facet determines the glacier's total mass balance. The mass balance controls the discharge of ice, which is the driving force producing glacial erosion. Therefore, a continuous, unbroken time-link between the climate, glacier erosion and mass balance exists today as it has for the past million or more years. The model is calibrated by minimizing the error of regressing several sets of daily balance variables with each other (for example, the balance *vs* the zero-balance-altitude, or the balance exchange *vs* the accumulation area ratio), which assumes there is an internal consistency in the link between mass balance and climate that is controlled by the glacier's area–altitude distribution.

THE PTAA MODEL

Two data sets are needed for application of this model to a specific glacier:
–   Meteorological observations from a nearby weather station or stations (daily precipitation and maximum and minimum temperatures).
–   The area–altitude distribution of the glacier (the AA profile).
Input to the model for the Langtang Glacier are daily precipitation and temperature observations at the Kathmandu airport, located 60 km south of the Langtang Glacier and at an altitude of 1546 m. The available temperature record at this site is for 1969–

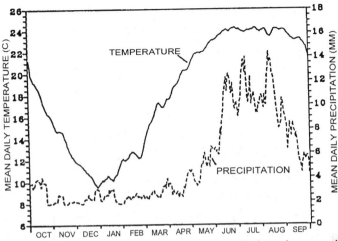

Fig. 2 Mean daily precipitation and temperature at Kathmandu averaged for the 1987–1997 period.

1997, and the precipitation record is for 1987–1997. Missing temperature observations were reconstructed by interpolating from observations on adjacent days. The precipitation record is complete. Average daily precipitation for the 1987–1997 period at Kathmandu is shown in Fig. 2. Both precipitation and temperature observations at Kathmandu closely agree with previously published mean monthly records at this weather station (Wernstadt, 1972).

The glacier and the surrounding area was digitized by the Department of Meteorology and Hydrology in Kathmandu using a 200-m grid, from a 1:50 000 topographic map (Austrian Alpine Club, 1990). Each grid point was given one of three designations: glacier ice, debris-covered ice, or rock. There were 984 grid points of glacier ice and 887 grid points of debris cover, indicating that the total glacier is 74.8 km^2, with 35.5 km^2 of debris cover (47.4%). Figure 3 shows the distribution of glacier ice and debris cover. Using the digitized data, the glacier area was divided into twenty-five 100-m altitude intervals. Figure 4 shows the area–altitude distribution for the total and the debris-covered glacier area.

The PTAA model has been tested on other glaciers (Tangborn, 1997, 1999) and has produced mass balance results that agree with independent measurements made by geodetic means. Detailed explanations of the model's key algorithms and the calibration procedure are provided in these earlier reports and duplication of these earlier explanations is not considered necessary here. However, a brief description of its application to the Langtang Glacier is included in the following section.

Model explanation

Precipitation and temperature observations at Kathmandu are converted to precipitation (as snow or as rain) and ablation at each of the twenty-five 100-m altitude intervals of the glacier by algorithms that use 15 coefficients. By application of the simulated temperature and precipitation at each interval, the occurrence of snow or rain

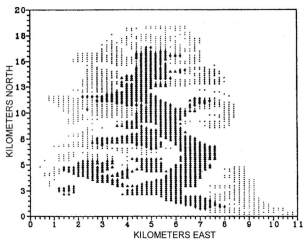

Fig. 3 Results for digitizing the Langtang Glacier on a 200 m grid. The small points designate glacier ice, the large triangles designate debris cover, which is 47% of the total glacier area of 75 km². These data were used to calculate the area–altitude distribution shown in Fig. 4.

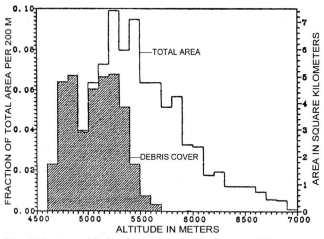

Fig. 4 The area–altitude distribution of the glacier in 100 m increments. The area of each area interval of the glacier that is covered by debris (47%) is hatched.

is determined; if the simulated temperature is 0°C or less, precipitation occurs as snow; if greater than 0°C, as rain.

It is proposed that the same physical laws operate on a glacier regardless of time or altitude, therefore the same set of coefficients is used for each day of the period and for each altitude interval. Thus over 100 000 values of each balance variable are calculated from a single set of coefficients. The lapse rates of both temperature and precipitation between Kathmandu and each altitude interval on the glacier are calculated by algorithms that use one or more of the 15 coefficients. Ablation is determined from the mean temperature and from the diurnal temperature range (an index of cloudiness and solar radiation). The mass balance at each altitude interval is calculated by the difference between snow accumulation and ablation (of both snow and ice), and the balance for the total glacier is found by integrating area and balance for all intervals. Both the snow-line altitude and the zero-balance altitude are determined each day by separate algorithms.

RESULTS

Simulated daily snowfall averaged for the period is shown in Fig. 5. Mean annual precipitation simulated for the entire glacier is 1.65 m (compared with 1.41 m at Kathmandu). Precipitation occurs as snowfall 73% (1.21 m), and as rain, 27% (0.44 m) of the time.

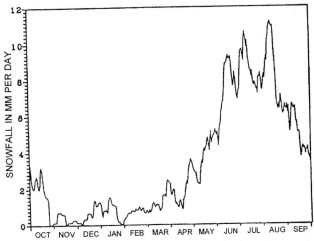

Fig. 5 The mean daily snowfall averaged over the glacier area and for the 1987–1997 period. Precipitation occurs as snow when the mean daily temperature at the AA interval is 0°C or less. Approximately 75% of total annual precipitation as snow occurs during the summer monsoon season (June–September).

The extensive debris cover on this glacier complicates ablation measurements, both in the field and by model simulation. To account for the debris cover on the lower glacier in the model, a change was made in the ablation algorithm from previous model applications.

Considering only the radiation component of ablation:

$$A(i, z) = C_1 D(i) (C_2 (1 - E(z)/S(i)) F(z) \qquad (1)$$

where $A(i, z)$ is ablation due to solar radiation on day i and at altitude z, in mm per day, $D(i)$ is the diurnal temperature range on day i, $E(z)$ is the altitude interval z in metres, $S(i)$ is the snow-line altitude in metres on day i, $F(z)$ is the fraction of altitude interval z covered by debris, and C_1, C_2 are coefficients determined by calibration. The fraction of debris cover $F(z)$ is then the only change in this algorithm from previous PTAA model applications. When the factor $(1 - E(z)/S)$ is less than zero, $A(i, z)$ is made equal to zero, therefore, ablation due to radiation derived from the temperature range is assumed to occur only below the snow line (high albedos at these altitudes precludes a significant direct radiation component of total ablation, however snowmelt still occurs due to indirect effects of radiation).

Measurements of ablation over debris-covered ice were conducted in 1995 on the Lirung Glacier, located 12 km west of Langtang Glacier (Rana *et al.*, 1998). Results of these measurements, made at 4350 m altitude, from 18 to 21 June 1995 at 22 points with varying depths of debris thickness, are shown in Fig. 6. Measured ablation rates varied from a maximum of 450 mm per day for a debris thickness of 26 mm, to 160 mm per day when the thickness was 120 mm. The rate was 230 mm per day if no debris was present and the average rate for the 22 sites was 260 mm of ablation per day.

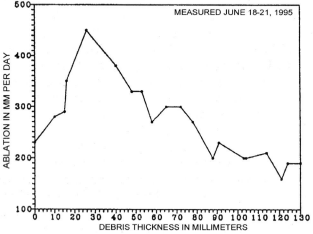

Fig. 6 Measured ablation at 22 points on the Lirung Glacier (at 4350 m altitude), for the period 18–21 June. Maximum ablation occurred when the debris thickness was 260 mm.

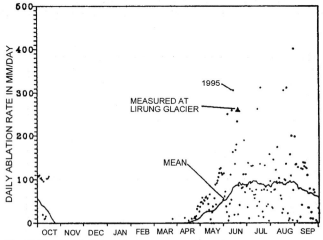

Fig. 7 Simulated daily ablation, averaged for the 1987–1997 period (solid line), and for the 1995 water year (October 1994–September 1995, dots). Measured ablation on nearby Lirung Glacier averaged for 22 points during the period 18–21 June 1995 (large triangle) is shown for comparison with simulated ablation during the same time period. The measured ablation is at 4350 m on the Lirung Glacier and the simulated is for 4550 m altitude on the Langtang Glacier (the lowest possible point).

Simulated ablation for the same period but at 200 m higher altitude (4550 m) on the Langtang Glacier averaged 113 mm per day (as the Langtang Glacier terminus is at 4500 m, ablation could not be simulated at the same altitude as measurements on the Lirung Glacier). Taking into account the difference in altitude, and assuming 25% probable errors in both simulated and measured ablation rates, the two methods are in reasonable agreement. A comparison of measured and simulated daily ablation rates for 1995 is demonstrated in Fig. 7.

Observations of the surface glacier melt rates are reported for Yala Glacier, a debris-free glacier located in the same valley, 7 km east of Langtang Glacier (Motoyama & Yamada, 1989). During a period from 23 August to 3 September 1987, at an altitude of 5100 m, ablation equalled 12.7 mm °C^{-1} day^{-1}, and during 3 September to 3 October 1987 at 5300 m, it equalled 19.2 mm °C^{-1} day^{-1}. The PTAA model results for the same elevations and time periods on the Langtang Glacier gave 11.6 mm °C^{-1} day^{-1} at 5100 m and 37 mm °C^{-1} day^{-1} at 5300 m. The reason for the large difference at 5300 m is unknown but could be caused by Yala Glacier being debris-free and Langtang Glacier having a significant debris cover at this altitude. The values calibrated for the same period by the HBV3–ETH model for lower elevations reasonably agree with measured ablation but for higher elevations the calibrated values are one-third of the observed. (Braun *et al.*, 1993).

The daily balance for each interval is simply the difference between accumulated snowfall and ablation. The average cumulative daily balance over the total glacier throughout the year is shown in Fig. 8. The winter, summer and annual balances are found by averaging for the period of record the cumulative snowfall (winter balance), cumulative ablation (summer balance) and the resulting annual balance for each altitude interval (Fig. 9). (Note: the terms winter and summer balance are not appropriate for Himalayan glaciers because much of the snow accumulation occurs during the summer monsoon season. *Accumulation balance* and *ablation balance* are considered more correct and will be used henceforth in this report). The cumulative daily balance for the 1987–1997 period (Fig. 10) shows a significant difference in the

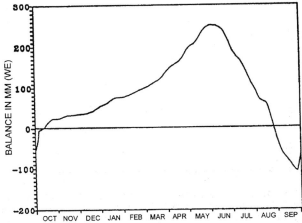

Fig. 8 The mean daily simulated mass balance averaged over the glacier for the 1987–1997 period. The balance is equal to daily snowfall minus daily ablation, cumulated from 1 October 1 to 30 September each year.

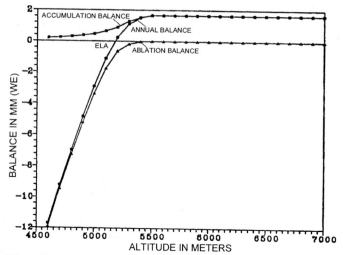

Fig. 9 The simulated accumulation (winter), ablation (summer) and annual balance as a function of altitude, averaged for the 1987–1997 period. The simulated ablation rate at the terminus during the 1 June 1–30 September season averages 98 mm day^{-1}. The ELA is approximately 5280 m.

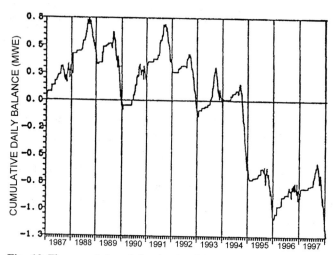

Fig. 10 The cumulative daily simulated balance for the 1987–1997 period (4015 days). The mean annual balance for this period is –0.11 m (water equivalent).

time distribution of balance from year to year. The average accumulation balance is 1.24 m (water equivalent), the ablation balance is –1.35, thus the mean annual balance for the 1987–1997 period is –0.11 m (water equivalent).

Runoff from the glacier is the sum of precipitation as rain and total ablation of snow and ice. Internal water storage is likely a factor in daily runoff variations but is not taken into account in this preliminary study. The mean daily and maximum simulated runoff for the total glacier, shown in Fig. 11, is similar in magnitude and variation as observed runoff for the Lirung Glacier basin (Rana *et al.*, 1997). Mean annual simulated runoff is 1.76 m; precipitation accounts for 94% and 6% is derived from the loss in glacier mass. The mean maximum simulated discharge is approximately 20 m^3 s^{-1} and usually occurs in early August. The mean simulated discharge for the year is 4.3 m^3 s^{-1}.

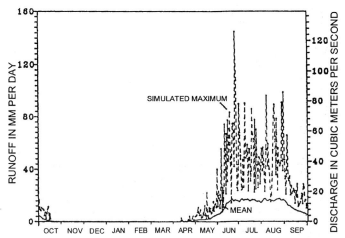

Fig. 11 Simulated runoff in millimetres per day from the glacier is the sum of total ablation and precipitation as rain averaged over the total glacier area (solid line) and the simulated maximum (dashed line). The storage and release of water from internal storage may be a significant factor but is not considered here. Discharge in cubic metres per second (right-hand scale) is the daily mean and maximum for the period of record.

CONCLUSIONS

These preliminary results indicate that realistic mass balance and runoff can be simulated for the Langtang Glacier using meteorological observations at Kathmandu and the glacier's AA profile. The agreement between measured and simulated ablation is within reasonable error limits. Further investigation by the application of the PTAA model to this glacier to calculate the mass and energy exchange at a large number of surface facets may yield fruitful results regarding the effect of debris cover on glacier mass balance and runoff.

Acknowledgements Raju Aryal and Sarju Vaidhya of the Department of Hydrology and Meteorology in Kathmandu digitized the glacier elevations. Funding was provided by the Nepal Department of Hydrology and Meteorology, and by HyMet Company. Two anonymous referees supplied numerous helpful criticisms. We also wish to thank Andrew Fountain for critical editing and suggested revisions to the initial manuscript.

REFERENCES

Austrian Alpine Club (1990) *1990 Expedition Maps, 0/10 (West) and 0/11 (East)*. Scale 1:50 000.
Braun, L. N., Grabs, W. & Rana, B. (1993) Application of a conceptual precipitation–runoff model in the Langtang Khola basin, Nepal Himalaya. In: *Snow and Glacier Hydrology* (ed. by G. J. Young) (Proc. Kathmandu Symp., November 1992), 221–237. IAHS Publ. no. 218.

Mattson, L. E. & Gardner, J. S. (1989) Energy exchange and ablation rates on the debris-covered Rakhiot Glacier, Pakistan. *Z. Gletscherk. Glaziolgeol.* **25**(1), 17–32.

Motoyama, H. & Yamada, T. (1989) Hydrological observations in Langtang Valley, Nepal Himalayas during 1987 monsoon-postmonsoon season. *Bull. Glacier Res.* **7**, 195–201.

Østrem, G. (1959) Ice melting under a thin layer of moraine and the existence of ice cores in moraine ridges. *Geogr. Ann.* **41**, 686–694.

Rana, B., Nakawo, M., Fukushima, Y. & Ageta, Y. (1996) Runoff modeling of a river basin with a debris-covered glacier in Langtang Valley, Nepal Himalaya. *Bull. Glacier Res.* **14**, 1–6.

Rana, B., Nakawo, M., Fukushima, Y. & Ageta, Y. (1997) Application of a conceptual precipitation–runoff model (HYCYMODEL) in a debris-covered glacierized basin in the Langtang Valley, Nepal Himalaya. *Ann. Glaciol.* **25**.

Rana, B., Nakawo, M., Ageta, Y., Seko, K., Kubota, J. & Kojima, A. (1998) Glacier ablation under debris cover: field observations on Lirung Glacier, Nepal Himalayas. In: *Proceedings of International Conference on Ecohydrology of High Mountain Areas* (Kathmandu, 1996), 393–403.

Tangborn, W. V. (1997) Using low-altitude meteorological observations to calculate the mass balance of Alaska's Columbia Glacier and relate it to calving and speed. In: *Calving Glaciers: Report of a Workshop, February 28– March 2, 1997* (ed. by C. J. Van der Veen), 141–161. BPRC Report no. 15, Byrd Polar Research Center, The Ohio State University, Columbus, Ohio.

Tangborn, W. V. (1999) A mass balance model that uses low-altitude meteorological observations and the area–altitude of a glacier. *Geogr. Ann.* December 1999, Proceedings of the Tarafala Mass Balance Workshop.

Wernstadt, F. (1972) *World Climatic Data*. Climatic Data Press.

Debris-Covered Glaciers (Proceedings of a workshop held at Seattle, Washington, USA, September 2000).
IAHS Publ. no. 264, 2000.

109

Computations of melting under moraine as a part of regional modelling of glacier runoff

VLADIMIR KONOVALOV

*Central Asian Hydrometeorological Research Institute, 72 K. Makhsumov Str.,
Tashkent 700052, Uzbekistan*

e-mail: fyyf98@silk.org

Abstract This paper considers: (a) measurements on melting under moraine
cover on glaciers of central Asia, the Caucasus and the Altai; (b) a
mathematical model of the influence of moraine cover on glacier melting;
(c) regional formulae to compute melting under moraine; (d) determination of
the mean moraine depth $h_C(Z_E)$ at the glacier terminus and modelling of the
spatial distribution of $\overline{h}_C$ within the ablation area of a glacier.

INTRODUCTION

The moraine cover on glaciers within the Pamir-Alai river basins varies between 2%
and 26% according to current estimations and totals 676.4 km². The author has
developed a regional model of glacier runoff that incorporates the method of
computation of total ice melting $M(h_C)$ under a moraine cover of depth h_C. The formula
used in a regional model for calculation of the total volume of glacier melt $v_M(t)$ at
time t is:

$$v_M(t) = M_C(\tilde{z}_{im},t)S_{im} + M(\tilde{z}_i,t)S_i + M(\tilde{z}_f,t)S_f + M(\tilde{z}_{ws},t)S_{ws} + M(\tilde{z}_{ss},t)S_{ss} \quad (1)$$

where $M_C = M\,f(h_C)$ is the intensity of icemelt under the moraine cover; M is the
intensity of bare ice melting; $f(h_C)$ is the function of change in ice melt under moraine
cover h_C; $\tilde{z}$ is mean weighted altitude for area S of a particular glacier surface.
Subscripts used in (1) are:

im is ice under moraine,
i is bare ice,
f is old firn,
ws is winter snow,
ss is summer snow.

To obtain the total melt volume V_M and icemelt runoff W_{gl} it is necessary to compute
and summarize the proper components of (1):

$$V_M = \sum_{t_1=D_{SC}}^{t_2=D_{EC}} v_M(t)$$

$$W_{gl} = \sum_{t_3=D_{SI}}^{t_4=D_{EI}} M_C(\tilde{z}_{im},t)S_{im} + M(\tilde{z}_i,t)S_i + M(\tilde{z}_f,t)S_f$$

where D_{SC} and D_{EC} are dates of the beginning and the end of the calculation period,
which include melting of all types of glacier surface; D_{SI} and D_{EI} are dates of the

beginning and the end of the icemelt period. Equation (1) is the regional model REGMOD of glacier mass balance and runoff formation in high mountain areas of central Asia, which has been elaborated in Konovalov (1985; 1997a,b).

The following methods and information are necessary to calculate the volume of icemelt under moraine using equation (1):

(a) Data on the area of solid moraine cover S_{im}.
(b) Modelling and computation of the interannual variability of $S_{im}(t)$ related to the movement of the seasonal snow line $Z_{SSL}(t)$ on glaciers at the condition:

$$Z_E < Z_{SSL}(t) < Z_{UML}$$

(c) Regional or local functions $f(h_C) = M(h_C)/M$ of icemelt change dependent upon depth h_C of solid moraine cover.
(d) Data on the spatial distribution of the mean moraine depth $\bar{h}_C$ for the debris-covered glacier area S_{im} or part of this area $S_{im}(t)$, located between altitudes Z_E and $Z_{SSL}(t)$, where Z_E is the altitude of the glacier terminus and Z_{UML} is the highest altitude of solid moraine distribution.

The mean moraine depth $\bar{h}_C$ at $Z_{SSL}(t) \quad Z_{UML}$ may be defined as:

$$\bar{h}_C = \frac{1}{\Delta Z_C} \int_{Z_E}^{Z_{UML}} h_C(z) \, dz \tag{2}$$

where $\Delta Z_C = Z_{UML} - Z_E$. But when $Z_E < Z_{SSL}(t) < Z_{UML}$:

$$\bar{h}_C(t) = \frac{1}{\Delta Z_C(t)} \int_{Z_E}^{Z_{SSL}(t)} h_C(z) \, dz \tag{3}$$

where $\Delta Z_C(t) = Z_{SSL}(t) - Z_E$.

The generalized values of S_{im} and Z_E used in the REGMOD model could be obtained from Glacier Inventory data. The interannual variability $S_{im}(t)$ when $Z_E < Z_{SSL}(t) < Z_{UML}$ is expressed by:

$$S_{im}(t) = \int_{Z_E}^{Z_{SSL}(t)} s(z) \, dz$$

where $s(z)$ is the distribution of the glacier area as a function of altitude. The method of estimating $Z_{SSL}(t)$ is described by Konovalov (1985, 1997a,b) and $s(z)$ by Schetinnikov (1997). All regionally available experimental measurements of ice melt under moraine are analysed further as the empirical basis to model $f(h_C)$, $h_C(Z_E)$ and $h_C(z)$ in REGMOD. Here $h_C(Z_E)$ is the mean moraine depth at the altitude of the glacier terminus.

REGIONAL MEASUREMENTS OF MELTING UNDER MORAINE COVER

At present field measurements of ice melting under moraine are made on at least 15 central Asian glaciers. Similar data are available for the glaciers of the Caucasus and Altai. Averaged data of measurements in the form of relative melting values $M(h_C)/M$

Table 1 Relative intensity of ice melt under moraine cover (f(h_C) in %). Names of glaciers and references are given in Konovalov (1985).

h_C (cm)	0	0.2	0.5	0.8	1.0	2.0	5.0	10	20	30	50	100	150	200	250	300
f(h_C)	100	106	110	105	102	86	60	43	26	17	12	8	5	3	1	1

are used to plot $M(h_C)/M = f(h_C)$ which shows that this function has its maximum value at $h_C > 0$ and two characteristic points where $f(h_C) = 1$. One of these points represents the relative intensity of ice melt without moraine. The existence of the other is explained by total absorption inside layer h_C of the additional heat obtained due to the albedo difference between ice and moraine. The generalized numerical values f(h_C) for different moraine depths are presented in Table 1 and Fig. 1.

The temporal variability of f(h_C) in the central Asia region has been estimated by combining all available measurements M and $M(h_C)$ on glaciers at different depths of

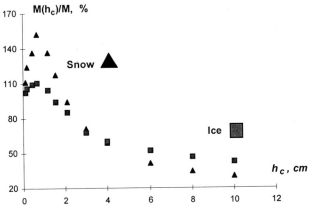

Fig. 1 Empirical curves of the melting intensity under different depths of moraine. From data of Konovalov (1985), Schetinnikov (1997), Kamalov (1974), Fujii (1977).

Table 2 Values of f(h_C) in central Asia (as % of the melting of bare ice). The names of more then 15 central Asian glaciers and sources of data used in this table are given in Konovalov (1985).

Months	Ten days	Depth of the moraine cover (cm): 5	10	20	30	50
July	I	69	41	26	16	
	II	66	38	23	16	
	III	72	49	34	16	15
Mean for month		70	44	29	16	
August	I	64	50	33	18	11
	II	72	67	36	28	
	III	67	48	37	21	15
Mean for month		67	53	35	22	16
September	I	67	38	37	13	
	II	43	30	21	10	
	III	41	22	8	4	
Mean for month		52	28	22	8	
Mean for July–September		68	49	34	22	16

moraine cover. These data averaged for some values of h_C are presented in Table 2. The list of glaciers used in both tables and the sources of the data are given by Konovalov (1985).

The results given in Table 2 are for altitudes 3000–3400 m a.s.l. To determine the generalized values $f(h_C)$ for the period July–September some additional data are taken into account which are not used to compute monthly values of $f(h_C)$. The temporal variability of $f(h_C)$ for certain h_C values in the Table 2 can be explained partly by the absence of quantitative characteristics of bare surfaces of the glacier. However the main reasons for changes of $f(h_C)$ have not yet been properly studied. Therefore, one of the main objectives of this paper is to evaluate the variability of $f(h_C)$ as a function of spatial and temporal coordinates.

MODEL OF MORAINE INFLUENCE ON THE MELTING PROCESS

For the purposes of the computation of melting under moraine with thickness h_C, it is useful to obtain the analytical form of $f(h_C,)$ which when $h_C = 0$ gives the ice melt value for a bare ice surface. We may use a common approach to solve this problem by considering the daily fluxes of heat onto bare ice (P_i), moraine surface $P_C(0)$, and to the moraine–ice interface $P(h_C)$ at $h_C > 0$.

Let us assume that the process of heat assimilation in the layer h_C could be described by a simple differential equation:

$$\frac{dP_C}{dh_C} = -\beta P_C \tag{4}$$

After integrating (4) we obtain:

$$P(h_c) = P_c(0)\exp(-\beta h_c) \tag{5}$$

and, after dividing both parts of (5) by $P_C(0)$ and taking only the first two terms of decomposition $\exp(-\beta h_C)$ to the power series,

$$\frac{P(h_c)}{P_c(0)} \approx \frac{1}{1+\beta h_c} \tag{6}$$

where β is the coefficient of heat absorption.

As can be seen, formula (5) and its approximate version (6) characterize the exponential extinction of heat flux at the moraine–ice boundary at $h_C > 0$ related to $P_C(0)$, the heat flux to the moraine surface. The relation between heat fluxes P_i and $P_C(0)$ can be written as $P_C(0) = P_i + \Delta P$, where ΔP is stipulated by increasing absorbed solar radiation due to differences in the albedo. After that the approximate formula (6) will be as follows:

$$\frac{P(h_c)}{P_i} = \frac{1+\dfrac{\Delta P}{P_i}}{1+\beta h_c} \tag{7}$$

A similar formula was obtained earlier by Khodakov (1972), but it doesn't meet with the experimental data at $h_C = 0$, since it gives $M(h_C) > M$. Equation (7) must be transformed in order to satisfy the conditions given earlier. It is obvious that fulfilling these conditions, i.e. $f(h_C) = 1$ at $h_C = 0$ and $f(h_C) = \max$ at $h_C > 0$ is possible if the argument of (7) is presented as $\xi = (h_C - h_0)^2$, where h_0 is a parameter having the dimension of length. Changing h_C by means of a power expression is necessary to preserve the positive sign of the product in the denominator of (7) at $h_C < h_0$. Thus instead of (7) it is suggested that:

$$\frac{P(h_c)}{P_i} = \frac{1 + \dfrac{\Delta P}{P_i}}{1 + \beta_1 (h_c - h_0)^2} \tag{8}$$

Then, using the condition $f(h_C) = 1$ at $h_C = 0$, we may define:

$$h_0 = \sqrt{\frac{\Delta P}{\beta_1 P_i}} \tag{9}$$

It follows from (9) that the parameter h_0 provides adjustment of $P_C(0)$ to P_i. The analysis of heat fluxes inside a moraine cover based on the multi-phase and multi-component theory is performed by Denisov (1980). Finally he obtained $f(h_C)$, which agrees well with known experimental data. However Denisov's solution could not be used for regional calculations since it includes many specific physical parameters (moraine density, wind velocity, air temperature and vapour pressure above and inside the moraine, etc).

METHOD TO COMPUTE MELT UNDER MORAINE

Analysis of $f(h_C)$ in the form of (8) shows that this function has maximum at $h_C = h_0$ and two characteristic points where $f(h_C) = 1$ at $h_C = 0$ and $h_C = 2h_0$. Therefore formula (8) satisfies all conditions for the correct computation of ice melt under moraine if values of melting, $M(h_C)$ and M, are used instead of heat fluxes $P(h_C)$ and P_i, i.e.

$$\frac{M(h_c)}{M} = \frac{1 + \dfrac{\Delta P}{c_* M}}{1 + \beta_1 (h_c - h_0)^2} \tag{10}$$

where c_* is the specific heat of phase transition.

For an approximate evaluation of $\Delta P/c_* M$ we suggest that $\Delta P = \Delta B_S$, where $\Delta B_S = B_{SM} - B_{SI}$ is the difference between values of absorbed solar radiation at the ice surface and moraine surface. The difference ΔB_S may be presented as $\Delta B_S = Q_o(1 - A_{SM}) - Q_o(1 - A_{SI}) = Q_o(A_{SI} - A_{SM})$ where Q_o is the global radiation; A_{SM} the albedo of the moraine; and A_{SI} the albedo of ice. Thus we may write $Q_o(A_{SI} - A_{SM}) = B_{SM} - B_{SI}$ and after simple transformation of this expression:

$$\frac{B_{SM}}{B_{SI}} = 1 + \frac{Q_o(A_{SI} - A_{SM})}{Q_o(1 - A_{SI})} = \frac{1 - A_{SM}}{1 - A_{SI}} \tag{11}$$

or:

$$B_{SM} = B_{SI} \frac{(1 - A_{SM})}{(1 - A_{SI})} \tag{12}$$

The nondimensional expression (12) presenting the coefficient of magnification of absorbed solar radiation was introduced first by the author (Konovalov, 1967) when considering the effect of artificial impact on glacier melting. Therefore, for ΔB_S we may write:

$$\Delta B_S = B_{SI} \left(\frac{1 - A_{SM}}{1 - A_{SI}} - 1 \right) = B_{SI} \left(\frac{A_{SI} - A_{SM}}{1 - A_{SI}} \right) \tag{13}$$

and, after substitution into (10), we get:

$$\frac{M(h_C)}{M} = \frac{1 + \dfrac{B_{SI}}{c_* M} \left(\dfrac{A_{SI} - A_{SM}}{1 - A_{SI}} \right)}{1 + \beta_1 (h_C - h_0)^2} \tag{14}$$

Equation (14) represents the general form of $f(h_C)$ where the right-hand components should be defined as regional or local functions of spatial coordinates and time. It is obvious that the relation $\phi = B_{SI}/c_* M$ characterizes the influence of absorbed solar energy on ice melt. An analysis of the spatial variability of ϕ reveals that in the central Asia region it may be defined adequately as a linear function of elevation Z (in km), i.e. $\phi(Z) = a_0 + b_0 Z$. Both parameters of $\phi(Z)$ have temporal variability, which is determined empirically as follows:

$$a_0(t) = 87.67 - 0.525 * t + 0.000\,841 * t^2$$

$$b_0(t) = 0.179 * t - 0.000\,28 * t^2 - 29.99$$

where t is the number of the day in the hydrological year, i.e. October–September period. The next equation to compute the mean monthly albedo of slightly dusted ice A_{SId} is obtained by data from long-term measurements on central Asia glaciers:

$$A_{SId}(T) = 0.0068 * T^2 - 0.1086 * T + 0.72$$

where T is the number of the month during the May–October period. The correlation coefficient of this empirical formula is 0.931. The albedo of the moraine is defined by field estimations as: $A_{SM} = 0.12 \approx$ constant. Ultimately we have equation (15) describing the influence of moraine cover on ice melt during May–October:

$$f(h_C)_{Id} = \frac{1 + (a_0(t) + b_0(t) * Z) * [(A_{SId}(T) - 0.12)/(1 - A_{SId}(T))]}{1 + \beta_1 (h_C - h_0)^2} \tag{15}$$

Similar formulae may be obtained for clean ice, firn and snow. The components of (15) β_1 and h_0 are considered so far as permanent parameters.

Adopting permanent averaged values of albedos and ϕ we may write equation (14) as follows:

$$\frac{M(h_C)}{M} = \frac{K_C}{1 + \beta_1 (h_C - h_0)^2} \tag{16}$$

where from our research (Konovalov, 1969, 1972, 1985) $K_C = 1.34$ at $\bar{\phi} = 0.80$, $\bar{A}_{SM} = 0.12$, and $\bar{A}_{SI} = 0.38$ for clean ice. Values for β_1 and h_0 may be obtained by combining experimental measurements of $M(h_C)$ and M, with equation (9).

The common approach states that melting under moraine can be computed regardless of the type of glacier surface. This means that the value of K_C in formula (16) depends upon the albedo of any natural surface A_S whether it is ice, firn or snow. The relationship $K_C = f(A_S)$ attains a general form if $B_S/c_*M = 0.80 \approx$ constant, $A_{SM} = 0.12$, and if we use the averaged values of albedo for the different types of glacier surface. Those revealed by the author earlier (Konovalov, 1969, 1972) are as follows: clear ice ($A_S = 0.38$), old snow/firn ($A_S = 0.47$), wet snow/clear firn ($A_S = 0.58$), clear dry snow ($A_S = 0.76$). Having used the least squares fit for $K_C = f(A_S)$ we finally obtain the universal formula:

$$M(h_c) = M \frac{0.97 + 0.0145 A_S^{2.18}}{1 + \beta_1 (h_c - h_0)^2} \tag{17}$$

for computation of the melting under moraine dependent on its depth h_C and intensity of melting M on the bare glacier surface (ice, firn, snow). The coefficients in (17) are considered as constants which in some cases may be accepted as a satisfactory approximation.

Several values of A_S listed above may be used to represent graphically the function (16). The set of these curves is characterized by the location of maximum $M(h_C)$ and speed of the function changes in its vicinity. The analysis of this graph is useful since it explains first the variability of dots on the empirical dependencies $f(h_C)$ and secondly it facilitates selecting an optimal option of glacier dusting in the numerical modelling of artificially modifying glacier melt.

An example of the function $f(h_C)$ is shown on Fig. 1 which presents empirical curves of the relative melting intensity under moraine on the surface of ice and snow. Data published by Kamalov (1974, Schetinnikov (1997), and Fujii (1977) have been used to prepare this graph. These curves make it easy to determine the value h_0, which equals certain h_C where each of the functions $f(h_C)$ are at their maximum and to find the coefficient β_1 in (17). Then $\beta_1 = (K_C - 1)/h_0^2$ if $h_C = 2h_0$, and $f(h_C) = 1$. For example, $\beta_1 = 6.0$ cm^{-2}, when $\bar{A}_S$ for snow is 76%, and $\beta_1 = 0.58$ cm^{-2} when $\bar{A}_S$ for ice is 30%.

MODEL FOR MORAINE DISTRIBUTION ON GLACIER SURFACE

In order to estimate the form of function $h_C(z)$ we use the equation of moraine mass changing along the length of a glacier suggested by Glazyrin (1969):

$$\frac{dm}{dz} = -\frac{\Phi_m B(z)}{v_{GL} \sin \lambda} \tag{18}$$

where $B(z)$ is the balance of accumulation and ablation of ice, Φ_m is the coefficient characterizing the long-term input of moraine material from outside; v_{GL} and λ are respectively the glacier velocity and slope at altitude Z. Adopting certain averaged values of B, v_{GL} and λ for altitudes $\Delta Z_C = Z_{UML} - Z_E$ we may write:

$$\frac{\Phi_m \overline{B}}{v_{GL} \sin \lambda} = \chi_C = \text{constant} \tag{19}$$

Integrating by z the simplified version of (18), i.e. $dm/dz = -\chi_C$ we get the expression $m(z) = m(z_0) - \chi_C(z - z_1)$ where $z_1 = Z_E$, and $z \in \Delta Z_C$. Using the obvious condition $m(z) = 0$ at $z = Z_{UML}$ we have:

$$\chi_C = \frac{m(Z_E)}{Z_{UML} - Z_E} \tag{20}$$

Here Z_E is the elevation of the glacier terminus; Z_{UML} is the elevation of upper solid moraine limit. Using the expression for χ_C we obtain:

$$m(z) = m(Z_E) - \frac{m(Z_E)}{Z_{UML} - Z_E}(z - Z_E) = m(Z_E)\frac{Z_{UML} - z}{Z_{UML} - Z_E} \tag{21}$$

After dividing both parts of equation (21) by the moraine density we get a mean depth of moraine distribution along the glacier surface:

$$h_C(z) = h_C(Z_E)\frac{Z_{UML} - z}{Z_{UML} - Z_E} \tag{22}$$

It is necessary to have data on $h_C(Z_E)$ in order to compute $h_C(z)$ by formula (22). The suggested solution of this task is based on the empirical dependence $h_C(Z_E) = f(\Omega)$, where $\Omega = S_m/S_{ab}$ is the ratio between areas of solid moraine S_m and ablation S_{ab} of a glacier. The form of dependence $h_C(Z_E) = f(\Omega)$ is shown in Fig. 2 based on the author's data and other measured data (Konovalov, 1985). This dependence is approximated by:

$$h_C(Z_E) = 88 * \Omega \text{ cm} \tag{23}$$

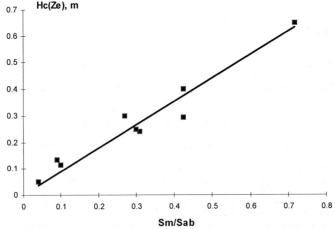

Fig. 2 Dependence of the moraine mean depth at the glacier terminus on the relative area of solid moraine. The glaciers presented on the graph are located in the following regions: Caucasus (the Shkheldy and Amanauz glaciers), Pamir (the Medvezhii, Fedchenko and Bivachnii glaciers), Tien Shan (the Pakhtakor, Ayutor-2, Karabatkak and Inylchek glaciers).

The coefficient of correlation of (23) is 0.97. After $h_C(Z_E)$ is determined it is not difficult to compute the average thickness of moraine $\bar{h}_C(\Delta z)$ in the altitude interval $\Delta z = z - Z_E$ at $Z_{UML} \geq z \geq Z_E$ by the formula:

$$\bar{h}_C(\Delta z) = 0.5 * h_C(Z_E) * [1 + (Z_{UML} - z)/(Z_{UML} - Z_E)]$$
$$= 44 * \Omega * [1 + (Z_{UML} - z)/(Z_{UML} - Z_E)] \quad cm \tag{24}$$

CONCLUSION

The most significant outcome of this research is as follows:
- The results of regional field experimental measurements of ice melt under moraine cover are collected and analysed.
- A simple and physically substantiated model of the influence of moraine cover on glacier melting is elaborated. This model is based on the empirical function $f(h_C)$ for the melting intensity under a moraine cover.
- A general analytical expression is obtained for $f(h_C)$. The recommended working formulae for $f(h_C)$ may be used in the regional model of glacier runoff both with permanent and distributed parameters.
- The function of mean moraine thickness distribution is obtained for the debris-covered area of ablation on a glacier. This is necessary to calculate the total volume of ice ablation under moraine cover, which represents an essential part of the area of a glacier.

Acknowledgement This research is performed within the framework of the scientific project "Glaciers of central Asia and their relation to the global hydrological cycle", kindly supported by NATO CL Grant ENVIR 974676.

REFERENCES

Denisov, Yu. M. (1980). Metod rascheta vliyania morennyh otlozhenii na tayanie lednikov (Method to compute the influence of moraine on glacier melting). *Trydy SANII* **71**(152), 67–80.

Fujii, Y. (1977) Field experiment on glacier ablation under a layer of debris cover. *J. Japan. Soc. Snow Ice (Seppyo)* **39**, 20–21.

Glazyrin, G. E. (1969) Ablatsionnie moreny kak istochnik informatsii o protsessah, proishodyaschih v verhov'yah lednikov (Ablation moraine as the source of information about the processes in a glacier head). *Meteorologiya i Gidrologiya* no. 2, 71–77.

Kamalov, B. A. (1974) Sovremennoe oledenenie i stok lednikov v basseine Syr-Daryi (State of contemporary glaciers and their runoff in the Syrdarya River basin). *Trudi SARNIGMI* **12**(93).

Konovalov, V. G. (1967) Izmenenie teplovogo balansa ablatsii i svoistv deyatelnoi poverhnosti snega i l'da pod deistviem iskusstvennogo zachernenia (Changing the ablation heat balance and features of the snow and ice surface after artificial dusting). *Trudi SANIGMI* **30**(45), 51–57.

Khodakov, V. G. (1972) Raschet ablatsii l'da pod sloem moreny (Calculation of ice ablation under a moraine layer). *MGI* (Data of Glaciological Studies), no. 20, 105–107.

Konovalov V. G. (1969) Problemi klassifikatsii i prostranstvennaya izmenchivost albedo odnorodnoi poverhnosti lednikov v period ablatsii. *Trudi SANIGMI* **44**(59), 102–107.

Konovalov, V. G. (1972) O srednih znacheniah albedo lednikov v period ablatsii (On the mean values of glacier albedo during of the ablation period). *Trudi SARNIGMI* **65**(80), 111–122.

Konovalov, V. G. (1985) *Tayanie i Stok s Lednikov v Basseinah rek Srednei Azii* (Melting and glacier runoff within central Asia river basins). Gidrometeoizdat, Leningrad.

Konovalov, V. G. (1997a) The hydrological regime of Pamir-Altai Glaciers. ICSI (IAHS), UNESCO Symp. on Glacier Mass Balance (Innsbruck, Austria, September 1994). *Z. Gletscherk. Glazialgeol.* **33**(2), 125–131.

Konovalov, V. G. (1997b) Regional model of runoff for high mountain basins: main components and results of realization in the Pamirs and Hindukush river basins. *Data of Glaciological Studies* no. 81, 21–29. Moscow.

Konovalov, V. G. (1997c) Snow line and formation of glacier-derived runoff in glacial basins. In: *34 Selected Papers on Soviet Glaciology, 1940s–1980s* (compiled and ed. by V. M. Kotlyakov), 402–410. Moscow.

Schetinnikov, A. S. (1997) *Morfologia Oledenenia Rechnih Basseinov Pamiro-Alaya po Sostoyaniu na 1980 god. Spravochnik* (Morphology of glaciers in 1980 within the Pamir-Altai river basins. Reference book). Izd-vo SANIGMI, Tashkent.

Debris-Covered Glaciers (Proceedings of a workshop held at Seattle, Washington, USA, September 2000).
IAHS Publ. no. 265, 2000.

Role of supraglacial ponds in the ablation process of a debris-covered glacier in the Nepal Himalayas

AKIKO SAKAI

*Institute for Hydrospheric–Atmospheric Sciences, Nagoya University, Furo-cho, Chikusa-ku,
Nagoya 464-8601, Japan*
e-mail: shakai@ihas.nagoya-u.ac.jp

NOZOMU TAKEUCHI*

*Basic Biology, Faculty of Bioscience and Biotechnology (c/o Faculty of Science), Tokyo
Institute of Technology, 2-12-1, O-okayama, Meguro-ku, Tokyo 152-8551, Japan*

KOJI FUJITA & MASAYOSHI NAKAWO

*Institute for Hydrospheric–Atmospheric Sciences, Nagoya University, Furo-cho, Chikusa-ku,
Nagoya 464-8601, Japan*

Abstract There are many supraglacial ponds on debris-covered glaciers in the Nepal Himalayas. The heat absorbed at the surface of a pond was estimated from heat budget observations on the Lirung Glacier in Langtang Valley, Nepal. The results indicated an average heat absorption of 170 W m^{-2} during the summer monsoon season. This rate is about 7 times the average for the whole debris-covered zone. Analysis of the heat budget for a pond suggests that at least half of the heat absorbed at a pond surface is released with the water outflow from the pond, indicating that the water warmed in the pond enlarges the englacial conduit that drains water from the pond and produces internal ablation. Furthermore, the roof of the conduit could collapse, leading to the formation of ice cliffs and new ponds, which would accelerate the ablation of the debris-covered glacier.

INTRODUCTION

In the Himalayas almost all large valley glaciers with lengths of several kilometres are covered with debris in their ablation zone. These types of glaciers occupy more than 80% of the glacier area in the Himalayas (Fujii & Higuchi, 1977). It is necessary, therefore, to examine the ablation process of debris-covered glaciers for assessment of their changes with climate and impact on water resources.

It has long been realized that a thin debris layer on a glacier surface enhances the ablation of the ice underneath, whereas thick debris inhibits melting (e.g. Østrem, 1959; Fujii, 1977; Mattson *et al.*, 1993). Inoue & Yoshida (1980) measured the ablation rate on the debris-covered zone at a number of points across the width of the glacier. Nakawo *et al.* (1993) and Rana *et al.* (1997) established a model to estimate the average melt rate for a rather large area of a debris-covered glacier by using surface temperature data estimated from satellite imagery.

---

* *Now at*: Frontier Observational Research System for Global Change, International Arctic Research Center, University of Alaska at Fairbanks, 930 Koyukuk Drive, PO Box 757335, Fairbanks, Alaska, USA.

There are many ice cliffs and ponds on debris-covered glaciers. Eyles (1979) and Iwata *et al.* (1980) indicated that the ablation rate of ice cliffs around a supraglacial pond is higher than that of thick debris-covered glacier ice. The ablation rate was found to be about 10 times higher at ice cliffs than the average for the whole debris-covered zone (Sakai *et al.*, 1998). However, there have been no studies of the ablation process at supraglacial ponds, and the morphological evolution due to heterogeneous ablation remains unclear. In this paper, we examine the heat absorbed at the water surface of a supraglacial pond, the pond heat balance, and the consequent effect on ice ablation.

DESCRIPTION OF OBSERVATIONS

Observations were carried out on the Lirung Glacier in Langtang Valley, Nepal. The accumulation zone is debris free. On the other hand, the ablation zone is covered with debris. Figure 1 shows a schematic map of supraglacial ponds and ice cliffs located in the ablation zone of the glacier. There were 53 ponds. Seventeen were partly surrounded by ice cliffs of 3–20 m in height (Aoki & Asahi, 1998). Figure 2 shows a photograph of one of the supraglacial ponds with an ice cliff.

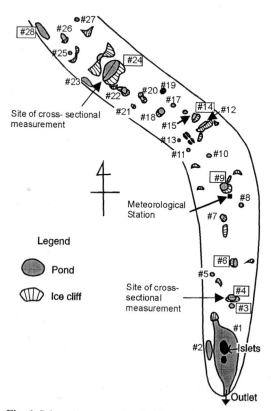

Fig. 1 Schematic map of main observed ponds and ice cliff distribution at ablation zone on the Lirung Glacier. The sign # indicates the number of the pond. Ponds where water temperature and relative water level were observed intermittently are indicated by pond numbers enclosed in a box. The cross-section and water temperature distribution were measured at pond #4 and #24.

Fig. 2 Photo of one of the supraglacial ponds (#22) on the Lirung Glacier. The pond is surrounded by a debris slope and the ice cliff faces north.

Surface and bottom water temperature and water level were observed at several ponds (#3, #4, #6, #9, #14, #24 and #28) at intervals of 1 h for several days. Measurement accuracy was ±0.4°C for temperature and ±2 mm for water level. Cross-sections of two ponds with ice cliffs were measured with a tape at 1-m intervals horizontally along a line across the pond (#24 on 14 June and #4 on 13 July). A meteorological station was installed in the central part of the debris-covered zone (Fig. 1). Air temperature, relative humidity, wind speed, surface temperature of the supraglacial debris, downward and upward solar radiation, and net radiation were monitored at an interval of 5 min from 11 May to 23 October 1996, including the summer monsoon season. Respective errors were ±0.12°C, ±4%, 0.024 m s^{-1}, ±2°C, 4 W m^{-2}, 0.4 W m^{-2}, and 7 W m^{-2}. Details of observations and preliminary results were described by Fujita *et al.* (1997).

HEAT TRANSFER ON THE GLACIER SURFACE

Heat balance of supraglacial ponds

The water level in ponds varied diurnally. The ponds receive water from a surrounding surface watershed and discharge water through englacial conduits. It is necessary, therefore, to take into account the heat associated with the inflow to and outflow from the pond. The heat storage S of the pond is changed by the net heat input at the water surface Q, by advection from meltwater inflow I, by heat lost with the water outflow D, by latent heat for icemelt under the debris layer M_d, and bare ice in the pond, M_i (Fig. 3). The heat balance for the pond is given by:

$$\frac{dS}{dt} = Q + I - D - M_d - M_i \qquad (1)$$

where t is time. The melting point of ice (0°C) is taken as the reference for heat content, and hence water at melting point is regarded here as containing no heat. The water temperature of meltwater inflow is probably 0°C, since it is supplied from the ice–debris interface or englacial water channels. Hence the heat with inflow I is zero. The heats M_d and M_i enlarge the pond and produce ablation. The discharged heat D enlarges the outflow water channels and produces internal ablation.

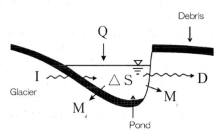

Fig. 3 Schematic figure of the heat balance at a supraglacial pond. ΔS: The change in heat storage of the pond; Q: net heat input at the water surface; D: the heat released from the outflow; I: the heat by meltwater inflow into the pond; M_d: the latent heat of fusion for icemelt under the debris layer at the bottom of the pond; and M_i: for icemelt at exposed ice cliff under the water surface.

Change of stored heat in ponds, dS/dt

Figure 4 shows the daily fluctuations in water level and water temperature (bottom and surface) for pond #6 from 28 May to 6 June. The mean bottom and surface water temperatures were similar, since the bottom ice was insulated by a thick debris layer

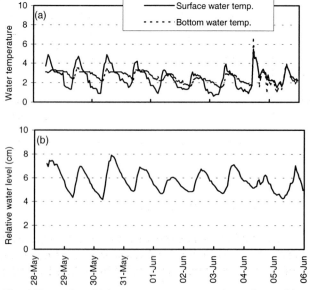

Fig. 4 Fluctuations (a) in water temperatures at the surface and bottom and (b) relative water level observed at pond #6 from 28 May to 5 June at hourly intervals.

(about 1 m). The temperature varied more at the surface than the bottom. Similar diurnal fluctuations were also observed at the other ponds.

The stored heat in the pond is given by:

$$S = c_w \rho_w T_i(t) A z_i(t) \tag{2}$$

Here c_w is the specific heat of water ($= 4.2 \times 10^3$ J °C^{-1} kg^{-1}) and ρ_w is the water density ($= 1000$ kg m^{-3}). A and z_i represent the area and the mean depth of the pond, where A is assumed to be independent of the water level.

The average depth and the surface length were 5 m and 70 m, respectively, at a supraglacial pond near Tsho Rolpa Glacier Lake in Rolwaling Valley. These dimensions were measured at only two ponds on the Lirung Glacier, averaging about 7 m in depth and 90 m in length at pond #24, and 1.6 m and 15.5 m at pond #4, respectively. The ratio of the average depth to the surface length, β, ranged from 0.07 to 0.10. The depth of the other ponds where the water depth was not measured was estimated from the surface geometry by assuming β to be 0.08 as listed in Table 1.

The change in stored heat was calculated for each pond at 1-h intervals using equation (2) and the data for surface temperature and water level. Since the relative water level and water temperature fluctuated with relatively small amplitudes, the mean values of dS/dt averaged over a number of days were usually negligibly small with an upper limit of 4.5 W m^{-2} (Table 1).

Table 1 Size of ponds, bare ice areas, heat transfer coefficient and average calculated heat components at these ponds during each observation period. Changes in storage heat, dS/dt, less than 10^{-2} W m^{-2} were indicated by ~0. Heat with outflow, D, was calculated as the residual value of Q, M_i and M_d from equation (1).

Pond no.	Period	Pond surface area (m²)	Average pond depth (m)	Exposed ice area (m²)	Bulk heat transfer coefficient ×10⁻³	dS/dt (W m⁻²)	Q (W m⁻²)	M_d (W m⁻²)	M_i (W m⁻²)	D (W m⁻²)
#3	10–22 May	45	0.4*	0	2.06	−0.5	148	1.8	0	147
#4	10–18 May	204	1.6	31	1.79	~0	144	1.2	38	105
	17 July–5 Sept.					−2.0	192	0.9	29	164
#6	28 May–5 June	385	1.0*	15	1.86	~0	156	1.1	10	145
#9	28 May–3 June	113	1.1*	15	1.86	~0	171	1.4	41	129
#14	2–6 July	250	1.9*	45	1.76	~0	238	0.6	22	216
	6 Sept.–12 Oct.					−4.0	172	0.1	3	173
#24	15 Aug.–14 Sept.	5805	7.0	630	1.54	+4.5	177	0.6	10	162
#28	10–19 July	100	4.4*	0	1.61	~0	116	3.6	0	112

* Estimated.

Absorbed heat at a supraglacial pond surface, Q

Heat input to the water surface Q is expressed by the following equation involving shortwave radiation SR, longwave radiation LR, sensible heat flux H, latent heat flux E, heat flux with rainfall P, and heat flux with rockfall from the edge of the ice cliff F:

$$Q = SR + LR + H + E + P + F \tag{3}$$

All fluxes are taken to be positive when they are toward the water surface.
    The net shortwave radiation was calculated by

$$SR = (1-\alpha)SR^{\downarrow} \tag{4}$$

Here $SR^{\downarrow}$ is the downward shortwave radiation and α is the albedo of the pond water, which depends on solar elevation h (in degrees). At Tsho Rolpa Glacier Lake in the Nepal Himalayas the following relationship was found during the monsoon season (Yamada, 1998):

$$\alpha = 0.78h^{-0.45} \tag{5}$$

The water was muddy, containing abundant suspended sediment. The turbidity was about 100 mg l^{-1}, and the transparency was less than 10 cm at the surface (Yamada, 1998). Turbidity of ponds on the Lirung Glacier was also high (50–300 mg l^{-1}). Therefore, almost all the shortwave radiation should be absorbed near the surface and would not reach the base of the pond.
    Net radiation NR, downward shortwave radiation $SR^{\downarrow}$, upward shortwave radiation $SR^{\uparrow}$ and surface temperature T_{ms} were observed at the meteorological station, where the surface was debris covered. Downward longwave radiation $LR^{\downarrow}$ was estimated by:

$$LR^{\downarrow} = NR - SR^{\downarrow} + SR^{\uparrow} + \varepsilon_d \sigma T_{ms}^4 \tag{6}$$

Here ε_d is the emissivity of the debris surface (= 0.98) (Oke, 1978) and σ is the Stefan-Boltzmann constant. It was assumed that $LR^{\downarrow}$ was uniform over the ablation area, including the supraglacial ponds. Net longwave radiation incoming to the pond surface is hence expressed by:

$$LR = LR^{\downarrow} - \varepsilon_w \sigma T_s^4 \tag{7}$$

Here ε_w is the emissivity of the water surface (= 0.95) (Oke, 1978) and T_s is the surface water temperature (K).
    Sensible and latent heat fluxes were calculated by bulk aerodynamic formulae presented by Kondo (1998), which were established for lake water surfaces with length from 1 to 10^4 m. Here, the bulk sensible and latent heat transfer coefficients are assumed to be equal, so that

$$H = c_p \rho_a CU(T_a - T_s) \tag{8}$$

$$E = l\rho_a CU(q_a - q_s) \tag{9}$$

where

$$C = 0.189\kappa \left[\ln\left(\frac{z}{z_0}\right) \right]^{-1} \left(\frac{X}{z_0}\right)^{-0.1} \tag{10}$$

Calculated values of C are summarized in Table 1. c_p, ρ_a and l are the specific heat of air at constant volume, air density at 4000 m a.s.l., and latent heat for evaporation from the water surface, respectively. U, q_a and q_s respectively represent the wind velocity at 1.5 m height, specific humidity of the air over the pond, and specific humidity at the pond surface q_s which is later assumed to be the saturated vapour pressure at the water surface temperature T_s. κ, z, z_0, and X are Kalman constant, measurement height (1.5 m), roughness height (2.7×10^{-5} m), and the length of the pond surface, respectively.

When the temperature of rainfall is assumed to be equal to the air temperature the average heat flux from rainfall would be about 1.6 W m^{-2}. Usually rainfall is colder than the air, so the value of 1.6 W m^{-2} should be an upper limit. Since this heat flux is relatively small compared to other heat flux components, it was not included in the total heat input to the pond.

An upper limit for the heat flux from rockfall at the edge of the ice cliff surrounding pond #14 was estimated as follows. The pond area was 250 m^2 and was bordered by an ice cliff with a horizontal length of 20 m. The debris temperature was assumed to be a uniform 30°C, which was the maximum observed debris surface temperature. Average debris thickness measured at the ice cliff edges was about 1 m. The ice cliff retreat rate was 7.2 cm day^{-1} (Sakai *et al.*, 1998). The above data indicate the heat flux from a rockfall should be less than 3.5×10^{-4} W m^{-2}, which is negligible. There would also be a contribution of rock potential energy to the heat in the lake. A cliff height of 20 m predicts heating of the order of 1.0×10^{-2} W m^{-2}, which is also negligible.

Figure 5 shows an example of the absorbed heat balance components at pond #6. The net absorbed heat was dominated by shortwave radiation. The contributions for individual heat flux components are given in Table 1. The total heat input for the observed ponds ranged from 110 to 240 W m^{-2} with an average of 170 W m^{-2}. That heat would melt ice at a rate of 4.8 cm day^{-1} if it were dissipated over the same pond surface area.

Errors of the heat from shortwave radiation, longwave radiation, sensible and latent heat are ±3.5 W m^{-2}, ±23 W m^{-2}, 6.7 W m^{-2} and 5.1 W m^{-2}, respectively. The total error of the incoming heat to the pond surface is ±40 W m^{-2}.

Heat for icemelt, M_d, M_i and D

The ice at the bottom of the pond was covered with thick debris and sediment. The particle size was between clay and silt, and the permeability negligible (Terzaghi &

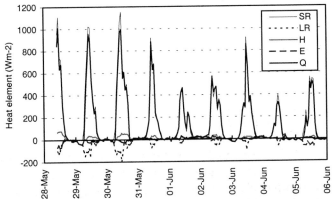

Fig. 5 Fluctuations in incoming heat elements (*SR*: shortwave radiation; *LR*: longwave radiation; *H*: sensible heat; *E*: latent heat; and *Q*: net absorbed heat) calculated at hourly intervals at pond #6 from 28 May to 5 June.

Peck, 1967). Therefore, convection in the debris is not possible and heat transfer is by conduction through the thickness of Δz. The thermal conductivity of the debris k was assumed to be 0.4 J K^{-1} m^{-1} s^{-1} like melting permafrost (Higashi, 1981). The heat flux M_d for unit area of the pond surface becomes

$$M_d = k\frac{T}{\Delta z}\cdot\frac{A_d}{A} \tag{11}$$

T is the temperature difference between water and the ice melting point, and A_d is the debris-covered area at the bottom of the pond, which was assumed to be equal to the pond surface area, A. The debris thickness at the bottom of the pond Δz was assumed to be the thickness observed at the edge of the ice cliff. On this basis, the heat available for melting under the debris layer at the bottom of the pond (M_d) was thus estimated to be approximately 1 W m^{-2} typically and 4 W m^{-2} maximum (Table 1). It is negligible in comparison with the heat incoming to the pond surface Q.

Weeks & Campbell (1973) applied an equation for the average heat transfer coefficient for the fully turbulent flow of a fluid over a flat plate (Eckert & Drake, 1959) to the melt rate of an iceberg at sea. Here, the expression was adopted for melt rate in pure water for application to the ponds as follows:

$$K = 7.14\times10^{-6}\left(\frac{v^{0.8}}{x^{0.2}}\right)\Delta T \tag{12}$$

where v and x are flow velocity of pond water (m s^{-1}) and the contact length of the ice with the water in the water flow direction (m). K is the melt rate (m s^{-1}). Equation (12) was adapted to icemelt in the pure water by changing the constant, which depends on the thermal conductivity, kinematic viscosity and specific heat of the fluid. The contact length x in equation (12) was assumed to be the vertical length of the bare ice in the pond. Since the temperature of the pond water was less than 4°C (temperature of maximum water density), heating from the surface would drive vertical circulation. The flow velocity of the pond was assumed to be less than 0.02 m s^{-1} since it was observed to be 0.02 m s^{-1} at the Tsho Rolpa Glacier Lake with ponds much larger than those on the Lirung Glacier. This prediction of heat transport to the submerged ice cliff gives the following melt rate per unit area of pond surface:

$$M_i = \rho_i L\cdot K\frac{A_i}{A} \tag{13}$$

where ρ_i, L and A_i are the respective density of ice, latent heat of icemelt and area of ice exposed under the water surface. In this calculation, the bare ice area in pond A_i was approximated from the horizontal length of the ice cliff and the average depth of the pond (Table 1). Observation of some ponds that drained suddenly showed that bare ice was restricted to the ice cliffs, so the above estimation of bare ice area should be reasonable. Calculated heat was at most 41 W m^{-2}, which was less than half of the absorbed heat at the pond surface Q.

The outflow heat D can be calculated as a residual value from equation (1) using the above estimates for Q, M_i, M_d and I, which indicates that D was at least 100 W m^{-2} (73% of Q) (Table 1).

Total melt amount for each type of surface

The surface of the debris-covered area can be divided into three kinds: ice cliffs, ponds and debris. The total heat absorbed by the whole debris-covered zone (8.9×10^{14} J or 28 W m^{-2}) is estimated from Rana *et al.* (1997). Our measurements provide estimates for the contribution from ice cliffs and ponds. The total for melt under the debris can then be estimated as a residual. Table 2 shows the total areas of each kind of surface and the corresponding total net heat absorbed over each area during the observation period. (The area of pond #1 was not included in the above total pond area, because its outflow heat was discharged directly out of the glacier (Fig. 1) and melt at the pond base during the observation period was negligible compared to the total heat absorbed by the ponds.) Although the absorbed heat per unit area was about 7 times greater on the ponds than the average for the whole debris-covered zone, the total absorbed in the ponds (0.25×10^{14} J) accounted for only 3% of the total absorbed over the debris-covered zone. The heat for icemelt under the surface debris (7.1×10^{14} J or 21 W m^{-2}) corresponds to an icemelt rate of 0.6 cm day^{-1}.

Table 2 Area and absorbed heat at each type of surface during the observation period (167 days) in 1996 on the Lirung Glacier.

	Whole debris-covered area	Pond	Ice cliff	Debris
Area (km^2)	2.30	0.01	0.04	2.16
Net absorbed heat (W m^{-2})	26*	170	256†	21
Net absorbed heat amount ($\times 10^{14}$ J)	8.9	0.3	1.5	7.1

* After Rana *et al.* (1997).
† After Sakai *et al.* (1998).

Water balance at the ponds

The heat discharged from the ponds D is substantial. In order to provide an additional check on the estimates of D, we estimate the water discharge q_o from a pond required to carry the heat out and examine whether melting in the watershed of the pond can provide that water. The required discharge is given by:

$$q_o = D/c_w \rho_w T_s \tag{14}$$

The corresponding water inflow is given from change in water storage and outflow as

$$q_i = A \frac{d z_i}{d t} + q_o \tag{15}$$

Figure 6 shows two examples (pond #6 and #24) of the inflow q_i calculated at 1-h intervals. The storage change was relatively small, possibly because the water level was controlled by spillways. Table 3 gives the mean daily inflows needed to transport D as calculated from equations (14) and (15) for ponds #6 and #24. Table 3 also shows the sources of water from ice cliffs (q_{ii}) and melting under the debris (q_{id}) that can provide the inflow. These sources were estimated as follows: q_{ii} was evaluated from the area of ice cliff surrounding each pond and the melt rate typical of ice cliffs

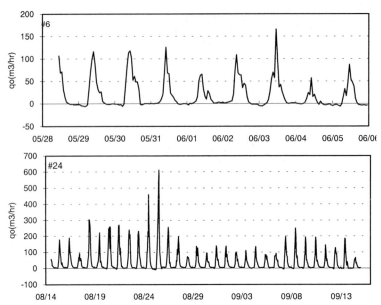

Fig. 6 Fluctuation of inflow to pond #6 and #24 at 1-h intervals calculated from equations (14) and (15).

(7.2 cm day^{-1}; Sakai *et al.*, 1998); q_{id} was calculated from the debris-covered area of the watershed indicated by the map from Aoki *et al.* (1998) and mean icemelt rate under the debris (0.6 cm day^{-1} from Table 2).

For pond #6 the required total inflow to transport D and the sum of the sources (q_{ii} + q_{id}) are essentially the same. This indicates an internal constancy that supports the heat balance calculations of the previous sections.

On the other hand, inferred inflow to transport D is much larger than estimated sources (q_{ii} + q_{id}) for pond #24. There are several possible explanations for this discrepancy. The discharge water temperature of pond #24 may have been higher than the surface water temperature observed locally. Given the relatively large size of pond #24, a sizeable temperature excess seems possible. A temperature about 6°C higher than observed would be required to account for the discrepancy. An additional source of water inflow from an englacial conduit could also help to explain it, but the englacial conduit would have to have a source area including more than half of the total debris-covered area or substantial input from the debris-free area. The latter supplies more than half of the total meltwater from glacier area (Rana *et al.*, 1997). Thus, this second explanation cannot be dismissed.

Table 3 Inflow amount estimated from heat discharge, D and inflow amount from ice cliff (q_{ii}) and from watershed debris-covered area (q_{id}) at ponds #6 and #24.

Pond no.	Inflow amount calculated from D (m^3 day^{-1})	q_{ii}: Area (m^2)	Meltwater amount (m^3 day^{-1})	q_{id}: Area (m^2)	Meltwater amount (m^3 day^{-1})	Total q_{ii} + q_{id} (m^3 day^{-1})
#6	460	4 860	350	20 000	120	470
#24	13 810	11 400	820	123 000	738	1558

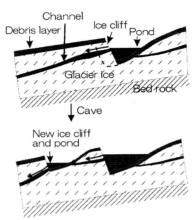

Fig. 7 Schematic figure of supraglacial pond formation by caving of the englacial water channel roof. The water channel enlarges as heat is absorbed at the pond surface, and the channel roof collapses to create a funnel-shaped depression. A new pond, surrounded by ice cliffs, is then formed. Formations of pond and ice cliffs accelerate the ablation rate at the debris-covered zone due to the high ablation rate at the pond and ice cliffs.

DISCUSSION

At least half of the heat absorbed at the surfaces of ponds was released with outflow. The melting caused by this heat is focused in the drainage paths such as englacial conduits or along the ice-debris interface of supraglacial trenches.

The temperature of water released from ponds should be close to the surface temperature (about 2°C). The potential for enlargement of englacial channels is considerable. (For example, Koizumi & Naruse (1994) found experimentally that 0.13°C water entering an initially small conduit of length 8 cm and initial diameter of 1.5 mm enlarged to 2.6 mm in a 13 minutes.) Some supraglacial ponds were observed suddenly to drain away during the melting season, probably by the thermal enlargement of their drainage channels or lowering of their floors. Although the absorbed heat at the ponds is smaller (0.3×10^{14} J) than the heat absorbed in the whole ablation zone (8.9×10^{14} J), its focused delivery to the ice could create large englacial or supraglacial channels.

Kirkbride (1993) suggested that supraglacial ponds aligned along an englacial conduit may be created by the collapse of the conduit roof. We suggest that heat absorbed in the ponds can accelerate this process by more rapid enlargement of the englacial conduit, roof collapse and formation of funnel-shaped hollows (Fig. 7). Even if water discharges from ponds along the debris–ice interface, the heat may melt trenches with overhanging bounding ice cliffs that can also collapse. Actually, funnel-shaped hollows appeared at three sites during the observation period, and they could be the sites of future ponds. Ice cliffs and the ponds absorb 10 and 7 times more heat than the debris-covered ice. Furthermore, absorbed heat at newly produced ponds could cause subsequent collapse of water channels and create more ice cliffs and ponds. This positive-feedback process could thereby accelerate the ablation rate of debris-covered glaciers.

Acknowledgements We wish to thank two anonymous reviewers and Charlie Raymond for their helpful comments and suggestions. We would like to express our thanks to the Department of Hydrology and Meteorology, Ministry of Water Resources, His Majesty's Government of Nepal. We also thank Yutaka Ageta, Jumpei Kubota and all of the members of the Project for their valuable support getting these observations. Financial support was provided respectively, by a Grant-in-Aid for Scientific Research (Project no. 06041051, no. 09490018 and Aid for the Japan Society for the Promotion of Science (JSPS) Research Fellow) from the Ministry of Education, Science, Sports and Culture of the Japanese Government, and Cooperative Research under the Japan–US Cooperative Science Program from JSPS.

REFERENCES

Aoki, K. & Asahi, K. (1998) Topographical map of the ablation area of the Lirung Glacier in the Langtang Valley, Nepal Himalaya. *Bull. Glacier Res.* **16**, 19–31.

Eckert, E. R. G. & Drake, R. M. (1959) *Heat and Mass Transfer.* McGraw-Hill, New York.

Eyles, N. (1979) Facies of supraglacial sedimentation on Icelandic and Alpine temperate glaciers. *Can. J. Earth Sci.* **16**, 1341–1361.

Fujii, Y. (1977) Field experiment on glacier ablation under a layer of debris cover. *J. Japan. Soc. Snow Ice (Seppyo)* **39**, special issue, 20–21.

Fujii, Y. & Higuchi, K. (1977) Statistical analyses of the forms of the glaciers in Khumbu Himal. *J. Japan. Soc. Snow Ice (Seppyo)* **39**, special issue, 7–14.

Fujita, K., Sakai, A. & Chhetri, T. B. (1997) Meteorological observation in Langtang Valley, Nepal Himalayas, 1996. *Bull. Glacier Res.* **15**, 71–78.

Higashi, A. (1981) *Fundamentals of Cold Regions Engineering Science.* Kokon-shoin Co., Ltd Japan.

Inoue, J. & Yoshida, M. (1980) Ablation and heat exchange over the Khumbu Glacier. *J. Japan. Soc. Snow Ice (Seppyo)* **41**, special issue, 26–33.

Iwata, S., Watanabe, O. & Fushimi, H. (1980) Surface morphology in the ablation area of the Khumbu Glacier. *J. Japan. Soc. Snow Ice (Seppyo)* **41**, special issue, 9–17.

Kirkbride, M. P. (1993) The temporal significance of transitions from melting to calving termini at glaciers in the central Southern Alps of New Zealand. *The Holocene* **3**(3), 232–240.

Koizumi, K & Naruse, R. (1994) Experiments on formation of water channels in a glacier (abstract in English). *J. Japan. Soc. Snow Ice (Seppyo)* **56**(2), 137–144.

Kondo, J. (ed.) (1998) *Meteorology in the Water Environment.* Asakura, Tokyo.

Mattson, L. E., Gardner, J. S. & Young, G. J. (1993) Ablation on debris covered glaciers: an example from the Rakhiot Glacier, Punjab, Himalaya. In: *Snow and Glacier Hydrology* (ed. by G. J. Young) (Proc. Kathmandu Symp., November 1992), 289–296. IAHS Publ. no. 218.

Nakawo, M., Moroboshi, T. & Uehara, S. (1993) Satellite data utilization for estimating ablation of debris covered glaciers. In: *Snow and Glacier Hydrology* (ed. by G. J. Young) (Proc. Kathmandu Symp., November 1992), 75–83. IAHS Publ. no. 218.

Oke, T. R. (1978) *Boundary Layer Climates*, second edn. John Wiley, New York.

Østrem, G. (1959) Ice melting under a thin layer of moraine and the existence of ice cores in moraine ridges. *Geogr. Ann.* **41**, 228–230.

Rana, B., Nakawo, M., Fukushima, Y. & Ageta, Y. (1997) Application of a conceptual precipitation–runoff model (HYCYMODEL) in a debris-covered glacierized basin in the Langtang Valley, Nepal Himalaya. *Ann. Glaciol.* **25**, 226–231.

Sakai, A., Nakawo, M. & Fujita, K. (1998) Melt rate of ice cliffs on the Lirung Glacier, Nepal Himalayas, 1996. *Bull. Glacier Res.* **16**, 57–66.

Terzaghi, K. & Peck, R. B. (1967) *Soil Mechanics in Engineering Practice*, second edn. John Wiley & Sons, Inc., New York.

Weeks, W. F. & Campbell, W. J. (1973) Iceberg as a fresh-water source: an appraisal. *J. Glaciol.* **12**, 65, 207–233.

Yamada, T. (1998) *Glacier Lake and its Outburst Flood in the Nepal Himalaya.* Monograph no. 1, March 1998, Data Centre for Glacier Research, Japanese Society of Snow and Ice.

3 Origin and Transport

Debris-Covered Glaciers (Proceedings of a workshop held at Seattle, Washington, USA, September 2000).
IAHS Publ. no. 264, 2000.

Hydrological controls on sediment transport pathways: implications for debris-covered glaciers

NICK SPEDDING

*Department of Geography, University of Aberdeen, Elphinstone Road, Aberdeen, AB24 3UF,
UK*
e-mail: n.spedding@abdn.ac.uk

Abstract It is usual to associate the presence of an extensive debris mantle and large lateral moraine ramparts with passive transport of rockfall debris. This simple model does not provide sufficient explanation for past and present moraine formation at the Icelandic glaciers Gígjökull and Kvíárjökull. Here active transport of debris derived from subglacial bedrock makes important contributions to the drainage basin sediment budget. Extensive englacial debris bands, representing relict channel fills, and thick exposures of debris-rich basal ice are both thought to reflect a switch from subglacial to englacial drainage induced by terminal overdeepenings. This switch in hydrology disrupts the tendency of subglacial drainage to sweep the basal transport zone clear of debris. Incorporation of this concept of subglacial flushing into drainage-basin-scale models of debris transfer provides for a fuller understanding of debris-covered glaciers within the wider context of general glacier sediment transport theory.

INTRODUCTION

Recent work has significantly increased our understanding of the various ways in which glaciers entrain and transport sediment (see Kirkbride, 1995; and Alley *et al.*, 1997; for reviews). Particular emphasis has been given to subglacial sediment deformation (e.g. Murray, 1997), ice deformation (e.g. Hambrey *et al.*, 1999), and the direct and indirect impact of water flow within and beneath ice (e.g. Gustavson & Boothroyd, 1987; Kirkbride & Spedding, 1996; Näslund & Hassinen, 1996; Lawson *et al.*, 1998; Krüger & Aber, 1999; Glasser *et al.*, 1999; Ensminger *et al.*, 1999). Nevertheless, the idea that the sediment budget of temperate, alpine-type, debris-covered glaciers that build large moraines is dominated by passive transport of supraglacial rockfall debris remains established as a central feature of glacial geomorphic theory (e.g. Small, 1987a,b; Benn & Evans, 1998). [The terms "passive" and "active" transport, introduced by Boulton (1978), define the primary classification of glacier sediment transport processes: clasts in passive transport retain their original form, whereas clasts subject to active transport undergo extensive modification.] However, this simple rockfall/passive transport model does not provide sufficient explanation for the large Neoglacial moraine ramparts constructed by the Icelandic glaciers Gígjökull and Kvíárjökull. Rockfall source areas are limited at these glaciers, and clast analysis demonstrates that active transport of subglacially-derived debris accounts for a substantial part of both past and present moraine formation. This paper argues that glacier drainage acts as the key influence on these alternative transport pathways, and builds on the examples of Gígjökull and Kvíárjökull to suggest that a perspective giving fuller treatment to hydrology is likely to provide a more complete understanding of sediment transport by debris-covered glaciers.

STUDY GLACIERS: GÍGJÖKULL AND KVÍÁRJÖKULL

Both Gígjökull and Kvíárjökull drain small mountain ice caps (Fig. 1), which means that, in contrast to alpine valley glaciers, supraglacial debris inputs above the equilibrium line (EL) are small. Steep, long icefalls occupy the zones where the glaciers have cut through the volcanic escarpments; these give way to gentle terminal lobes at the junction of escarpments and *sandar* (outwash plains). Ice radar surveys show that pronounced overdeepenings lie beneath these terminal lobes (Fig. 2); observations of upwelling and moulin water levels standing within a few metres of the ice surface indicate high water pressures in these areas. However, direct data indicative of the glaciers' drainage systems are not available. Following Björnsson (1979), both glaciers are believed to be temperate. The volcanoes underneath Eyjafjallajökull and Öræfajökull last erupted in 1821–1823 and 1727 respectively, both events generating an outburst flood at the study glaciers. The time elapsed since makes it unlikely that the current patterns of sedimentation are dominated by the impact of *jökulhlaups*, although the possible impacts of elevated geothermal heat fluxes on the process regimes are unknown.

Large Neoglacial moraine ramparts enclose the glaciers' termini (Dugmore, 1989; Thórarinsson, 1956; Guðmundsson, 1998): Gígjökull's is ~60 m high, Kvíárjökull's ~100 m high. These motivated study of the two glaciers, although fieldwork focused on the character of contemporary sediments and transport pathways. Clast roundness analysis using standard procedures (Benn & Ballantyne, 1994), supported by observations of the sediments' matrix properties and wider field relationships (e.g. the spatial arrangement of debris relative to other debris, the glacier margins, and ice structures such as foliation), identified three distinct types of debris. Tephra forms a fourth distinct category, but its overall volume relative to the other three is negligible, so it was excluded from this study. Tables 1 and 2 summarize the most important details; Fig. 3 depicts the spatial distribution of the major debris types.

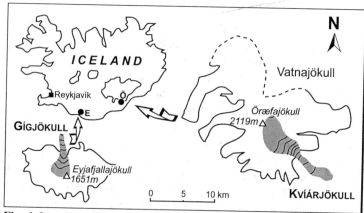

Fig. 1 Location of Gígjökull and Kvíárjökull. Surface contours shown for study glaciers at 200 m intervals.

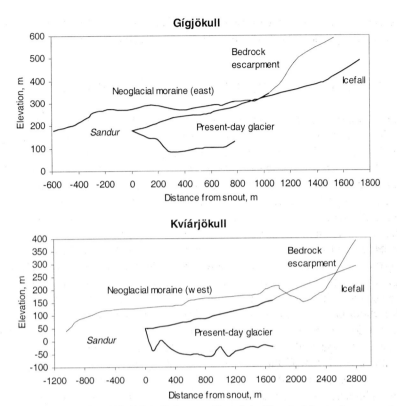

Fig. 2 Gígjökull and Kvíárjökull: long profiles of the Neoglacial moraine ramparts set against present-day, centre-line surface and bed topography. Thick lines represent data obtained by field survey, thin lines data taken from published maps. Although crude (centreline survey only, no migration of bed-return data), these profiles support the inference that the magnitude of the adverse bed slope relative to the ice surface slope is sufficient to induce glacio-hydraulic supercooling beneath the termini of both glaciers. Gígjökull ice depth data courtesy of A. J. Dugmore.

INTERPRETATION

Its angular character identifies Type A sediment as rockfall debris; field relationships demonstrate both above-EL sources (debris bands at Kvíárjökull) and below-EL sources (debris directly supplied to the ice surface at both Gígjökull and Kvíárjökull). Type B debris is clearly different from either Types A or C debris. The rounded character of the larger clasts, and the crude sorting of the matrix deficient in fine particles is atypical of rockfall or basal debris, but strongly suggests modification of the debris by water transport. The debris content of the source debris bands is unusually high (~60–70% debris concentration by mass), and a sharp contact exists between the debris bands and the surrounding, debris-free englacial (i.e. of meteoric origin) ice. Accordingly, Kirkbride & Spedding (1996) conclude that the debris bands from which Type B debris is derived represent channel fills, formed by sediments deposited in an englacial drainage system, subsequently to become separated from the water and returned to ice transport. This relict channel hypothesis is preferred to a

Table 1 Summary of clast roundness analysis.

Location	Debris type	No. of clasts in sample	Clast roundness: RA%	Mean	Std Dev.
Gígjökull	A	248	64.92	2.27	0.62
	B	487	1.03	3.86	0.75
	C	396	39.90	2.60	0.55
	Rampart	1083	15.82	3.17	0.76
Kvíárjökull	A	635	95.28	1.95	0.38
	B	545	19.27	3.11	0.77
	C	560	54.82	2.46	0.57
	Rampart, P	877	65.34	2.30	0.61
	Rampart, M	1291	52.98	2.52	0.71
	Rampart, D	1082	28.10	2.92	0.76

Clast roundness was assessed by Power's standard six-point scale. Very angular clasts were given the value 1, angular clasts 2, ...well-rounded clasts 6, so allowing calculation of roundness mean and standard deviation.

RA%   This is the RA index, a non-parametric measure of sample clast roundness (Benn & Ballantyne, 1994). It indicates the percentage of clasts in each sample classified as very angular or angular.

Rampart: Debris making up the Neoglacial lateral moraine ramparts enclosing the study glaciers. Because of the size of Kvíárjökull's Neoglacial moraine, the data set was divided into three parts according to distance along the ridge crest. These are denoted P (proximal), M (middle) and D (distal).

Table 2 Other important characteristics of the three major debris types.

Debris type	Matrix properties	Source of debris	Interpretation
A	Poorly sorted. Coarse matrix, deficient in fine sands, silts and clays.	(i) Sits on ice surface as clast-supported deposit, or, (ii) largely continuous englacial debris septa; irregular contact with surrounding ice; high debris content.	Rockfall debris; PASSIVE supraglacial or englacial transport.
B	Crude sorting. Medium–coarse matrix, often deficient in silts and clays.	Various englacial debris bands: continuous debris septa, interspersed with lenticular or trough-like pockets of sediment; smooth, sharp contact with surrounding ice; high debris content; ice occupies interstices.	Englacial channel fill deposits: "relict channel" debris bands. ACTIVE transport by running water; thereafter passive transport in englacial ice.
C	Poorly sorted; usually all grades of particles from gravels to silts and clays well represented.	Dirty ice exposures, sometimes >10 m thick; debris occurs as clots or sub-horizontal laminae, enclosed within ice; debris concentrations low to medium; occasional clasts >30 mm diameter; distinct bubble layers common; otherwise ice largely bubble-free.	Basal debris enclosed in basal ice; ACTIVE transport in the subglacial traction zone.

thrust origin because the debris bands are commonly wavy, closely spaced, and with a shallow dip; only in one instance was a connection to the glacier bed observed. These features do not match published accounts of thrusts (e.g. Hambrey *et al.*, 1999). If thrust development was responsible for debris band formation at the study glaciers, it is reasonable to expect entrainment of basal debris also, but this is not the case: the debris bands contain Type B material only. This observation further supports their inferred origin as channel fills.

The most probable source for the sediment in these debris bands is the subglacial bedrock some distance upglacier of the termini. Supraglacial debris sources above the ELs are limited, whereas entrainment of debris by surface streams at lower elevations is difficult to reconcile with the observed volume and routing of supraglacial drainage below the icefalls, and the transport distance likely to be required for significant rounding of the debris to occur. Thus it is inferred that the channels that gave rise to the debris bands must once have run subglacially. This switch from subglacial to englacial drainage is difficult to account for, but it is consistent with current ideas on the behaviour of water in overdeepenings (Lliboutry, 1983; Röthlisberger & Lang, 1987; Fountain, 1994; Hooke & Pohjola, 1994; Fountain & Walder, 1998). The adverse slope of an overdeepened basin acts to raise water pressures to levels sufficient to render discrete subglacial channels unstable. Recent work has focused on the impact of freezing induced by an energy deficit as water flows upslope beneath progressively thinner ice: growth of frazil and anchor ice accelerates the process of channel closure and rising water pressures, so that, in certain cases, water (and debris also) is diverted into smaller channels at higher levels within the ice (Hooke & Pohjola, 1994; Alley *et al.*, 1998; Ensminger *et al.*, 1999). This envisaged switch from subglacial to englacial drainage involves a loss in flow competence and capacity, likely to induce deposition of sediment within the ice—a process that clearly favours the production of channel fill debris bands (Kirkbride & Spedding, 1996).

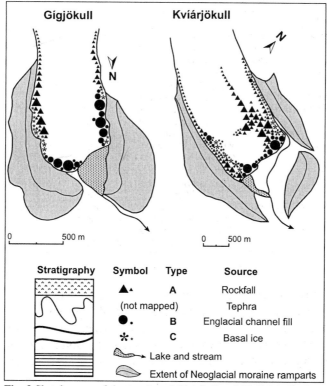

Fig. 3 Sketch maps of the termini of Gígjökull and Kvíárjökull, showing the distribution of the major debris types.

Its reduced angularity, indicative of active clast modification, differentiates Type C debris from the rockfall material, and supports an origin within the basal traction zone. The dirty ice from which it is derived shows many characteristics of basal ice produced by sliding over a hard bed (e.g. Jansson *et al.*, 1996): using the classification of Hubbard & Sharp (1995), the ice can be described as "stratified", consisting largely of a mixture of "laminated" and "clear" facies. Debris laminae suggest "Weertman-type" regelation (Hubbard & Sharp, 1993); clear pockets with muddy clots suggest flow of meltwater containing fine sediments through the vein network (Lliboutry, 1993; Knight & Knight, 1994), accompanied by plastic deformation and ice metamorphism; coarse clasts indicate bedrock fracture and tractive entrainment of debris. The climate is not conducive to net accretion of basal ice by freezing-on, so the observed thicknesses of basal ice are probably produced by tectonic thickening (cf. Sharp *et al.*, 1994). However, given the ice radar evidence of overdeepenings, which suggests that the adverse bed slopes exceed the ice surface slopes by more than the critical factor of 1.2–1.7 (Fig. 2), formation of basal ice by glacio-hydraulic supercooling in a residual subglacial drainage network is also plausible (Lawson *et al.*, 1998). The debris band evidence for englacial drainage is also consistent with this hypothesis.

Clast roundness analysis shows that much of the debris contained in the rampart moraines is not derived from rockfall: very angular or angular clasts make substantial contributions to the proximal (i.e. adjacent to the escarpment) portions only. Much of the moraine material closely resembles Type B or C sediments, so it is inferred that the same active transport pathways identified today operated for much of the Neoglacial, contributing large quantities of relict channel and basal debris to the moraine ridges.

DISCUSSION

Hydrological influences on sediment transport

It is the transition from icefall to overdeepening that seems to govern the disposition of sediments at the termini of Gígjökull and Kvíárjökull. This section explores the possibility that these circumstances permit development of a thick debris cover at temperate glaciers even in the absence of extensive rockfall inputs. At the core of this hypothesis is the inferred switch from predominantly subglacial to predominantly englacial drainage, induced by the ice and bedrock geometry. This favours both production of debris, and its retention within the ice for subsequent delivery to the glacier margins.

It is likely that much of the Types B and C debris mapped in Fig. 3 is produced by bedrock erosion associated with rapid sliding, widespread cavity formation and variable water pressures at the base of the icefalls (Hooke, 1991). Some of this debris will be picked up and carried away by the subglacial drainage; some will be incorporated into basal ice. Debris-rich basal ice of the type found at Gígjökull and Kvíárjökull is unlikely to survive in close proximity to major elements of subglacial drainage, because high power flows melt ice and remove debris (Hubbard & Sharp, 1995); however, destruction of basal ice, and consequent evacuation of its debris, beneath icefalls is likely to be limited because sliding suppresses both the growth and migration of channels. As noted above, both theoretical and empirical studies indicate that rising water pressures within an overdeepening can force a switch from predominantly subglacial to predominantly englacial drainage. The relict channel debris bands provide firm evidence of this at Gígjökull and Kvíárjökull (Kirkbride & Spedding, 1996), and provide clues to the possible structure of water flow. Their location, size and spacing imply distributed englacial networks of numerous small channels (cf. Hooke & Pohjola, 1994), possibly exploiting pre-existing fractures (cf. Ensminger *et al.*, 1999), preferentially routed close to the sides of the glaciers (cf. Lliboutry, 1983; Fountain & Walder, 1998).

It is possible that the extensive exposures of basal ice also represent ramifications of this hydrological switch:

(a) water running within englacial ice cannot attack basal ice and sediments, favouring accumulation of relatively thick, debris-rich basal ice layers;

(b) the transition from a lubricated "wet" bed to a sticky "dry" bed will enhance the compressive flow acting to thicken basal ice, and so carry it away from areas immediately adjacent to the glacier bed where it is most likely to be destroyed.

If this hypothesis is correct, the simultaneous presence of extensive relict channel debris bands and thick exposures of basal ice at Gígjökull and Kvíárjökull is causally-connected, not coincidental, and moraine formation, both present and past, is (was) related to a context dominated by water flow. The possibility of glacio-hydraulic supercooling enhancing basal ice formation strengthens this idea.

Implications for debris-covered glaciers

Although large areas are buried beneath sediments, Gígjökull and Kvíárjökull cannot be described as debris-covered; however, this does not mean that similar processes to those described above are not important at debris-covered glaciers. Arguably it is because their termini are not smothered by rockfall debris that alternative, active sediment transport pathways can be identified at Gígjökull and Kvíárjökull. It is probable that similar non-rockfall debris is buried in the surface mantles and lateral moraines of many debris-covered glaciers: e.g. relict channel debris features strongly in the debris cover of the Tasman and Mueller Glaciers in New Zealand (Kirkbride & Spedding, 1996), and both water-worked cobbles and polished, striated basal clasts are found amongst the rockfall debris of the Ghiacciaio del Miage in the Italian Alps (author's observations). This study highlights the impacts of overdeepenings, but it is feasible that other circumstances, such as storm events (e.g. Warburton & Fenn, 1994), surges (e.g. Sharp, 1985; Bennett *et al.*, 2000) or floods (Näslund & Hassinen, 1996; Krüger & Aber, 1999) that generate high basal water pressures will also give rise to relict channel debris bands. It is also clear from this study that the construction of large moraines is not restricted to glaciers with sediment budgets dominated by rockfall and passive transport.

A corollary of the passive transport model is the assumption that paucity of debris cover and small moraines are the result of restricted debris supply: e.g. because of resistant rocks, or small areas of supraglacial rockwalls. This is not necessarily true: sediment availability for moraine formation is a function of both debris supply and debris *retention*. Hydrology exerts a critical control on the latter. Highly erosive glaciers cannot build large moraines at the end of active transport pathways if the bulk of debris generated subglacially is swept away by the action of aggressive subglacial water flows. Alley *et al.* (1997) emphasize the efficacy of subglacial water transport, a notion which is also implicit in the use of proglacial sediment discharge to estimate subglacial sediment yields and erosion rates; however, the potential impact of subglacial flushing on the distribution of debris between different transport pathways and the ability of glaciers to form moraines does not figure strongly in the glacial geomorphic literature (Kirkbride, 1995), despite the rapid growth in our knowledge of glacier hydrology in the last 20 years or so. Gígjökull and Kvíárjökull can build large moraines without the aid of abundant rockfall inputs precisely because this flushing constraint is broken: large quantities of debris evade removal by water beneath the icefalls (sliding constraints on channel growth and migration), at the base of the overdeepenings (collapse of the subglacial drainage network), and within the ice of the terminal lobes (deposition of the relict channel debris bands). If this concept of flushing is applied to debris-covered glaciers, their thick debris mantles and large moraines are seen to indicate not only the presence of effective, rockfall-dominated debris supply, but also the *absence* of effective debris removal. Rockfall debris sits upon, or returns quickly to, the glacier surface, whereas water tends to find its way rapidly towards the glacier bed, so creating the necessary separation of debris and competent water flows required to break the flushing constraint for the high level part of the transport system.

CONCLUSION

The examples of Gígjökull and Kvíárjökull demonstrate the importance of hydrology as an influence on glacier sediment budgets, and suggest that the passive transport model provides a partial, and possibly misleading, account of debris cover formation and moraine accumulation. Accounts of sediment transport that stress the source and primary mode of entrainment of debris risk ignoring the possibility of more complex transport histories: debris can be shifted between different pathways within ice, or removed from ice transport altogether (in which case it cannot form true moraines). Glacier drainage is a major factor controlling this redistribution of debris. This study forms a small part of a growing body of work indicating that hydrology must be included alongside established factors such as relief, geology, climate and thermal regime when formulating glacier sediment transport models; use of such an extended framework provides for a more complete understanding of debris-covered glaciers in the full context of the different types of ice masses found worldwide.

Acknowledgements This study was part-funded by the Royal Society of London and the Carnegie Trust for the Universities of Scotland. Thanks to Peter Jansson and Andrew Fountain for their constructive appraisals of the original manuscript.

REFERENCES

Alley, R. B., Cuffey, K. M., Evenson, E. B., Strasser, J. C., Lawson, D. E. & Larson, G. J. (1997) How glaciers entrain and transport basal sediment: physical constraints. *Quatern. Sci. Rev.* **16**(9), 1017–1038.

Alley, R. B., Lawson, D. E., Evenson, E. B., Strasser, J. C. & Larson, G. J. (1998) Glaciohydraulic supercooling: a freeze-on mechanism to create stratified, debris-rich basal ice: II. Theory. *J. Glaciol.* **44**(148), 563–569.

Benn, D. I. & Ballantyne, C. K. (1994) Reconstructing the transport history of glacigenic sediments: a new approach based on the co-variance of clast-form indices. *Sediment. Geol.* **91**(1–4), 215–227.

Benn, D. I. & Evans, D. J. A. (1998) *Glaciers and Glaciation*. Edward Arnold, London.

Bennett, M. R., Huddart, D., McCormick, T. & Waller, R. I. (2000) Glaciofluvial crevasse- and channel-fills as indicators of subglacial dewatering during a surge, Skeiðarárjökull, Iceland. Accepted for *J. Glaciol.*

Björnsson, H. (1979) Glaciers in Iceland. *Jökull* **29**, 74–80.

Boulton, G. S. (1978) Boulder shapes and grain size distributions as indicators of transport paths through a glacier and till genesis. *Sedimentology* **25**(6), 773–799.

Dugmore, A. J. (1989) Tephrochronological studies of Holocene glacier fluctuations in south Iceland. In: *Glacier Fluctuations and Climatic Change* (ed. by J. Oerlemans), 37–55. Kluwer Academic Publishers, Dordrecht, The Netherlands.

Ensminger, S. L., Evenson, E. B., Larson, G. J., Lawson, D. E., Alley, R. B. & Strasser, J. C. (1999) Preliminary study of laminated, silt-rich debris bands: Matanuska Glacier, Alaska, USA. *Ann. Glaciol.* **28**, 261–266.

Fountain, A. G. (1994) Borehole water-level variations and implications for the subglacial hydraulics of South Cascade Glacier, Washington State, USA. *J. Glaciol.* **40**(135), 293–304.

Fountain, A. G. & Walder, J. S. (1998) Water flow through temperate glaciers. *Rev. Geophys.* **36**(3), 299–328.

Glasser, N. F., Bennett, M. R. & Huddart, D. (1999) Distribution of glaciofluvial sediment within and on the surface of a High Arctic valley glacier: Marthabreen, Svalbard. *Earth Surf. Processes and Landforms* **24**, 303–318.

Guðmundsson, H. J. (1998) Holocene glacier fluctuations and tephrochronology of the Öræfi district, Iceland. PhD Thesis, University of Edinburgh, UK.

Gustavson, T. C. & Boothroyd, J. C. (1987) A depositional model for outwash, sediment sources and hydrologic characteristics, Malaspina Glacier, Alaska: a modern analogue of the south-eastern margin of the Laurentide Ice Sheet. *Geol. Soc. Am. Bull.* **99**(2), 187–200.

Hambrey, M. J., Bennett, M. R., Dowdeswell, J. A., Glasser, N. F. & Huddart, D. (1999) Debris entrainment and transfer in polythermal valley glaciers. *J. Glaciol.* **45**(149), 69–86.

Hooke, R. Le B. (1991) Positive feedbacks associated with erosion of glacial cirques and overdeepenings. *Geol. Soc. Am. Bull.* **103**(8), 1104–1108.

Hooke, R. Le B. & Pohjola, V. A. (1994) Hydrology of a segment of a glacier situated in an overdeepening, Storglaciären, Sweden. *J. Glaciol.* **40**(134), 140–148.

Hubbard, B. & Sharp, M. J. (1993) Weertman regelation, multiple refreezing events and the isotopic evolution of the basal ice layer. *J. Glaciol.* **39**(132), 275–291.

Hubbard, B. & Sharp, M. J. (1995) Basal ice facies and their formation in the western Alps. *Arct. Alpine Res.* **27**(4), 301–310.

Jansson, P., Kohler, J. & Pohjola, V. A. (1996) Characteristics of basal ice at Engabreen, northern Norway. *Ann. Glaciol.* **22**, 114–120.

Kirkbride, M. P. (1995) Processes of transportation. In: *Modern Glacial Environments: Processes, Dynamics and Sediments* (ed. by J. Menzies), 261–292. Butterworth-Heinemann, Oxford.

Kirkbride, M. P. & Spedding, N. (1996) The influence of englacial drainage on sediment transport pathways and till texture of temperate valley glaciers. *Ann. Glaciol.* **22**, 160–166.

Knight, P. G. & Knight, D. A. (1994) Glacier sliding, regelation water flow and development of basal ice. *J. Glaciol.* **40**(136), 600–601.

Krüger, J. & Aber, J. S. (1999) Formation of supraglacial sediment accumulations on Kötlujökull, Iceland. *J. Glaciol.* **45**(150), 400–402.

Lawson, D. E., Strasser, J. C., Evenson, E. B., Alley, R. B., Larson, G. J. & Arcone, S. A. (1998) Glaciohydraulic supercooling: a freeze-on mechanism to create stratified, debris-rich basal ice: I. Field evidence. *J. Glaciol.* **44**(148), 547–562.

Lliboutry, L. (1983) Modifications to the theory of intraglacial waterways for the case of subglacial ones. *J. Glaciol.* **29**(102), 216–226.

Lliboutry, L. (1993) Internal melting and ice accretion at the bottom of temperate glaciers. *J. Glaciol.* **39**(131), 50–64.

Murray, T. (1997) Assessing the paradigm shift: deformable glacier beds. *Quatern. Sci. Rev.* **16**(9), 995–1016.

Näslund, J.-O. &. Hassinen, S. (1996) Supraglacial sediment accumulations and large englacial water channels at high elevations in Mýrdalsjökull, Iceland. *J. Glaciol.* **42**(140), 190–192.

Röthlisberger, H. & Lang, H. (1987) Glacial hydrology. In: *Glacio-fluvial Sediment Transfer: an Alpine Perspective* (ed. by A. M. Gurnell & M. J. Clark), 207–284. Wiley, Chichester, UK.

Sharp, M. J. (1985) Sedimentation and stratigraphy at Eyjabakkajökull—an Icelandic surging glacier. *Quatern. Res.* **24**, 268–284.

Sharp, M. J., Jouzel, J., Hubbard, B. & Lawson, W. (1994) The character, structure and origin of the basal ice layer of a surge-type glacier. *J. Glaciol.* **40**(135), 327–340.

Small, R. J. (1987a) Englacial and supraglacial sediment: transport and deposition. In: *Glacio-fluvial Sediment Transfer: an Alpine Perspective* (ed. by A. M. Gurnell & M. J. Clark), 111–145. Wiley, Chichester, UK.

Small, R. J. (1987b) The glacial sediment system: an alpine perspective. In: *Glacio-fluvial Sediment Transfer: an Alpine Perspective* (ed. by A. M. Gurnell & M. J. Clark), 199–203. Wiley, Chichester, UK.

Thórarinsson, S. (1956) On the variations of Svínafellsjökull, Skaftafellsjökull and Kvíárjökull in Öræfi. *Jökull* **14**, 67–75.

Warburton, J. & Fenn, C. R. (1994) Unusual flood events from an Alpine glacier: observations and deductions on generating mechanisms. *J. Glaciol.* **40**(134), 176–186.

Debris-Covered Glaciers (Proceedings of a workshop held at Seattle, Washington, USA, September 2000).
IAHS Publ. no. 264, 2000.

Debris entrainment and polythermal structure in the terminus of Storglaciären

PETER JANSSON, JENS-OVE NÄSLUND,
RICKARD PETTERSSON*,
CECILIA RICHARDSON-NÄSLUND & PER HOLMLUND*

Department of Physical Geography, Stockholm University, S-10691 Stockholm, Sweden
e-mail: peter.jansson@natgeo.su.se

Abstract Ground penetrating radar recordings and measurements of ice motion have provided a detailed picture of movement and internal structure of the terminus of Storglaciären, Sweden. The glacier is polythermal with a cold surface layer resulting in a frozen rim along the glacier margins and terminus. Englacial debris layers emerge at the glacier surface, forming supra-glacial ice-cored ridges. Measurements show that surface velocity decreases sharply by ~50% across the ridge line. The transport mechanism through the cold ice to the surface is inferred to be through shearing of clean ice intercalated with the debris layers and not along discrete "shear planes". The sediment is likely frozen on at the glacier bed. However, the way in which the sediment layers are brought up into the ice and sandwiched between clean ice layers is not answered.

INTRODUCTION

Many glaciers have extensive debris-covered termini. The debris cover is of interest since it alters ablation and complicates the glaciers response to climate change. In Scandinavia ice cored lateral moraines have survived almost 100 years without being noticeably affected by the climate change driving general glacier retreat over the last century (Østrem, 1964). In areas with large debris-covered glaciers, such as the Himalaya, debris affects assessment of freshwater resources (Nakawo *et al.*, 1999).

In many cases the debris cover is mainly derived from rockfalls (e.g. Nakawo *et al.*, 1999). However, much uncertainty revolves around the mechanics of entrainment of debris at the base of a glacier and subsequent transport of such debris towards the surface in narrow bands (e.g. Hambrey *et al.*, 1999). The fact that debris can be entrained in the basal ice has been shown from theory and observations for both cold and temperate ice (e.g. Alley *et al.*, 1997). The problem lies in the mechanisms responsible for moving basally entrained material towards the glacier surface in discrete bands (discussions in Weertman, 1961; Alley *et al.*, 1997; Hambrey *et al.*, 1999).

This paper deals with the internal structure of a cold-based terminus with emerging debris bands and the associated ice flow in order to better define the processes involved in bringing basal debris into the glacier and up to its surface.

* *Also at*: Climate Impacts Research Centre, The Space and Environmental Research Institute (MRI-CIRC), Björkplan 6A, S-98142 Kiruna, Sweden.

DEBRIS PLANES AND DEBRIS-COVERED RIDGES

The incorporation of debris into basal ice and mechanisms for transporting such debris to the glacier surface has been discussed by many authors (e.g. Alley *et al.*, 1997; Hambrey *et al.*, 1999 and references therein). Whereas processes for basal entrainment of till into ice are generally accepted, processes for subsequent lifting and transport in the glacier ice are still under debate. Weertman (1961) argued forcibly against the so-called *shear plane* mechanism. Hooke *et al.* (1972) and Nickling & Bennett (1974) found additional evidence against shearing within sediment-rich layers from laboratory experiments. Their results showed that the creep rate and shear strength of ice increase with increasing sediment concentration. However, with a very small volume fraction of sediment, creep rates are higher than both for clean ice and for higher volume fractions (Hooke *et al.*, 1972). Yet, many still argue for shear motion along discrete sediment-rich planes (e.g. Clarke & Blake, 1991; Murray *et al.*, 1997; Hambrey *et al.*, 1999).

The occurrence of debris-rich layers is common in polythermal glaciers (Boulton, 1970). Entrainment of debris under temperate ice conditions has traditionally been associated with regelation. Walder (1986), theoretically, and Iverson (1993), experimentally, showed that ice can regelate into subglacial debris. Knight (1989) found that isotopic composition of ice in a stacked sequence of debris bands indicated regelation whereas intercalated ice was isotopically similar to glacier ice above the sequence and hence not formed by regelation.

In addition to the processes described above, folding (e.g. Hudleston, 1976) and englacial drainage (Kirkbride & Spedding, 1996; Näslund & Hassinen, 1996) have also been suggested as means of incorporating and, perhaps primarily, transporting debris towards the glacier surface.

STORGLACIÄREN

Storglaciären, northern Sweden, (Fig. 1) is extensively studied (e.g. Jansson, 1996) including annual glacier mass balance measurements since 1946 (e.g. Holmlund & Jansson, 1999). The retreat of the glacier in response to a rise in air temperature around 1910 (Holmlund, 1987) has halted partly due to positive mass balance on the glacier during the last decade (Holmlund & Jansson, 1999). Steepening of the terminus indicates that an advance may be imminent. The glacier is polythermal with a cold surface layer of varying thickness (≤60 m) in the ablation area (Holmlund & Eriksson, 1989). The glacier margins and a frontal zone of ≤200 m width is frozen to the glacier bed (Holmlund *et al.*, 1996). Hence any glacier advance will have to occur over a frozen terminus region. The glacier is underlain by a till layer which has been shown to deform (e.g. Iverson *et al.*, 1994).

SUPRAGLACIAL DEBRIS ON STORGLACIÄREN

Several englacial debris bands emerged on the surface near the terminus in 1994 and formed ice-cored ridges as a result of differential melting (Fig. 2). The debris bands are parallel to foliation in the ice and hence have an arcuate shape (Figs 1 and 2). Between

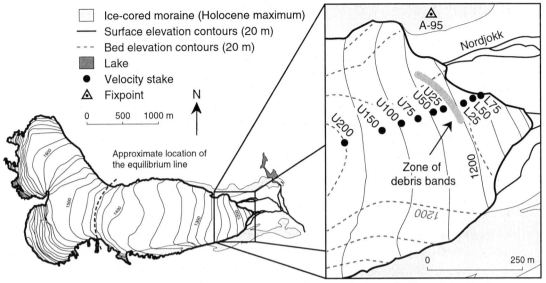

Fig. 1 Map of Storglaciären showing surface and bed topography. Inset shows location of debris-covered ridges and of surveyed stakes and fixed points used in this study.

the debris bands there is cleaner ice that can be divided into two types: (a) largely bubble-free ice consisting of large crystals and (b) ice rich in bubbles elongated in the plane of foliation along the direction of flow. Bubble-free ice occurs immediately below the sediment layers whereas bubble-rich ice is found immediately above the layers. Typically, large crystals indicate non-deforming ice whereas elongated bubbles are an indication of actively deforming ice. A bulk sample from one debris band gave a sediment concentration of 78% by weight or ~51% by volume assuming an average density of 2.65 kg m^{-3}. The debris is unsorted, somewhat rounded, and devoid of clasts >0.1–0.2 m. Rockfall debris typically contains more angular particles and also larger concentrations of coarse particles relative to typical subglacially worked tills (Boulton, 1978). Hence, the origin of material in the debris bands is inferred to be of subglacial origin.

GROUND-PENETRATING RADAR OBSERVATIONS

Detailed surveying of bed topography and the internal structure of the glacier was carried out during the fall of 1995 with a continuous wave step-frequency ground-penetrating radar (based on a Hewlett Packard Network Analyzer, HP8753B). The equipment sends out a continuous sine wave at 201 frequencies evenly distributed over a user-defined bandwidth. The signal penetration depth varies depending on the frequencies covered by the bandwidth (780–1080 MHz in our case). The radar system thus allows recording of both thermal structure and ice thickness although not necessarily simultaneously. Details of the equipment can be found in Hamran *et al.* (1995) and Richardson *et al.* (1997). For the present study the radar system was mounted on a sled and pulled by hand. During the survey an approximately constant travel speed was maintained between stakes along the survey line. In interpreting the radar image we consider travel speed between individual stakes to be constant. Since stake positions are known, they constitute known reference points along the profile. In the case of a somewhat varying travel velocity between different *sets* of stakes, these reference points aided in the interpretation of the radar image.

Fig. 2 (a) The moraine ridges seen from fixed point A-95 (northern moraine) in fall 1995. (b) Close up of the ridge looking south. The ridge is approximately 1 m high.

Figure 3(a) shows a radar image of the glacier terminus. The uppermost strong horizontal reflection is the upper ice surface. The glacier surface is not corrected for topography and therefore appears flat. The depth scale, calculated from a radar signal travel velocity of 168 m μs^{-1}, is shown relative to the ice surface. An automatic gain control was applied in the data processing. Internal structures are readily seen in the terminus (Fig. 3(a)) that show thermal zonation, debris bands and possibly water pockets. Figure 3(b) shows the interpretation of the profile in Fig. 3(a). For easier evaluation, data have here been adjusted to show true surface topography.

The radar image shows a strong sharp bed reflection close to the terminus where the ice-bed interface is frozen. The transition from cold-based to wet-based conditions occurs at ~200 m from the terminus (Holmlund *et al.*, 1996, fig. 6, p. 152). Upstream from this point, bed reflection weakens considerably. Instead the radar image shows the englacial transition from cold surface layer to temperate ice below as a less sharp, diffuse reflection (Fig. 3). Here, the strength of the signal that reaches and returns from the bed is drastically reduced due to scattering of the radar signal by liquid water within the temperate ice body that obscures the bed. Another strong reflector can be followed from the location of the debris-covered ridges to a point near the cold-temperate transition at the bed. This reflector is interpreted as a continuous debris

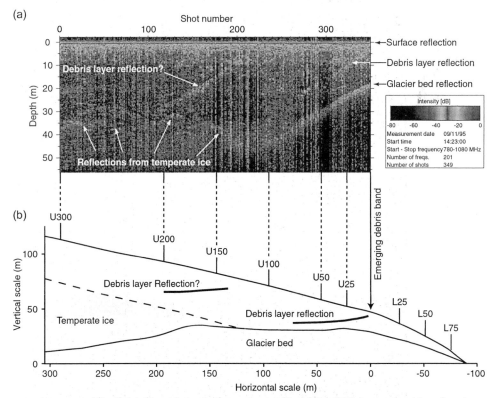

Fig. 3 (a) Ground-penetrating radar profile of ice thickness and cold surface layer thickness along the line of stakes (Fig. 1) on the terminus Storglaciären. (b) Interpretation of the radar profile. The bed topography is based on several ground-penetrating radar soundings (unpublished).

band, emanating from the base of the glacier and reaching the surface at the ridges. The radar image also shows a second englacial reflector further up-glacier, which terminates before reaching the surface. This feature is interpreted to be a second debris band that should soon emerge on the glacier surface between stake U100 and U150 (Fig. 3). To date no sign of this inferred second debris band has appeared on the glacier surface.

SURFACE VELOCITY

Repeated surveys of nine stakes (Fig. 1) were made in 1995 from the fixed point A-95 using standard surveying techniques (Geodimeter™ 440 total station: $\pm 0.0005^g$ for angles and ± 5mm + 10 ppm for distances). The errors in calculated velocities are negligible due to the length of the survey period. The velocity along the profile is shown in Fig. 4. As expected from continuity, horizontal surface velocity, u_H, decreases towards the terminus. However, across the point of emergence of the debris bands u_H decreases from 9.1 to 3.6 m year^{-1} (>50% reduction in u_H) over a distance of 50 m. The vertical velocity u_V is variable and close to zero along the profile.

   Emergence velocity u_E gives the vertical flux of ice that interacts with the net balance to determine the evolution of the surface profile. For most of the measured stake profile u_E is ~2.5–3.5 m year^{-1} (Fig. 4). The lowermost stakes yield u_E near zero. Typical net balance in this region is ~2–3 m year^{-1} and varies by ~0.2–0.4 m year^{-1} over the area covered by the stake profile. Thus, the terminus is near a balanced state. The lowermost section of the profile, on the other hand, is in a state of strong wastage, caused by a lack of influx of ice into the section. The emerging debris bands separate the two dynamic regimes observed on the terminus. It therefore seems reasonable to

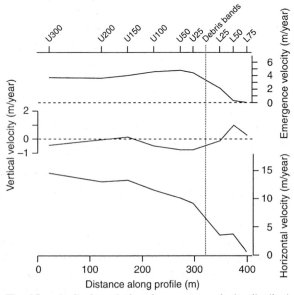

Fig. 4 Longitudinal, vertical, and emergence velocity distributions along a longitudinal profile on the terminus of Storglaciären.

conclude that the ice down-glacier of the ridges is stagnant or moving very slowly. This is not surprising since no or very little sliding can occur in this area because of the frozen bed. The ice up-glacier from the emerging debris bands is part of the active glacier that is now responding to changes in net balance.

OBSERVATIONS VERSUS THEORY

Our study of the terminus region of Storglaciären suggests that the ice wedge down-glacier and possibly beneath the debris band is slower moving (cf. Nye, 1967). The ice up-glacier of the debris bands is active and approximately in balance with the local net balance of the glacier indicating near steady-state conditions or, possibly, glacier growth. Extrapolating the debris band reflection back towards the bed indicates that it originates at or near the current transition between temperate and cold basal conditions. Thus, it is possible to suggest, as did Clarke & Blake (1991), that the debris bands are forming where this transition occurs. The transport to the glacier surface would take ~14 years at the present surface velocity. This is a conservative estimate since the speed at depth is slower than at the surface. Since Storglaciären has been in steady retreat for most of the twentieth century, it is likely that the cold–temperate transition has retreated with the glacier terminus. Hence, it is not certain that the debris was entrained at the cold–temperate transition. If the second reflector, visible in the radar images at a location ~100 m upstream from the emerging debris bands, also constitutes a debris band, the cold–temperate transition cannot be the only location for incorporation and additional mechanisms must be sought.

With the relatively high concentrations of debris in the debris bands on Storglaciären, the difference in competence (e.g. Hobbs *et al.*, 1976, p. 67) between the debris bands and the intercalated ice is quite large. Any shear deformation occurring in and around these bands must therefore occur in the cleaner ice. The observations of bubble orientation in the bubble-rich ice in our section supports this idea. The strong velocity gradient observed across the sequence also indicates that significant shearing occurs in this zone of the glacier. However, a significant portion of apparently non-shearing ice (i.e. bubble-free layer) is also moved along beneath the debris band. Knight (1989) concluded that the debris-rich and debris-poor layers in a stacked sequence had different origins, the debris-rich parts being consistent with freezing-on and the debris-poor being similar to overlying glacier ice. It seems likely that the observed sequence on Storglaciären is similar, except for the possible division of the debris-free layers into deforming and non-deforming layers.

In order for debris bands to be carried to the surface it is necessary for ice below the debris band to maintain a significant degree of shear motion. However, that presents a problem at the base of the glacier. Suppose that debris is frozen on as a result of cooling of temperate ice flowing into the region of the cold–temperate transition. Furthermore, re-freezing of relatively clean ice must occur as well in order to maintain an ice layer sufficiently weak for shearing beneath the debris. However, this combination does not seem possible if we assume that the quasi-steady-state location of the cold–temperate transition dips down into the till and underlying bedrock in the down-glacier direction. This would give a situation where subglacial water cannot reach beyond the debris band, resulting in no re-freezing beneath the debris band. If the mechanism outlined above was in operation, the result would be a slow depletion of the ice wedge beneath the debris band. The effect of this process on a glacier in steady-state will be that the emergence point of the debris band would move further down-glacier and closer to the bed and eventually consume the wedge.

With our current knowledge, the layers emerging on the surface of Storglaciären are difficult to explain in terms of the entrainment process. Obviously further investigations into the origin of ice surrounding the layers are needed. However, the process of entrainment of till into the ice evidently is associated with phase changes either due to a cold–temperate transition at the bed or regelation, while the process by which debris is lifted off the bed remains poorly known.

CONCLUSIONS

Debris emerging on the terminus of Storglaciären that forms ice-cored supra-glacial ridges can be traced into the glacier as a reflector in radar images. Velocity measurements show a more than 50% drop in surface velocity over a distance of ~50 m across the ridges in the down-glacier direction. The emerging debris layer is complex and shows a very distinct repetitive sequence of ice containing numerous bubbles elongated in the direction of foliation indicating shearing, debris bands with ~50% by volume sediment content, and coarse-grained bubble-free ice indicating no shearing. The structure in the ice is similar to other debris bands described in the literature where sediment is frozen on at the base of the glacier and where the intercalated ice is glacier ice brought up with the entrained sediment layer. However, the question regarding the process by which the sediment is lifted and brought up from the base into the ice remains unanswered.

Acknowledgements The careful reviews by Dr U. H. Fischer and one anonymous reviewer significantly helped us improve the paper. We are most grateful to Prof. C. F. Raymond who provided additional suggestions, well beyond his duties as scientific editor, to help us focus the paper further.

REFERENCES

Alley, R. B., Cuffey, K. M., Evenson, E. B., Strasser, J. C., Lawson, D. E. & Larson, G. J. (1997) How glaciers entrain and transport basal sediment: physical constraints. *Quatern. Sci. Rev.* **19**(9), 1017–1038.

Boulton, G. S. (1970) On the origin and transport of englacial debris in Svalbard glaciers. *J. Glaciol.* **9**(56), 213–229.

Boulton, G. S. (1978) Boulder shapes and grain size distribution as indicators of transport paths through a glacier and till genesis. *Sedimentology* **25**(6), 773–799.

Clarke, G. K. C. & Blake, E. W. (1991) Geometric and thermal evolution of a surge-type glacier in its quiescent state: Trapridge Glacier, Yukon Territory, Canada, 1969–89. *J. Glaciol.* **37**(125), 158–169.

Hambrey, M. J., Bennett, M. R., Dowdeswell, J. A., Glasser, N. F. & Huddart, D. (1999) Debris entrainment and transfer in polythermal valley glaciers. *J. Glaciol.* **43**(149), 69–86.

Hamran, S. E., Gjessing, D. T., Hjelmstad, J. & Aarholt, E. (1995) Ground penetrating synthetic pulse radar: dynamic range and modes of operation. *J. Appl. Geophys.* **33**, 7–14.

Hobbs, B. E., Means, W. D. & Williams, P. F. (1976) *An Outline of Structural Geology.* John Wiley & Sons, New York.

Holmlund, P. (1987) Mass balance of Storglaciären during the 20th century. *Geogr. Ann.* **69A**(3–4), 439–447.

Holmlund, P. & Eriksson, M. (1989) The cold surface layer on Storglaciären. *Geogr. Ann.* **71A**(3–4), 241–244.

Holmlund, P. & Jansson, P. (1999) The Tarfala mass balance program. *Geogr. Ann.* **81A**(4), 621–632.

Holmlund, P., Näslund, J.-O. & Richardson, C. (1996). Radar surveys on Scandinavian glaciers, in search of useful climate archives. *Geogr. Ann.* **78A**(2–3), 147–154.

Hooke, R. LeB., Dahlin, B. B. & Kauper, M. T. (1972) Creep of ice containing dispersed fine sand. *J. Glaciol.* **11**(63), 327–336.

Hudleston, P. J. (1976) Recumbent folding in the base of the Barnes Ice Cap, Baffin Island, Northwest Territories, Canada. *Geol. Soc. Am. Bull.* **87**(12), 1684–1692.

Iverson, N. R. (1993) Regelation of ice through debris at glacier beds: implications for sediment transport. *Geology* **21**(6), 559–562.

Iverson, N. R., Jansson, P. & Hooke, R. LeB. (1994) *In-situ* measurement of the strength of deforming subglacial till. *J. Glaciol.* **40**(136), 497–503.

Jansson, P. (1996) Hydrology and dynamics of a polythermal valley glacier. *Geogr. Ann.* **78A**(2–3), 171–180.

Kirkbride, M. & Spedding, N. (1996) The influence of englacial drainage on sediment-transport pathways and till texture of temperate valley glaciers. *Ann. Glaciol.* **22**, 160–166.

Knight, P. G. (1989) Stacking of basal debris by layers without bulk freeze-on: isotopic evidence from West Greenland. *J. Glaciol.* **35**(120), 214–216.

Murray, T., Gooch, D. L. & Stuart, G. W. (1997) Structures within the surge front at Bakaninbreen, Svalbard, using ground-penetrating radar. *Ann. Glaciol.* **24**, 122–129.

Nakawo, M., Yabuki, H. & Sakai, A. (1999) Characteristics of Khumbu Glacier, Nepal Himalaya: recent change in the debris-covered area. *Ann. Glaciol.* **28**, 118–122.

Näslund, J.-O. & Hassinen, S. (1996) Correspondence. Subglacial sediment accumulations and large englacial water conduits at high elevations in Mýrdalsjökull, Iceland. *J. Glaciol.* **42**(140), 190–192.

Nickling, W. G. & Bennett, L. (1984) The shear strength characteristics of frozen coarse granular debris. *J. Glaciol.* **30**(106), 348–357.

Nye, J. F. (1967) Plasticity solution for a glacier snout. *J. Glaciol.* **6**(47), 695–715.

Østrem, G. (1964) Ice-cord moraines in Scandinavia. *Geogr. Ann.* **46**(3), 282–337.

Richardson, C., Aarholt, E., Hamran, S. E., Holmlund, P. & Isaksson, E. (1997) Spatial distribution of snow in western Dronning Maud Land, east Antarctica, mapped by a ground-based snow radar. *J. Geophys. Res.* **102**(B9), 20 343–20 353.

Walder, J. S. (1986) Motion of sub-freezing ice past particles with application to wire regelation and frozen soils. *J. Glaciol.* **32**(112), 404–414.

Weertman, J. (1961) Mechanism for the formation of inner moraines found near the edge of cold ice caps and ice sheets. *J. Glaciol.* **3**(30), 965–978.

Debris-Covered Glaciers (Proceedings of a workshop held at Seattle, Washington, USA, September 2000).
IAHS Publ. no. 264, 2000.

153

On the formation of supraglacial lakes on debris-covered glaciers

JOHN M. REYNOLDS

Reynolds Geo-Sciences Ltd, 2 Long Barn, Pistyll Farm, Nercwys, Mold, Flintshire CH7 4EW, UK
e-mail: rgsl@geologyuk.com

Abstract Analyses of satellite imagery obtained in 1989–1990 and topographic maps from 1966 have been undertaken for the glacierized areas of Bhutan. It has been found that where supraglacial lakes have formed since 1966, surface gradients of the glaciers concerned were in all cases less than 2°. At gradients of 2–10° supraglacial ponds can form but tend to be transient due to the opening and closing of crevasses. By identifying the conditions under which large supraglacial lakes form it is possible to use these criteria to predict where such lakes may develop in the future. This will allow suitable monitoring programmes to be introduced and, where necessary, suitable engineering remediation works to be undertaken in order to prevent the collection of large volumes of water that may be liable to form glacier lake outburst floods in the future.

INTRODUCTION

In October and November 1998 the author was commissioned by Norconsult A.S./NORPLAN Joint Venture to participate in a pre-feasibility study for a major hydropower project in Bhutan (Fig. 1). The project was undertaken in collaboration with the Division of Power, Royal Government of Bhutan. The author's task was to compile the first detailed inventory of glaciers and glacial lakes and to undertake the first assessment of glacial hazards in the Mangde Chhu River basin and to review the glaciers of Bhutan with respect to the formation of glacial lakes and their prospective rupture to form what are known in the Himalayas as Glacier Lake Outburst Floods (GLOFs). Images of over 300 glaciers were examined with 154 being studied in detail.

As part of the project access was provided to 1:50 000 scale prints of sub-scenes of panchromatic SPOT imagery of the whole of Bhutan. The imagery was obtained in December 1989 and in December 1990. Access was also provided to colour SPOT imagery at a scale of 1:125 000 obtained in December 1993 of the Lunana area in northern Bhutan. In addition, a set of topographic maps at the same scale and produced by the Survey of India was also made available. These maps dated from 1966 and were based on aerial photography acquired in 1956 and 1958 at an approximate scale of 1:32 000 with further ground truth provided in 1960–1962. It was clear from comparing the satellite images with the topographic maps that many of the glaciers present in 1958 had developed lakes over significant areas. While many glaciers exhibit supraglacial ponds that appear to be transient, some supraglacial ponds develop to form a single large supraglacial lake. This may develop further to lead to the separation of a significant stagnant or very slow moving ice mass from the upper reaches of the glacier. The formation of such lakes poses a potential threat should the

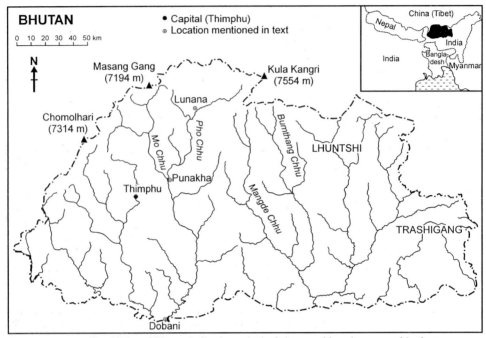

Fig. 1 Map of Bhutan indicating principal rivers and locations named in the text.

lakes burst through whatever is damming them. In the Himalayas there are many records of such catastrophic outbursts from moraine-dammed supraglacial lakes (Galay, 1987; Ives, 1986; Reynolds, 1998a; Yamada, 1993) resulting in loss of life and significant amounts of damage to property and strategic infrastructure. In Bhutan, 27 people were killed at Punakha following the outburst from Luggye Tsho (Fig. 2), Lunana region, in the eastern branch of the Pho Chhu on 7 October 1994.

Analysis undertaken by the present author of the SPOT imagery for Bhutan has indicated a large number of potentially dangerous glacial lakes in Bhutan and no river system that drains from the high Himal is immune. Consequently, it is of considerable importance to Bhutan for strategic reasons that such glacial lakes are identified and areas where other lakes may form are identified for planning purposes, and especially in relation to the development of hydropower (Reynolds, 1998b).

As glaciers continue to recede in response to climate change, the number and volume of potentially dangerous glacial lakes in the Himalayas are increasing (Richardson & Reynolds, 2000a). Consequently it is important to be able to recognize how such lakes have formed in the past and thus where they may form in the future.

PHYSICAL SETTING IN BHUTAN

Bhutan comprises an area of 47 182 km^2 on the southern boundary of the Tibetan Plateau. Ground elevations range from less than 300 m on the southern border with northern India to over 7000 m in the northern high Himal. Bhutan is dissected approximately north–south by major river systems that drain the high mountains

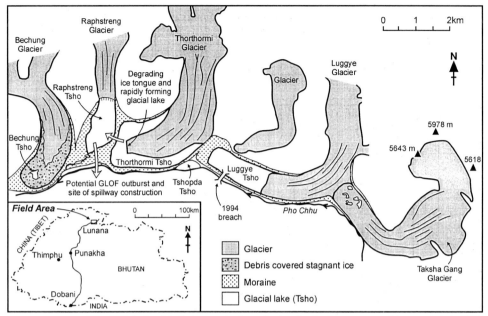

Fig. 2 Relationship between the key glaciers in the Lunana area (shown at their 1962 extent). Tshoju Glacier is located about 5 km west of Bechung Glacier.

towards the south and into northern India as tributaries of the Brahmaputra River which then flows through Bangladesh.

The main areas covered by glaciers are the high Himal in the northern part of the country and especially in the west (east of Chomolhari, 7314 m) and central regions (south of Masang Gang, 7194 m, and Kula Kangri, 7554 m) and to a lesser extent in the regions of Lhuntshi and Trashigang in the east. The glaciers range from small remnant cirque and niche glaciers through to major icefields and outlet and valley glaciers in the north. The highest glaciers appear to be dominated by radiation and may be cold-based as many of them produce little meltwater. In common with other similar regions of the Himalayas, the glaciers in Bhutan are generally in recession although there appear to be some exceptions that are at least maintaining their spatial extent in the short term (decadal scale).

PREVIOUS GLACIOLOGICAL STUDIES IN BHUTAN

There have been no previous specific glaciological investigations in Bhutan that have been published other than as part of other broad geological studies (Gansser, 1983). However, a desk study on glacier lakes was undertaken by Norconsult and Norpower as part of the "Bhutan Power System Master Plan Project" in 1992–1993. A review of available satellite imagery was carried out by the Division of Geology and Mines (DGM), Ministry of Trade and Industry (Norbu, 1996). Both desk studies were reviewed and the primary data re-analysed by the present author as part of the commission with Norconsult/NORPLAN and the Division of Power in October/November 1998. The results of this work have been described within the official project report submitted to the Royal Bhutanese Government in 1999. The only other previous literature relating to glaciers and glacial lakes in Bhutan are unpublished reports relating to investigations into potentially problematic glacial lakes near Lunana (Sharma *et al.*, 1984, 1987) and into the GLOF from Luggye Tsho in the Lunana area in October 1994 (Tashi, 1994; Bhargava, 1995; Leber *et al.*, 1999).

Following the review and analysis undertaken by the author, and building upon the extensive previous experience in the Nepalese Himalayas (Reynolds, 1998a, 1999), in the Andes (Reynolds, 1990, 1992, 1998b; Reynolds *et al.*, 1998), as well as in the Antarctic (Reynolds, 1981) it has been possible to consider the formation of supraglacial ponds and lakes.

SURFACE TOPOGRAPHY AND PRESENCE OF SUPRAGLACIAL LAKES

By comparing the 1966 topographic maps at a scale of 1:50 000 for Bhutan with the 1989–1990 SPOT imagery, it has been possible to consider the changes in the glaciers over the intervening 23–24 years and to identify why lakes form on some glaciers but not others.

Two areas in Bhutan (Fig. 1) were considered in detail: the Lunana region, due to the GLOF of 1994 and to its significance with respect to ongoing glacial lake remediation and hazard minimization (Leber *et al.*, 1999), and the Chomolhari area. In both areas, longitudinal profiles were taken from the 1966 topographic maps through glaciers that had subsequently developed large supraglacial lakes as well as neighbouring glaciers that had not. The longitudinal profiles from both sets of glaciers (with and without lakes) were compared and the longitudinal gradients examined.

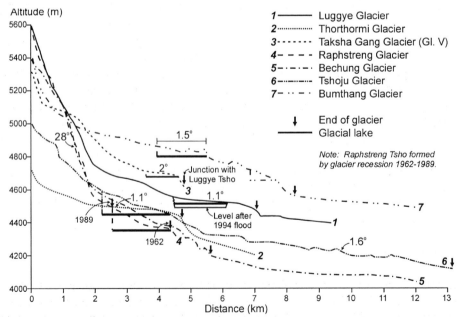

Fig. 3 Elevation profiles of six glaciers in the Lunana area of Bhutan with one from the Bumthang Chhu. The locations of large supraglacial lakes are indicated.

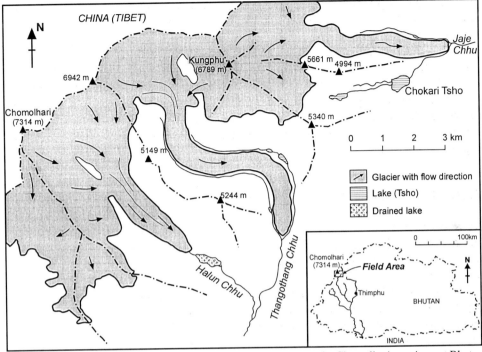

Fig. 4 Relationship between the named glaciers in the Chomolhari area in west Bhutan (shown at their 1962 extent).

The location of and relationships between selected glaciers in the Lunana area are shown in Fig. 2. The corresponding longitudinal elevation profiles are shown in Fig. 3 with the positions of the supraglacial lakes that had formed between 1966 and 1989 indicated. A longitudinal profile from the Bumthang Glacier, from the upper headwaters of the Bumthang Chhu (Fig. 1), is also shown.

The glaciers all have extremely steep headwalls, with elevations from 5600 m down to 4600 m, from which the glacier surfaces level out. In each case where a large supraglacial lake has developed, the glacier surface prior to 1966 had a slope of less than 2°. Where slopes were between 2° and 6°, discrete supraglacial ponds were evident. For slopes greater than 6° but less than 10°, small isolated ponds could be found. For slopes greater than 10° there was no evidence for supraglacial ponds.

Similarly a set of glaciers east of Chomolhari has been examined whose locations are shown in Fig. 4 with their corresponding longitudinal elevation profiles in Fig. 5. It is again evident that supraglacial lakes form at the shallowest surface gradients.

DISCUSSION

It appears that for supraglacial ponds to develop into larger supraglacial lakes the surface slope should be <2°. However, shallow slope angles in themselves are not sufficient for the formation of supraglacial ponds. There must be appropriate mass balance conditions to permit the formation of sufficient meltwater. It has been found in

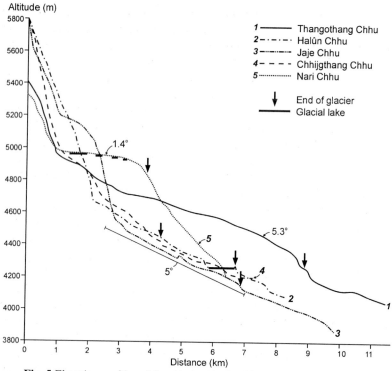

Fig. 5 Elevation profiles of five glaciers in the Chomolhari area in west Bhutan. The locations of large supraglacial lakes are indicated.

the Antarctic, for example, that large supraglacial ponds and lakes form when the surface slope is virtually flat, the local mass balance is in effect negative, the surface has low surface permeability and the drainage off the ice is limited (Reynolds, 1981). This restriction is usually due to the surface being flat.

Once a pond has formed it has a lower albedo that that of the surrounding snow and ice. Consequently, absorbed radiation into the water helps to develop further melting. Debris on adjacent ice may help to insulate it from radiation melting. As a pond develops its margins tend to steepen. Debris on the pond margins sloughs into the pond exposing adjacent glacier ice that then melts faster. Sub-aerial ice melts by backwasting and, given steep or near vertical ice cliffs, the local ice may respond rheologically and fail mechanically. These processes only serve to exacerbate the rate of pond development (Richardson & Reynolds, 2000b). Where algae begin to colonize the edges and floors of ponds, they can provide biological heating to the local water and increase the rate of melting of local ice substantially. For example, at Thulagi glacier lake in Nepal, measurements of temperature were made using a thermistor within a number of ponds on debris-covered ice. The lake water was generally found to be $1.4 \pm 0.3°C$. When the thermistor was placed just inside a mat of green algae the temperature was found to be $6.3°C$. Elsewhere, temperatures within algae mats were found to be between 5 and $8.5°C$ warmer than those of the surface water. Where temperature profiles with depth were completed, temperature gradients of around $5°C \, m^{-1}$ were found over shallow depths of 1–2 m. The measured temperatures were highest in the most dense concentrations of green algae. Biogenic heating of ponds over ice would appear to be significant where algae have become established. Once formed, lakes tend to be self-perpetuating through a combination of the above processes as long as the water remains in the pond.

It is also evident that once ponds have formed and the glacier surface lowers through ablation, they coalesce to form larger lakes. Eventually all the lakes will merge to form one large supraglacial lake. It is known from repeat observations that this process can take up to several decades to complete (Mool, 1995; Watanabe *et al.*, 1994). However, there are also examples in South America where this process can occur in less than 10 years (e.g. Hualcán, Cordillera Blanca, Peru; Reynolds, 1989).

The flow activity of a glacier is inherently related to surface slope (due to its relation to basal shear stress and to the general rheological flow of ice that is also dependent upon basal shear stress (Paterson, 1994)). Consequently, the steeper the surface slope the more active the flow is likely to be. Given the complex structures found in Himalayan glaciers, both within individual flow units and as composite glaciers, the surface structures (e.g. crevasses) are likely to open and close intermittently and thus allow drainage of surface water into and within the glacier. Transient supraglacial ponds are common on Himalayan glaciers. The relationship between glacial structures and supraglacial drainage is well known (e.g. Benn & Evans, 1998, p. 106; Reynolds, 1981). Further evidence for the control of glacial structures and flow dynamics on the shape of supraglacial lakes is also demonstrated by reference to Fig. 6. This shows a glacier in Bhutan (near Kajila, on the Nari Chhu, an upper tributary of the Mho Chhu) where there is a clear sequence with position downstream of the orientation of pear-shaped supraglacial lakes. With increasing distance downstream, the long axis of each pond rotates from being oblique to become transverse (Fig. 6). Furthermore, the ponds have formed in a depression caused by the junction between two convergent flow units. This example serves to reinforce the relationship between glacier structure and supraglacial drainage.

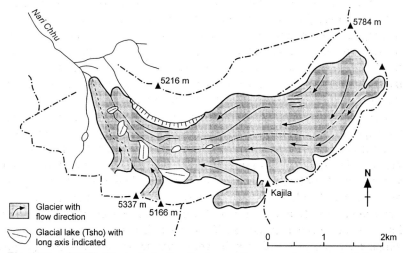

Fig. 6 Map of Kajila Glacier indicating the form of four supraglacial ponds that appear to have rotated from parallel to transverse to glacier flow with distance downstream.

Assuming that supraglacial lakes form where the surface gradient is <2°, given a negative mass balance, it should be possible to identify locations where such lakes may form in the future. If the proto-lake formation takes a decade or more, this may yield an early warning lead-in time of a similar time period sufficient to establish appropriate monitoring and maybe even early engineering remediation works to stop significant volumes of water forming. This may be prudent as part of a risk management strategy in locations where key infrastructure lies downstream. This is especially valid given the precarious nature of many glacial lakes in most river systems in Bhutan. Such monitoring procedures should be established urgently.

CONCLUSIONS

Meltwater forms on the surface of glaciers where the appropriate mass balance conditions exist. Flow activity within the glacier may cause structures to open and close giving rise to intermittent drainage of meltwater. However, the controlling factor that appears to influence the formation of supraglacial ponds is the glacier's surface gradient:
- *Surface gradient >10°* = all meltwater is able to drain away, no evidence of ponding;
- *Surface gradient in the range 6–10°* = isolated small ponds may form, transient due to local drainage conduits opening and closing due to ice flow;
- *Surface gradient in the range 2–6°* = supraglacial ponds form, may also be transient locally, but sufficiently large areas affected by presence of ponds;
- *Surface gradient in the range 0–2°* = formation of large supraglacial lake over stagnant or very slow moving ice body forms from the merging of many smaller discrete ponds.

By identifying areas with a surface gradient of less than 2° on glaciers with a negative mass balance, it should be possible to establish appropriate monitoring or even early engineering remediation works to stop the formation of large volumes of water that may later prove to be potentially dangerous. Given the precarious nature of many glacial lakes in most river systems in Bhutan, such monitoring procedures should be established urgently.

Acknowledgements I am very grateful to Dr Shaun D. Richardson, Reynolds Geo-Sciences Ltd, for fruitful technical discussions and for producing the figures. I am also very grateful to Mr Dorgi Namgay, Division of Power, Ministry of Trade and Industry, Royal Government of Bhutan, and Mr L.-E. Lørum and colleagues, Norconsult/NORPLAN Joint Venture, for inviting me to become involved with this work in Bhutan and for permission to publish the results.

REFERENCES

Benn, D. I. & Evans, D. J. A. (1998) *Glaciers and Glaciation*. Arnold, London.

Bhargava, O. N. (1995) *Geology, Environmental Hazards and Remedial Measures, Lunana Area, Gasa Dzongkhag: Report of 1995 Indo-Bhutan Expedition*. Geological Survey of India, Bhutan Unit, Samtse, India.

Galay, V. J. (1987) *Erosion and Sedimentation in the Nepal Himalaya*. His Majesty's Government of Nepal, Water and Energy Commission Secretariat, Ministry of Water Resources, Kathmandu, Nepal.

Gansser, A. (1983) *Geology of the Bhutan Himalaya*. Birkhauser Verlag, Basel, Switzerland.

Ives, J. D. (1986) *Glacial Lake Outburst Floods and Risk Engineering in the Himalaya*. ICIMOD Occasional Paper no. 5, International Centre for Integrated Mountain Development, Kathmandu, Nepal.

Leber, D., Häusler, H., Morawetz, R., Schreilechner, M. & Wangda, D. (1999) GLOF risk assessment in the northwestern Bhutanese Himalayas based on remote sensing sustained geo-hazard mapping and engineering geophysical methods. *J. Nepal Geol. Soc.* **20** (special issue), 141–142 (abstract).

Mool, P. K. (1995) Glacier lake outburst floods in Nepal. *J. Nepal Geol. Soc.* **11**, 273–280.

Norbu, P. (1996) *Glaciers and Glacier Lakes in the Headwaters of Major River Basins of Bhutan*. Division of Geology and Mines, Ministry of Trade and Industry, Thimpu, Bhutan.

Paterson, W. S. B. (1994) *The Physics of Glaciers*, third edn. Pergamon/Elsevier Science Ltd.

Reynolds, J. M. (1981) Lakes on George VI Ice Shelf, Antarctica. *Polar Record* **20**(128), 425–432.

Reynolds, J. M. (1989) Hazard assessment in the Callejón De Huaylas, Cordillera Blanca, Peru. Hidrandina S.A. Glaciología e Hidrología, Huaraz, Peru (unpublished).

Reynolds, J. M. (1990) Geological hazards in the Cordillera Blanca, Peru. *AGID (Assoc. Geoscientists for International Development) News*, (61/62), 31–33.

Reynolds, J. M. (1992) The identification and mitigation of glacier-related hazards: examples from the Cordillera Blanca, Peru. In: *Geohazards* (ed. by G. J. H. McCall, D. J. C. Laming, & S. C. Scott), 143–157. Chapman and Hall, London.

Reynolds, J. M. (1998a) High-altitude glacial lake hazard assessment and mitigation: a Himalayan perspective. In: *Geohazards in Engineering Geology* (ed. by J. G. Maund & M. Eddleston), 25–34. Geological Society, London, Engineering Geology Special Publ. no. 15.

Reynolds, J. M. (1998b) Managing the risks of glacial flooding at hydro plants. *Hydro Review Worldwide* **6**(2), 18–22.

Reynolds, J. M. (1999) Glacial hazard assessment at Tsho Rolpa, Rolwaling, central Nepal. *Quart. J. Engng Geol.* **32**(3), 209–214.

Reynolds, J. M., Dolecki, A. & Portocarrero, C. (1998) The construction of a drainage tunnel as part of glacial lake hazard mitigation at Hualcán, Cordillera Blanca, Peru. In: *Geohazards in Engineering Geology* (ed. by J. G. Maund & M. Eddleston), 41–48. Geological Society, London, Engineering Geology Special Publ. no. 15.

Richardson, S. D. & Reynolds, J. M. (2000a) An overview of glacial hazards in the Himalayas. *Quatern. International* **65–66**(1), 31–47.

Richardson, S. D. & Reynolds, J. M. (2000b) Degradation of ice-cored moraine dams: implications for hazard development. In: *Debris-Covered Glaciers* (ed. by M. Nakawo, C. F. Raymond & A. Fountain) (Proc. Seattle Workshop, September 2000). IAHS Publ. no. 264 (this volume).

Sharma, A. R., Ghosh, D. K. & Norbu, P. (1984) *Report on Lunana Lake Expedition—1984*. Geological Survey of India, Bhutan Unit, Samchi, Bhutan.

Sharma, A. R., Ghosh, D. K. & Norbu, P. (1987) *Report on Lunana Lake Expedition—1986*. Geological Survey of India, Bhutan Unit, Samchi, Bhutan.

Tashi, T. (1994) *Preliminary Report on the Investigation of Glacial Lakes at Phho Chhu Source and the Assessment of Flood Affected Areas in Lunana*. Natural Environment Commission, Thimpu, Bhutan.

Watanabe, T., Ives, J. D. & Hammond, J. E. (1994) Rapid growth of a glacial lake in Khumbu Himal, Himalaya: prospects for a catastrophic flood. *Mountain Res. Develop.* **14**(4), 329–340.

Yamada, T. (1993) *Glacier Lakes and their Outburst Floods in the Nepal Himalaya*. Water and Energy Commission Secretariat, Kathmandu, Nepal.

4 Supraglacial Lakes

Debris-Covered Glaciers (Proceedings of a workshop held at Seattle, Washington, USA, September 2000).
IAHS Publ. no. 264, 2000.

165

Expansion of glacier lakes in recent decades in the Bhutan Himalayas

YUTAKA AGETA

*Institute for Hydrospheric–Atmospheric Sciences, Nagoya University, Furo-cho, Chikusa-ku,
Nagoya 464-8601, Japan*
e-mail: ageta@ihas.nagoya-u.ac.jp

SHUJI IWATA

Department of Geography, Tokyo Metropolitan University, Hachioji, Tokyo 192-0397, Japan

HIRONORI YABUKI

Frontier Observational Research System for Global Change, Tokyo 105-0013, Japan

NOZOMU NAITO, AKIKO SAKAI

*Institute for Hydrospheric–Atmospheric Sciences, Nagoya University, Furo-cho, Chikusa-ku,
Nagoya 464-8601, Japan*

CHIYUKI NARAMA

Department of Geography, Tokyo Metropolitan University, Hachioji, Tokyo 192-0397, Japan

KARMA*

Geological Survey of Bhutan, Ministry of Trade and Industry, GPO Box 173, Thimphu, Bhutan

Abstract An inventory of glacier lakes was compiled based on observations
carried out for 30 glacier lakes in the northern and northwestern parts of
Bhutan in autumn 1998. Risk assessments for glacier lake outburst floods
were made for these glacier lakes. Historical variations of glacier lakes and
glacier termini were examined using photographs, satellite images, maps and
published observations. In the northern region of Bhutan, supraglacial ponds
on some debris-covered glaciers in the 1950s have subsequently grown into
moraine-dammed lakes. Also, proglacial lakes have expanded substantially as
a result of retreat of glacier termini.

INTRODUCTION

Glaciers in the Himalayas are shrinking more rapidly than glaciers in other regions of
the world (Fujita *et al.*, 1997). In the Himalayas, precipitation on the glaciers is intense
in summer during the summer monsoon. Winter is a dry season. A rise in summer air
temperature on these summer-accumulation type glaciers in the Himalayas has an
especially strong negative effect on mass balance (Ageta & Kadota, 1992). The
proportion of rain is increased by the temperature rise and snow accumulation
decreases; surface albedo is decreased by the snowfall decrease and ablation increases.
The monsoon precipitation in Bhutan in the eastern Himalayas is much higher than
that in Nepal and the western Himalayas (Eguchi, 1997). Therefore, a decrease in the

* *Present address*: Institute for Hydrospheric–Atmospheric Sciences, Nagoya University.

glacier mass balance and associated glacier retreat with similar summer warming is likely to be more pronounced in Bhutan. However, no study has been published on glacier variations in Bhutan after exploratory work in the 1960s by Gansser (1970).

Since the rapid change of glaciers impacts geo-hazards such as glacier lake outburst floods (GLOF), combined monitoring of the variations of glacier lakes and the surrounding glaciers is needed for assessment of the future risk potential. A joint project between the Geological Survey of Bhutan and Japanese glaciologists and geomorphologists was initiated in 1998 for preparation of the updated inventory of major glacier lakes and assessment of the danger of GLOF. Field research was executed in northern and northwestern parts of Bhutan along the route shown in Fig. 1 during the period from 11 September to 19 October 1998. On the basis of this research and other available information, 30 glacier lakes were identified and GLOF risk assessments were made (Ageta & Iwata, 1999). Related observations were also carried

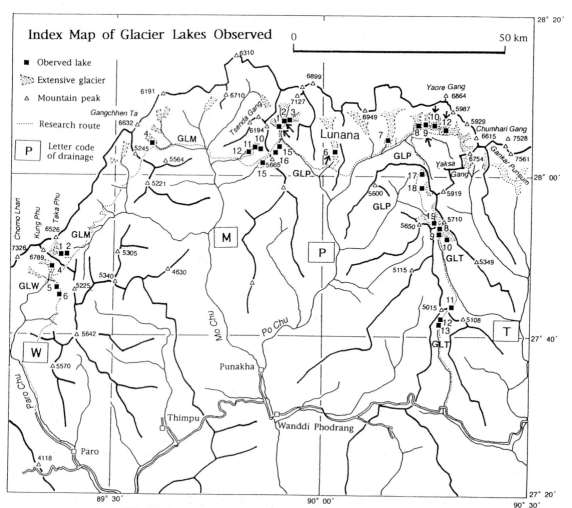

Fig. 1 Index map of glacier lakes listed in the glacier lake inventory. Code numbers of glacier lakes described in this paper are indicated by arrows.

out on glacier variations, climate and glacial geomorphology. Water temperature and lake depth distribution was measured at Raphsthreng Tsho (lake) in the Lunana region (GLP9), the upper stream of Po Chu (river) (Fig. 1).

Observations in 1998 aimed to obtain a broad view of conditions in a large area where ground observations have been scarce. In the present paper, brief results of the GLOF assessment are presented; the results on variations of selected glacier lakes and glacier termini are described as a basis for further study.

VARIATIONS OF GLACIER LAKES

Glacier lakes observed

An inventory of glaciers and glacier lakes in the headwaters of major river basins of Bhutan was published by the Division of Geology and Mines (1996); glaciers, glacier lakes and the first-order river basins were labelled and numbered in this inventory. Their code numbers are used here with some provisional additional numbers where required (Fig. 1).

Glacier lakes were classified into three types based on location, mode of formation and recent condition:
(a) *Supraglacial ice-melt ponds or lakes*: most of them are small and shallow in size, but they tend to connect to each other and grow into large contiguous lakes.
(b) *Moraine-dammed lakes*: some lakes store large quantities of water and have probability of GLOFs that could cause severe damage downstream.
(c) *Lakes located in basins far from glaciers or without glaciers*: they are located in cirques or glacial troughs which were scoured by Pleistocene glaciers. These lakes are stable because of solid rock spillways and no direct influence of glacier variation.

All of lakes of types (a) and (b) were associated with debris-cover on glacier ice that caused differential melting, and increased surface irregularities developed ponds or lakes.

Dimensions for the main glacier lakes of types (a) and (b) were measured on maps (1:50 000 toposheets made by the Survey of India using aerial photographs in 1956 and 1958), satellite images and literature. Examples are considered below. Code numbers of glacier lakes described in the next section are indicated by arrows in Fig. 1.

Expansion of glacier lakes and risk of GLOF

In Lunana region, several debris-covered glaciers extend their tongues into the flat valley floor of the eastern headwaters of Pho Chu; three glaciers form a contiguous chain of termini with large glacier lakes called Lugge Tsho (GLP12), Thorthomi Tsho (GLP10) and Raphsthreng Tsho (GLP9) (Fig. 2). This area appears to be the most vulnerable for GLOF along the observed route, since the lakes could interact with each other as described below.

Lugge Tsho (GLP12) and Drukchung Tsho (GLP13) Lugge Tsho (28°06′N, 90°18′E, 4520 m a.m.s.l.) is located at the eastern end of Lunana valley at the head of

Yutaka Ageta et al.

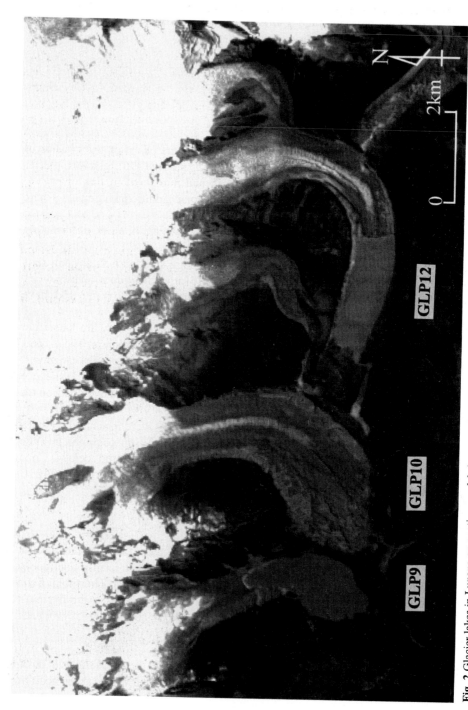

Fig. 2 Glacier lakes in Lunana on contiguous debris-covered glaciers. Lugge Tsho (GLP12), Thorthomi Tsho (GLP10) and Raphsthreng Tsho (GLP9) from east in a SPOT-XS satellite image taken on 11 December 1993 (copyright: CNES).

Po Chu. On 6–7 October 1994, GLOF from Lugge Tsho killed 21 persons and damaged many facilities. The outburst occurred by the sudden expansion of a small cleft at the lower end of the left lateral moraine of Lugge Glacier. Ice was observed in the cut through the moraine a week after the outburst, and failure of the moraine was probably induced by melting of its ice core (Division of Geology and Mines, 1996). Expansion of the outlet channel is easily recognized on the satellite images of SPOT taken before and just after the GLOF as illustrated in Fig. 3.

Evolution of Lugge Tsho since the 1950s is illustrated in Fig. 3. In the 1950s, there were no significant lakes on either Lugge Glacier or Drukchung Glacier which joins Lugge Glacier from the southeast. According to Gansser's observation in 1967, many supraglacial ponds had formed on both glaciers; he found clear signs of recent drainage of ponds on Drukchung Glacier (Gansser, 1970). From 1967 to 1988, these ponds joined together to form two large moraine-dammed lakes, Lugge Tsho and Drukchung Tsho. Drukchung Tsho reached a maximum area in 1988 (Fig. 3) and probably drained through a supraglacial channel of Lugge Glacier to Lugge Tsho. Lugge Tsho had a maximum area in 1993. It shrank after a 1994 outburst, when the western end of the lake receded by nearly 500 m.

If the outlet channel of Lugge Tsho were to become blocked in the future, a rise of the water level over its wide area would increase the risk of another GLOF. Possible causes of a blockage could be: (a) a landslide from the steep inner slope of the lateral moraine, (b) the large-scale failure of the inner slope caused by melting of the ice core in the lateral moraine. If GLOF from Lugge Tsho were to occur again, there might be a high risk of Thorthomi Tsho further downstream adding to the flood due to erosion of

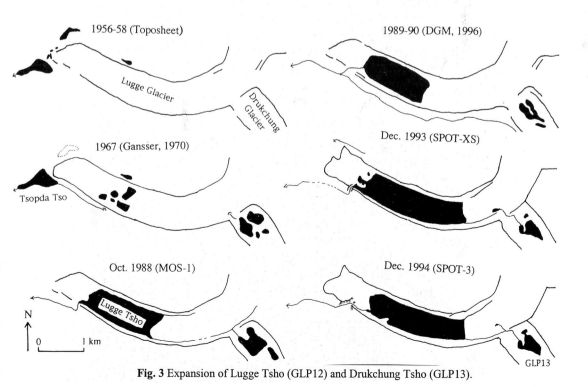

Fig. 3 Expansion of Lugge Tsho (GLP12) and Drukchung Tsho (GLP13).

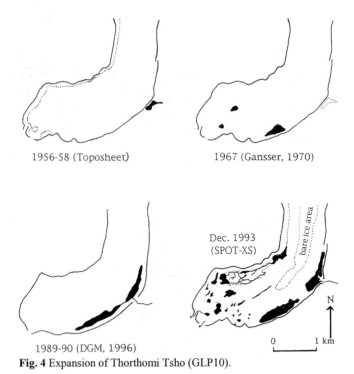

1956-58 (Toposheet)

1967 (Gansser, 1970)

Dec. 1993
(SPOT-XS)

bare ice area

N

0   1 km

1989-90 (DGM, 1996)

Fig. 4 Expansion of Thorthomi Tsho (GLP10).

the outer slope of its vulnerable left lateral moraine by the flood water as described below.

Thorthomi Tsho (GLP10) Expansion of supraglacial ice-melt lakes (28°06′N, 90°17′E, 4440–4480 m a.m.s.l.) on Thorthomi Glacier has accelerated in the 1990s as shown in Fig. 4. A continuing expansion of the lakes was documented by 1998 observations. The thin debris cover on the glacier surface, which accelerates ice melting, and the very gentle gradient of the snout may lead to the formation a large lake in the near future.

The left (southeast) lateral moraine is being eroded from both sides and the moraine ridge is becoming sharp and narrow; the inner slope is retreating because of expansion of the long lakes along the base. The outer slope is eroding its base by lateral and downward cutting of the river which discharges from Lugge Tsho (GLP12). In addition, a considerable amount of water is leaking from the left lateral moraine to the river channel from Lugge Tsho. There is therefore a potential for collapse of this moraine and associated release of water in the near future.

Raphsthreng Tsho (GLP9) Raphsthreng Tsho (28°07′N, 90°15′E, 4400 m a.m.s.l.) rapidly expanded between the 1950s and the 1980s from supraglacial lakes to a moraine-dammed lake, while in the 1990s the lake maintained almost the same state (Fig. 5). Lake expansion has halted, probably because the glacial bed steeply rises just upstream from the present terminus position.

The lake level of Raphsthreng Tsho is about 50 m lower than the levels of supraglacial lakes on Thorthomi Glacier to the east (Fig. 2). The moraine between

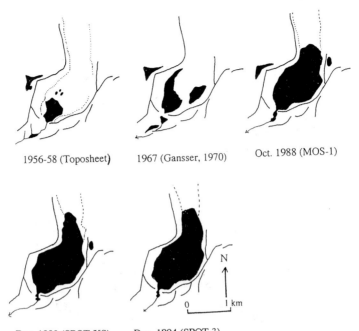

1956-58 (Toposheet)   1967 (Gansser, 1970)   Oct. 1988 (MOS-1)

Dec. 1993 (SPOT-XS)   Dec. 1994 (SPOT-3)

Fig. 5 Expansion of Raphsthreng Tsho (GLP9).

them is damming water flow from Thorthomi lakes to Raphsthreng Tsho. If this moraine dam were to break, the outburst from Thorthomi lakes could initiate a catastrophic outburst of Raphsthreng Tsho. Although the moraine looks stable at present, vulnerability of this moraine to failure could increase, if seepage from Thorthomi Glacier to Raphsthreng Tsho weakens this moraine. The probability of failure of the terminal moraine dam of Raphsthreng Tsho has been mitigated by artificial excavation of the outlet channel in 1996–1998. But the risk is still high because the lake contains a large volume of water (maximum depth about 100 m) with the additional danger from Thorthomi Glacier.

Tarina Lakes (Tarina Tsho GLP1 and Mouzom Tsho GLP2) These glacier lakes are located at the western headwaters of Pho Chu (Figs 1 and 6). The evolution of the Tarina Lakes is illustrated in Fig. 7. Comparison of 1998 observations with a photograph taken in 1967 by Gansser (1970) shows that the area of the upper lake (GLP2: 28°07′N, 89°55′E, 4340 m a.m.s.l.) expanded upstream due to retreat of the debris-covered tongue of the glacier. A satellite image in 1988 shows that the present condition with the terminus on the top of a rock cliff in the valley was already established 10 years ago (Fig. 7). Since upper ends of both of the glacier lakes GLP1 and GLP2 have been located at the foot of high rock cliffs, upvalley expansion of the lakes has been blocked. A fall of ice from the hanging ice masses of the glaciers terminating on the cliffs could displace water very rapidly causing overflow and downstream flooding.

Supraglacial ponds (GLP6) of Wachey Glacier Wachey Glacier is located about 15 km downstream of Tarina Lakes along the western branch of Pho Chu (Fig. 6). As

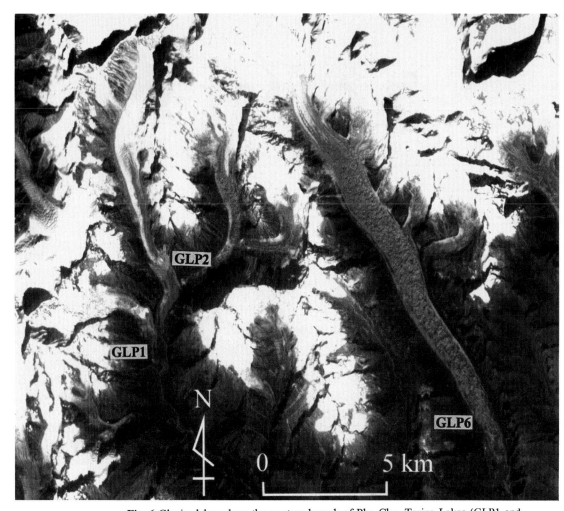

Fig. 6 Glacier lakes along the western branch of Pho Chu. Tarina Lakes (GLP1 and GLP2) and supraglacial ponds (GLP6) of Wachey Glacier in a SPOT-XS satellite image taken on 3 December 1993 (copyright: CNES).

shown in Fig. 8, only a few ponds were found in the map of Wachey Glacier in the 1950s. In 1967, Gansser (1970) found nine supraglacial ponds on the debris-covered area of this glacier. These ponds (28°03′N, 90°02′E, 4360–4440 m a.m.s.l.) more than doubled in area in December 1993 as seen in Fig. 8.

EXPANSION RATES OF PROGLACIAL LAKES UPVALLEY

Variations of glacier lakes and glacier termini can be detected from comparison of photographs, satellite images and maps in different years. For some glaciers, the variation can be measured from photographs taken in 1984 by T. Tsukihara and in 1998 by the authors. Between 1988 and 1993 Lugge Tsho expanded about 0.8 km (Fig. 3) in association with the glacier retreat. Raphsthreng Tsho expanded about 0.5

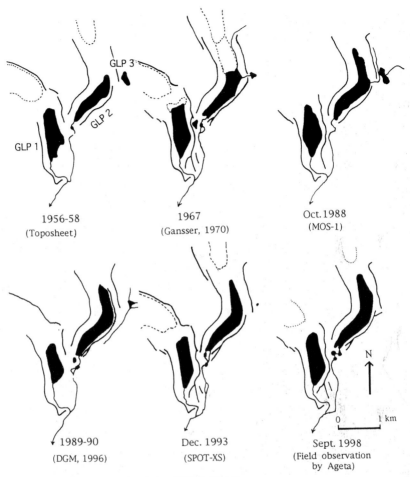

Fig. 7 Expansion of Tarina Lakes (GLP1, GLP2).

km between 1984 and 1998, and 0.3 km between 1988 and 1993 (Fig. 5). Tarina Lake (GLP2) expanded about 0.7 km from 1967 to 1988 (Fig. 7) and successive expansion was blocked by a cliff. The unnamed debris-free glacier, north of Gangrinchemzoe Pass (between GLP19 and GLT8 in Fig. 1), retreated about 0.4 km from 1984 to 1998; as a result, a small pond grew into a proglacial lake (GLP19: 27°55′N, 90°16′E, 5100 m a.m.s.l.). The above are examples of upvalley expansions of proglacial lakes accompanied by the corresponding retreat of glacier termini.

    Mean annual expansion distances of proglacial lakes during recent years and glacier lengths in Bhutan are compared with available data from the Nepal Himalayas (Tsho Rolpa: 27°50′N, 86°28′E, 4580 m a.m.s.l.; Imja Lake: 27°59′N, 86°56′E, 5010 m a.m.s.l.) in Table 1. Since the expansion of Lugge Tsho can be measured only for the period from 1988 to 1993, available data of other lakes for the same period are shown in a different column. The mean annual expansions of three lakes (GLP9 and GLP19 for 1984–1998, GLP2 for 1967–1988) in Bhutan converge in a range of 30–35 m year[-1]. However, the rates are variable with time as found for GLP9 and Tsho Rolpa (Table 1). Irregular calving of the glacier tongues is probably a major contribution to such variations.

Table 1 Mean annual expansion of proglacial lakes upvalley.

Glacier name (Lake code/name)	Expansion distance: m year[-1]	period	m year[-1] during 1988–1993	Glacier length (km)
Bhutan				
Lugge (GLP12)			160	5
Raphsthreng (GLP9)	35	1984–1998	60	3
Tarina (GLP2)	35	1967–1988	blocked by a cliff	8
unnamed* (GLP19)	30	1984–1998		3
Nepal				
Trambau (Tsho Rolpa)[a]	60	1983/84–1997	80	20
Imja (Imja)[b]	40	1984–1992		9

* The unnamed glacier, which is the only debris-free in the above glaciers, is located north of Gangrinchemzoe Pass.

[a,b] Based on figures in Yamada (1998) and Watanabe *et al.* (1995), respectively.

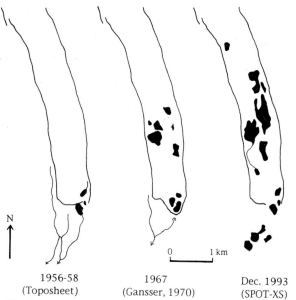

1956-58	1967	Dec. 1993
(Toposheet)	(Gansser, 1970)	(SPOT-XS)

Fig. 8 Expansion of supraglacial ponds (GLP6) on Wachey Glacier.

Comparison of the rates between Bhutan and Nepal from Table 1 is difficult. Absolute rates appear smaller in Bhutan than Nepal, but rates relative to the glacier lengths are larger. The retreat rate of the unnamed glacier, which is the only debris-free glacier in Table 1, is very large in comparison with those of small debris-free glaciers in Nepal, most of which are retreating at only several m year[-1] (Kadota, 1997).

For the further analyses of variations of proglacial lakes and glaciers, the interaction between them should be studied, such as calving and ice melting of glacier tongues by lake water. Proper criteria and methods to standardize the variation of debris-covered and debris-free glaciers with different scales are required for comparison of the glacier variations in different regions.

Acknowledgements The authors would like to express their gratitude to Mr Dorji Wangda, Head of Geological Survey of Bhutan, his staff and Dr Mutsumi Motegi, Japan International Cooperation Agency for kind support on the joint project, and to Mr Toshihiro Tsukihara, a member of Kyoto University Bhutan Himalaya Expedition, 1983 and 1984 for providing photographs on glaciers and glacier lake variations. This study was mostly supported by Grant-in-Aid for Scientific Research (Projects nos. 09041103 and 09490018) from the Ministry of Education, Science, Sports and Culture, Japanese Government.

REFERENCES

Ageta, Y. & Iwata, S. (eds) (1999) *Report of Japan–Bhutan Joint Research 1998 on the Assessment of Glacier Lake Outburst Flood (GLOF) in Bhutan*. Inst. for Hydrospheric–Atmospheric Sciences, Nagoya Univ., Nagoya, Japan.

Ageta, Y. & Kadota, T. (1992) Predictions of changes of glacier mass balance in the Nepal Himalaya and Tibetan Plateau: a case study of air temperature increase for three glaciers. *Ann. Glaciol.* **16**, 89–94.

Division of Geology and Mines (1996) *Glaciers and Glacier Lakes in the Headwaters of Major River Basins of Bhutan*. Ministry of Trade and Industry, Thimphu.

Eguchi, T. (1997) *Regional and Temporal Variations in Precipitation in the Eastern Part of the Himalayas*. Faculty of Humanities and Economics, Kochi Univ., Kochi, Japan.

Fujita, K., Nakawo, M., Fujii, Y. & Paudyal, P. (1997) Changes in glaciers in Hidden Valley, Mukut Himal, Nepal Himalayas, from 1974 to 1994. *J. Glaciol.* **43**, 583–588.

Gansser, A. (1970) Lunana: the peaks, glaciers and lakes of northern Bhutan. In: *The Mountain World 1968/69*, 117–131. Swiss Foundation for Alpine Research.

Kadota, T. (1997) Study on the relation between climate and recent shrinkage of small glaciers in the Nepal Himalayas. DSc Thesis, Nagoya Univ., Nagoya, Japan.

Watanabe, T., Kameyama, S. & Sato, T. (1995) Imja Glacier dead-ice melt rates and changes in a supra-glacial lake, 1989–1994, Khumbu Himal, Nepal: danger of lake drainage. *Mountain Res. Develop.* **15**, 293–300.

Yamada T. (1998) *Glacier Lake and its Outburst Flood in the Nepal Himalaya*. Monograph no. 1, Data Centre for Glacier Research, Japanese Society of Snow and Ice, Tokyo.

Debris-Covered Glaciers (Proceedings of a workshop held at Seattle, Washington, USA, September 2000).
IAHS Publ. no. 264, 2000.

177

Rapid growth of a supraglacial lake, Ngozumpa Glacier, Khumbu Himal, Nepal

DOUGLAS I. BENN

School of Geography and Geosciences, University of St Andrews, Fife KY16 9ST, UK
e-mail: doug@st-andrews.ac.uk

SEONAID WISEMAN

Department of Geography, University of Aberdeen, Aberdeen AB24 3UF, UK

CHARLES R. WARREN

School of Geography and Geosciences, University of St Andrews, Fife KY16 9ST, UK

Abstract Between October 1998 and October 1999, a supraglacial lake on the Ngozumpa Glacier, Khumbu Himal, Nepal, underwent rapid growth, mainly by a combination of calving retreat and basin flooding during the 1999 monsoon season. The lake is unlikely to develop into a large moraine-dammed lake, but while it persists, growth of the lake will probably continue to result in locally high rates of ablation, contributing to overall downwasting of the glacier surface.

INTRODUCTION

The Khumbu Himal contains a large population of debris-mantled glaciers, many of which have undergone significant downwasting in recent decades (e.g. Nakawo *et al.*, 1999). In many cases, downwasting has been associated with the rapid growth of supraglacial lakes, e.g. on the Imja Glacier, where a supraglacial lake *c.* 1.5 km long and 0.5 km across has developed since the 1950s (Yamada & Sharma, 1993; Watanabe *et al.*, 1994). Such lakes may generate catastrophic glacier lake outburst floods (GLOFs), which constitute a major hazard in the region (Yamada, 1998; Reynolds, 1999). If current glacier downwasting trends continue, more potentially dangerous moraine-dammed lakes can be expected to develop in the Khumbu Himal. However, little is known about the response of Himalayan debris-mantled glaciers to climatic inputs, and at present it is not possible to determine how many glaciers are at risk, or the likely time scale for the development of dangerous lakes.

This paper describes the rapid growth of a supraglacial lake on the Ngozumpa Glacier between 1998 and 1999. The study forms part of an ongoing programme of research on the Ngozumpa, which aims to identify the controls on lake growth and glacier downwasting, and their changes over time. The glacier was chosen because it is hemmed in by large latero-frontal moraines, a situation which may encourage the development of a large moraine-dammed lake if the current trend of downwasting continues. Study of the glacier will therefore allow the anticipation of possible future hazards in this heavily-frequented part of the Himalayas.

STUDY AREA

The Ngozumpa is the longest glacier in Nepal, flowing southward for *c.* 25 km from the slopes of Cho Oyu (8188 m) and Gyachung Kang (7922 m; Fig. 1). A major tributary, the Gaunara Glacier, is no longer dynamically connected to the Ngozumpa. Most of the lower 15 km of the glacier (below *c.* 5200 m) is mantled by supraglacial debris, which increases in thickness downglacier to *c.* 1–2 m on the lower snout. Much of the ablation area of the glacier is hemmed between large lateral moraines, which

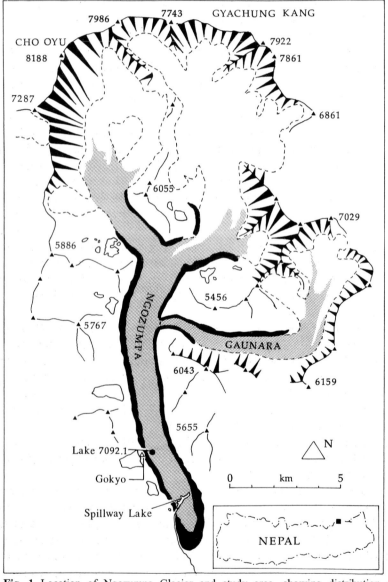

Fig. 1 Location of Ngozumpa Glacier and study area, showing distribution of avalanche faces (hachures) and debris-mantled ice (stippled). Lateral moraines are shown in black. Heights in metres.

typically stand 60–100 m above the glacier surface, attesting to significant downwasting in recent decades.

Meltwater leaves the glacier via a supraglacial lake (Spillway Lake) located *c.* 1 km from the glacier terminus. The lake drains through a channel cut into the right (west) lateral moraine of the glacier, and receives water from at least two subaerial portals close to the lake margins and two or three subaqueous portals, revealed by the presence of water upwelling to the surface. Integrated supraglacial drainage systems are not in evidence on the glacier snout, but in a number of places streams and sheet flow from ice faces enter moulins on the glacier surface. The presence of active portals and moulins suggests that much of the long-distance transport of supraglacial meltwater is *via* englacial conduits.

The debris-mantled surface of the ablation area is highly irregular, with a typical vertical relief between peaks and troughs of *c.* 20–50 m, and is studded with numerous supraglacial lakes. With the exception of Spillway Lake, none of the lakes observed to date have any apparent connection to the englacial drainage system, and are thus "perched lakes" supported by essentially impermeable glacier ice. The lakes are typically stagnant, except where disturbed by wind or falling debris, and show no evidence of either upwelling or drawdown of water. Lake levels are apparently controlled by inputs of meltwater, calved ice blocks and precipitation, outputs by evaporation, and changes in basin volume. There is abundant evidence that such lakes may drain englacially in certain circumstances. Lacustrine silts and sands drape the floors of several closed basins on the glacier surface and, in places, the sediment drapes are pierced by holes up to *c.* 1 m in diameter, into which feed systems of dry rills. It is inferred that water from the lakes drained through the holes, presumably when the lake floors became connected to englacial conduits. This potential drainage mechanism provides a limit to the growth of perched supraglacial lakes, because such lakes can only exist until their floor intersects a conduit or other void which is connected to the englacial drainage system, a possibility that becomes more likely as the lake grows larger.

Spillway Lake differs from the other lakes observed on the Ngozumpa, in that its level is controlled by the altitude of the overflow channel through the western lateral moraine. Its growth, therefore, is not constrained by new connections to the englacial drainage network and in the future, the lake may grow to occupy a large area of the lower snout, as has happened on the Imja, Tsho Rolpa, and other glaciers in the region (Yamada & Sharma, 1993; Chikita *et al.*, 1997, 1999; Yamada, 1998; Reynolds, 1999). At present, Spillway Lake is mainly surrounded by stable debris-mantled ice slopes, and between autumn 1998 and autumn 1999 modest growth occurred in only one part of the lake basin, where bare ice cliffs are exposed (Benn & Wiseman, unpublished data).

Observations to date indicate that ablation rates on the lower snout are negligible, except where the debris cover is broken and bare ice exposed. The future evolution of the Ngozumpa Glacier thus primarily will depend on (a) processes affecting the growth of Spillway Lake, (b) the growth rates and life cycles of perched supraglacial lakes elsewhere on the snout, and (c) the ablation of ice cliffs around moulins and other holes on the glacier surface. It is thus important to determine growth rates and average lifetimes for perched supraglacial lakes, due to the important role they play in the ablation of the lower glacier, and the consequent control that they exert on long-term downwasting rates.

This paper focuses on the evolution of one perched lake basin on the western side of the glacier adjacent to Gokyo, at an altitude of *c.* 4750 m (Fig. 1). During the study period, several perched lakes on the Ngozumpa underwent growth, whereas others drained. The studied lake is therefore not representative of all supraglacial lakes on the glacier, but provides an example of the rapid growth rates that are possible during a growth phase.

METHODS

Surveys of the lake basin (Lake 7092.1, Fig. 1) were conducted on 9–10 October 1998, and 3–4 October 1999 (lakes are labelled by their four-figure grid reference on the Survey of Nepal 1:50 000 maps). Triangulation from a measured baseline and single-station surveys were conducted using a Leica TR1000 theodolite and Dior 3002S distomat (1999) and Abney Level and Suunto compass (1998). Repeat measurements were made in 1999 of bearings taken to fixed points in 1998, and the 1998 measurements were found to be accurate to within ±0.5°, which equates to a horizontal accuracy of *c.* ±2 m for points in the surveyed areas. The 1999 measurements were considerably more accurate, with a horizontal accuracy of *c.* ±0.03 m. Bathymetric measurements were made on 27 October 1999, when the lake was frozen to a depth of *c.* 15 cm. Holes were cut in the ice, and soundings taken with a Lowrance LMS-350A sounder. The lake was also visited in April 1999, when a photographic survey was undertaken.

LAKE EVOLUTION 1998–1999

October 1998

In October 1998, three lakes occupied a large basin on the glacier surface, the floor of which had an area of *c.* 38 800 m^2 (Figs 2(a) and 3(a)). The largest lake (A, Fig. 3(a)) was in the southern part of the basin, with an area of 12 980 m^2. The eastern and southern margins of this lake were fringed by steep ice faces generally 25–33 m high, although much of the actual shoreline consisted of fallen ice blocks or talus. The western margin of the lake was bounded by active talus below the western lateral moraine of the glacier, whereas the northern margins were composed of hummocky debris-mantled ice. The second lake (B, Fig. 3(a)) occupied the east–central part of the basin, and had an area of 2730 m^2. The eastern margin of the lake was overlooked by a steep ice face up to 34 m high. The southern part of this face was fringed by talus, but the northern part formed a vertical and overhanging ice face rising directly from the water. The western shores of the lake were composed of ice-cored debris. The third and smallest lake (C, Fig. 3(a)) occupied the northern part of the basin, and had an area of 2180 m^2. The lake was fringed by talus on the northwest, and hummocky ice-cored topography on its other sides. The combined area of the three lakes was 17 890 m^2, or *c.* 46 % of the basin area.

(a)

(b)

(c)

Fig. 2 Photographs of the lake basin in (a) October 1998; (b) April 1999; and (c) October 1999. Note the detached ice block on the left of the October 1999 photo. This block collapsed on 12 October, 9 days after the photo was taken. A–D indicate reference boulders for comparison.

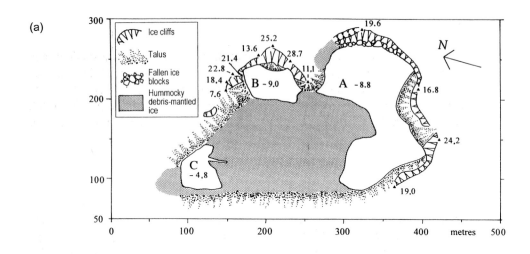

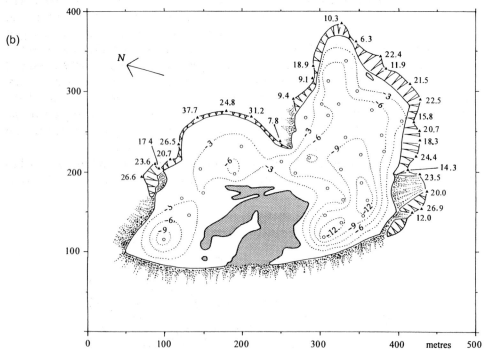

Fig. 3 Maps of the lake basin in (a) October 1998; and (b) October 1999. Spot heights and lake surface heights are in metres above and below the October 1999 lake level.

There is evidence that a deeper lake occupied the basin sometime prior to autumn 1998. Drapes of laminated silts and sands occur on the hummocky debris-mantled ice in the west–central part of the basin, attesting to water levels at least 12 m higher than the autumn 1998 level. Additionally, a lake filling most of the basin can be observed on several commercial photographs of the glacier, although lack of dating limits their scientific usefulness.

April 1999

When visited again in April 1999, the water level had risen causing the southern and central lakes to join (Fig. 2(b)). The water level was not measured, but it is estimated to be *c.* 2 m above the autumn 1998 level of the southern lake. In general, there was little change in the overall size of the basin between October 1998 and April 1999, although during April, calving of large spalls in the eastern and southeastern parts of the basin was leading to basin expansion in these areas.

October 1999

Large changes occurred in the basin between April and October 1999 (Figs 2(c) and 3(b)). Water level rose during the summer monsoon of 1999, forming a single large lake composed of two sub-basins joined by a narrow neck of water. The surface of this lake was 8.8 m above the autumn 1998 level of the southern lake. The lake basin also underwent dramatic expansion, particularly along the southern and eastern margins of the basin, where the lake was in direct contact with steep ice faces. At the beginning of October 1999, the basin floor had an area of *c.* 60 500 m^2, and the lake had an area of 52 550 m^2, or 87% of the basin. The greatest changes occurred in the southeastern part of the basin, where the ice cliff retreated by *c.* 100 m during the summer season. During the same period, ice-cliff retreat of *c.* 25 m occurred around much of the southern and northeastern perimeters. Active calving occurred in several parts of the basin during October 1999 (Fig. 2(c)). Calved blocks failed along pre-existing crevasse traces or along new fractures that developed parallel to the ice faces.

The shore of the October 1999 lake lay within the limits of the October 1998 lakes in only one area: the southwestern margin of the basin (Fig. 4). In this area, the basin

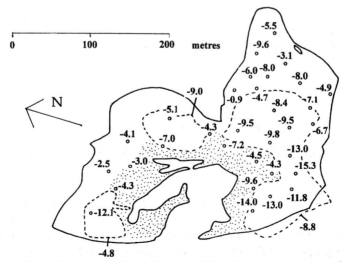

Fig. 4 Bathymetry of the October 1999 Lake. For comparison, the limits of the October 1998 lakes are also shown. The stippled area was hummocky debris-mantled ice in 1998.

margin consists of talus fed by the unstable ice-proximal slopes of the western lateral moraine, and the change in lake configuration in this area is therefore attributed to talus progradation.

The deepest portions of the October 1999 lake were in the southwestern and northwestern parts, within the areas occupied by the southern and northern lakes in 1998 (Figs 3 and 4). Some of the measured depths fall close to the position of the 1998 lake shorelines, but have depths rather less than should be expected from the amount of flooding that occurred in the basin between 1998 and 1999 (e.g. the depths of 5.1 and 4.3 m in the east–central part of the basin, and the depths of 7.1 and 6.7 m in the southern part, Fig. 4). These locations are close to the 1998 positions of active talus cones, and it is inferred that the anomalous measurements reflect basin infilling between the survey dates. Depth measurement points that fall within the area occupied by hummocky debris-mantled ice in 1998 (stippled area, Fig. 4) indicate generally shallow water in 1999. Comparison of the subaerial part of this hummocky area in 1998 and 1999 (Fig. 3(a) and (c)) reveals that several distinctive boulders have the same positions in both years. Taken together with the shallow soundings in the flooded part of the hummocky area, this evidence suggests that little or no downwasting occurred over most of the basin floor between the survey dates. In contrast, the soundings in the southeastern embayment of the 1999 lake were occupied by substantial thicknesses of ice in 1998, indicating that a layer of ice up to 20 m thick was removed from this part of the glacier between the two surveys. In total, approximately 340 000 m^3 of ice was removed from the basin, mainly by calving of ice faces. The exceptionally rapid backwasting of the southeastern margin of the lake probably relates to the presence of closely spaced longitudinal crevasse traces in this area, providing pre-existing weaknesses to be exploited by calving.

The dramatic flooding that occurred during the 1999 summer monsoon can be attributed to a number of causes:
(a) increased precipitation during the summer months;
(b) melting in the catchment and subsequent runoff into the basin;
(c) reduced evaporation from the lake surface due to frequent cloud cover;
(d) input of calved ice blocks adding water to the lake, and
(e) input of rock debris partially infilling the basin.
It is suggested that flooding of the basin encouraged calving retreat because, as the water deepened, talus and ice-block aprons were submerged and more ice faces were brought into direct contact with water, whereupon undercutting by thermo-erosional notching could occur. Additionally, deeper water reduced the likelihood of talus accumulation above the waterline, and fallen icebergs were more likely to be removed by wind drifting. It therefore appears likely that water deepening and calving retreat form a positive feedback cycle, together leading to rapid growth of the lake.

CONCLUDING REMARKS

Lake 7092.1 is located *c.* 2.7 km from, and *c.* 50 m above, the Spillway Lake outfall. Therefore, it is anticipated that the lake will continue to grow only until it is intercepted by an englacial conduit, at which time it will fully or partially drain.

During the study period, the lake expanded across *c.* 30% of the width of the glacier, and its growth is thus a major contributor to ablation on this part of the glacier. While the lake exists, therefore, rapid ice loss is likely to continue. Ongoing research on the Ngozumpa is focused on the distribution, density, and life cycle of several supraglacial lakes, to determine their aggregate contribution to glacier downwasting.

Acknowledgements Fieldwork was funded by The Carnegie Trust for the Universities of Scotland, and the Universities of Aberdeen and St Andrews. Grateful thanks are offered to Kathryn Hands, Tim Harrington, Sue Fielding, Andrew Wakefield and Stephen Varga for field assistance, to Jack Jarvis for help with equipment and data analysis, and to Raju Aryal and other staff at the Department of Hydrology and Meteorology, Kathmandu, for helpful advice and permission to work in Nepal.

REFERENCES

Chikita, K., Yamada, T., Sakai, A. & Ghimire, R. P. (1997) Hydrodynamic effects of the basin expansion of Tsho Rolpa Glacier Lake in the Nepal Himalaya. *Bull. Glacier Res.* **15**, 59–69.

Chikita, K., Jha, J. & Yamada, T. (1999) Hydrodynamics of a supraglacial lake and its effect on the basin expansion: Tsho Rolpa, Rolwaling Valley, Nepal Himalaya. *Arct., Antarct. Alp. Res.* **31**, 58–70.

Nakawo, M., Yabuki, H. & Sakai, A. (1999) Characteristics of Khumbu Glacier, Nepal Himalaya: recent change in the debris-covered area. *Ann. Glaciol.* **28**, 118–122.

Reynolds, J. M. (1999) Glacial hazard assessment at Tsho Rolpa, Rolwaling, Central Nepal. *Quart. J. Engng Geol.* **32**, 209–214.

Watanabe, T., Ives, J. D. & Hammond, J. E. (1994) Rapid growth of a glacial lake in Khumbu Himal, Himalaya: prospects for a catastrophic flood. *Mountain Res. Develop.* **14**, 329–340.

Yamada, T. (1998) *Glacier Lake and its Outburst Flood in the Nepal Himalaya.* Monograph no. 1, Data Centre for Glacier Research, Japanese Society of Snow and Ice, Tokyo.

Yamada, T. & Sharma, C. K. (1993) Glacier lakes and outburst floods in the Nepal Himalaya. In: *Snow and Glacier Hydrology* (ed. by G. J. Young) (Proc. Kathmandu Symp., November 1992), 319–330. IAHS Publ. no. 218.

Debris-Covered Glaciers (Proceedings of a workshop held at Seattle, Washington, USA, September 2000).
IAHS Publ. no. 264, 2000.

187

Degradation of ice-cored moraine dams: implications for hazard development

SHAUN D. RICHARDSON & JOHN M. REYNOLDS

Reynolds Geo-Sciences Ltd, 2 Long Barn, Pistyll Farm, Nercwys, Mold, Flintshire CH7 4EW, UK
e-mail: rgsl@geologyuk.com

Abstract Field and geophysical studies have allowed us to identify processes leading to ice-cored moraine degradation for three natural dams investigated in Peru and Nepal. As potentially hazardous lakes form on the snouts of debris-covered glaciers they may separate a stagnant ice body from the upper reaches of the glacier to form an ice-cored end-moraine complex. The ice-cored moraines appear to degrade through ablation beneath the debris cover, by localized thermokarst development, and by associated mass movement. Relict glacier structures serve as a focal point for the onset of accelerated thermokarst degradation. Once exposed, the ice core then undergoes accelerated wastage through the combined affects of solar radiation and mechanical failure due to the rheological response of the ice to deepening kettle forms. Continuing degradation reduces the lake freeboard, weakens the moraine dam, and can lead to its catastrophic failure.

INTRODUCTION

Outburst floods from moraine-dammed glacial lakes represent significant natural hazards in many glaciated regions (Lliboutry *et al.*, 1977; Clague & Evans, 1994; Richardson & Reynolds, 2000). Moraine-dammed glacial lakes are commonly associated with periods of glacier wasting and recession, particularly by debris-covered glaciers. During periods of ice wastage, ice at the glacier margins in the ablation zone may be preferentially insulated by the thick debris cover and can become incorporated within terminal and lateral moraines to form substantial ice cores. Wasting of stagnant ice within ice-cored moraine dams by a variety of thermokarst processes (Clayton, 1964; Healy, 1975) can affect the development and stability of potentially hazardous glacial lakes.

We have investigated several moraine dams during assessments of potentially dangerous glacial lakes in the Himalayas and the Andes. Three examples are presented here from Nepal and Peru where buried ice has played an important role in affecting moraine dam stability. Our studies consisted of topographical surveying, geomorphological mapping of moraine landforms and glacial structures, sedimentological characterization, photography of key features, Ground Penetrating Radar (GPR) and electrical resistivity studies of moraine structure, and interpretation of oblique and vertical aerial photographs.

HUALCÁN, PERU

A Neoglacial end-moraine complex near Hualcán, Cordillera Blanca, Peru (Fig. 1), was studied during a successful hazard assessment and mitigation programme

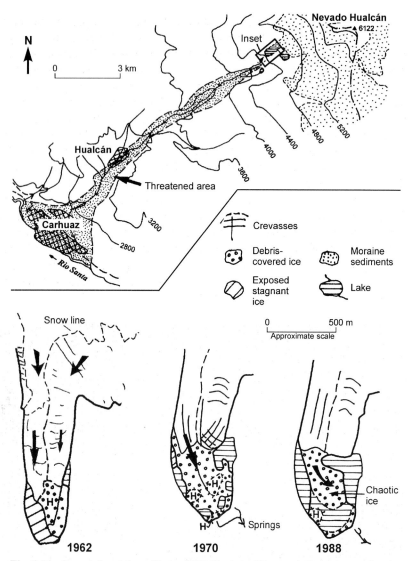

Fig. 1 The hazard threat from "Lake 513", Hualcán, Peru, and sketch maps showing the growth of the lake between 1962 and 1988. Map of the potential flood route from Reynolds *et al.* (1998).

undertaken between 1988 and 1993 (Reynolds *et al.*, 1998). "Lake 513" developed on a composite glacier that flowed westwards from Nevado Hualcán (6122 m a.s.l.) into an elongated bedrock basin. Aerial photographs show that between 1948 and 1962 the debris-covered glacier snout was losing mass by downwasting rather than by retreat. Small ponds up to *c.* 100 m across began to form on the glacier snout between 1962 and 1970. By 1988 individual ponds had coalesced to form a single lake separating an ice-cored end-moraine complex from the upper reaches of the glacier (Fig. 1). By 1993 the lowermost part of the glacier had ablated completely and the glacier had retreated to form a highly unstable ice tongue on the steep slope descending into the basin.

Melting of the glacier and formation of the lake left a prominent end-moraine ridge with steep inner flanks at the former position of the glacier terminus (Fig. 2). Electrical resistivity was used to investigate the internal structure of the moraine ridge to assist the design of a suitable hazard remediation programme. It was confirmed that the moraine was cored with stagnant glacier ice up to *c.* 8 m thick, directly overlying bedrock. The ice core was overlain by at least 0.5 m of diamict containing angular and sub-angular boulders. Detailed topographical levelling showed that the moraine surface had subsided by 4 m across much of the end-moraine complex between 1985 and 1988. This was interpreted as melting of the ice core beneath the debris cover, lowering at an average rate of about 11 cm per month (Reynolds, 1992). Water from the lake was flowing over the ice core and draining via two springs on the distal side of the moraine.

Lowering of the moraine's ice core reduced the lake freeboard to less than 1 m in 1988, leaving the moraine vulnerable to overtopping by displacement waves. It was thought that if nothing had been done to mitigate the situation, the moraine might have failed in 1989, possibly destroying Carhuaz and part of Hualcán with the loss of many thousands of lives. An emergency remediation programme was initiated in 1988–1989, employing siphons and an engineered tunnel to successfully lower the lake level (Reynolds, 1992; Reynolds *et al.*, 1998).

Fig. 2 Composition of the moraine dam at Lake "513", Hualcán, clearly showing the angular and blocky nature of sediment indicative of supraglacial transport.

TSHO ROLPA, ROLWALING HIMAL, CENTRAL NEPAL

Tsho Rolpa glacier lake lies at the head of the Rolwaling Valley in northern Central Nepal and, with a length of 3.2 km and volume of *c.* 10^8 m^3, it is the country's largest glacial lake. The lake formed by the coalescence of supraglacial ponds on the debris-covered Trakarding Glacier (Mool, 1995) and is dammed by a 150 m high moraine ridge complex. The potential for the lake to burst catastrophically from behind its moraine dam prompted a detailed hazard assessment (Reynolds, 1998) and a remediation scheme to lower the lake level through an engineered channel (Rana *et al.*, 1999).

Morphological and geophysical studies of the end-moraine between 1994 and 1999 provide evidence for degradation processes and rates. Degradation has been greatest in the terminal area where two lobate ridges of angular supraglacial debris mark the extent of the last Neoglacial advance (Fig. 3). Between the lobate ridges and the lake shoreline, on the inner flank of the end-moraine complex, is an area of hummocky moraine. Steep gullies and scarps up to 2 m deep bound the hummocky moraine. Comparison of photographs taken between 1994 and 1999 indicates that the scarps and gullies are deepening and that the hummocky moraine is subsiding relative to the lobate end-moraine ridges. Also in this area are two well-developed sinkholes, each up to 45 m across (indicated "M" and "S", Fig. 3). Sinkhole formation plays an important role in moraine surface lowering. Between 1996 and 1999 the moraine surface subsided by 19.5 m into one sinkhole (Fig. 4). At least 13 m of this subsidence occurred between October 1996 and

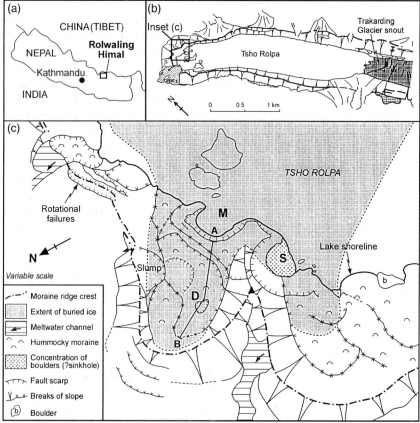

Fig. 3 Geomorphology of the degrading ice-cored moraine dam at Tsho Rolpa, Rowaling Himal, Nepal. A–B marks the location of the GPR and electrical resistivity data shown in Fig. 5. The main thermokarst features are indicated "D", "M" and "S".

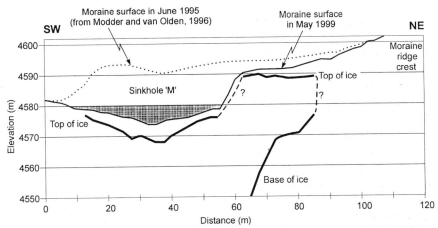

Fig. 4 Cross-section through the inner flank of the Tsho Rolpa end-moraine highlighting variable degradation rates, 1995–1999. The location of sinkhole "M" is indicated on Fig. 3.

May 1997, equating to a maximum lowering rate of 22.3 m year^{-1}. Adjacent to the sinkhole the surface lowering rates over the same period were up to 1.05 m year^{-1}. Further evidence for moraine degradation is provided by rotational failures on the inner flank of the end-moraine ridge (Fig. 3). Each backscarp is up to 40 m long and 3 m high. Geophysical profiles through the rotational failures show that the moraine is not ice-cored at this location. The failures are interpreted as relating to an adjacent supporting ice mass beneath the lake, with slippage occurring as the ice gradually melts.

Degradation landforms on the Tsho Rolpa end-moraine, including subsiding hummocky moraine, kettle-form sinkholes and rotational failures, are coincident with the extent of buried ice as mapped geophysically. The internal structure of the moraine beneath a developing sinkhole (indicated "D", Fig. 3) has been studied using GPR and electrical resistivity to determine possible controls on degradation (Fig. 5). At 61 m along the shown GPR radargram, there is a depression in the interpreted top of ice at a depth of *c*. 4.5 m below moraine surface (circled, Fig. 5(a)). A flat prominent bright reflection above the cusp coupled with a strongly attenuated zone beneath suggests that this depression is water-filled but penetrates into the ice mass below. The same feature is imaged in the electrical resistivity tomogram as an inclined low resistivity zone that dips towards the lake separating two highly resistive bodies to a depth of 15–20 m (Fig. 5(b)). The higher resistivity values observed (reaching 100 000 Ω m^{-1}) are clearly indicative of buried ice. It is clear that there is a significant discontinuity in the buried ice mass that is consistent with this zone being a debris and/or water filled crevasse that reaches to the base of ice. Correlation of a newly developing sinkhole in the moraine surface above a water and debris filled crevasse in the underlying ice core suggests that relict ice structures may act as foci for moraine degradation.

The role of relict ice structures in facilitating moraine degradation was observed in 1997 when an exposed block of ice >100 m^3 gradually became detached along the line of a former crevasse. The ice block had been exposed in the side wall of a sinkhole into which the lake had encroached. Undercutting of the ice cliff at the water line was aiding calving and causing the ice block to rotate into the lake, failing along well developed crevasses (Fig. 6). In the process of calving, flakes of ice were spalling from the undercut ice cliff. Sub-aqueous calving was also observed involving ice blocks of up to 4 m³. Behind the rim of the sinkhole a series of sub-parallel gullies in the moraine surface were becoming activated. These were interpreted as crevasses being reactivated in response to the creep of ice towards the developing sinkhole. Sub-horizontal debris filled conduits exposed in the face of the ice cliff periodically issued pulses of saturated sediment. Connectivity of the conduits with the crevasses behind the sinkhole was inferred, allowing water and debris to drain from the widening crevasses.

THULAGI, CENTRAL NEPAL

Thulagi Glacier lake in Manaslu Himal, Nepal, is 2.2 km long and has a volume of c. 32 million m³. At the downstream end of the lake is a complex of ridges and hummocky sand and gravel through which the main outlet river drains (Fig. 7). Exposures in the ridges show predominantly silt grade material overlain by angular to sub-rounded gravels and cobbles. They have been interpreted as erosional remnants of a former lake bed (Hanisch *et al.*, 1998). GPR and electrical resistivity measurements over the area indicate the presence of a major ice body below 10–35 m of sediment (Hanisch *et al.*, 1998). The ice is approximately 100 m thick, at least 550 m long and extends for 500 m across the entire valley. This stagnant ice and overlying veneer of silts, sands and gravels forms a dam that is at least 550 m wide.

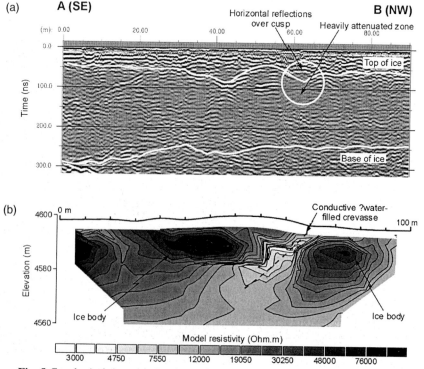

Fig. 5 Geophysical data showing internal structures of the Tsho Rolpa end-moraine. (a) is a GPR profile, and (b) is an electrical resistivity tomogram. The profile location is indicated on Fig. 3.

Fig. 6 Stagnant glacier ice exposed within the Tsho Rolpa terminal moraine in May 1997. Note (a) the undercut ice cliff, (b) active crevasse behind calving ice block, and (c) debris filled conduit within the ice core.

Fig. 7 The ice-cored dam complex at Thulagi, Nepal, showing (a) hummocky sands and gravels, and (b) erosional ridges of silts and sands. The field of view is *c.* 700 m wide.

Evidence for degradation of the dam complex is restricted to the flanks of the ridges adjacent to the hummocky sand and gravel. Small slope failures within the finer silts and sands are evident where vegetation has not stabilized the ridge slopes. Within the hummocky area itself there are several depressions up to 8–10 m across containing concentrations of larger boulders. These have been interpreted as sinkhole drainage centres, although these features are relatively immature (cf. Clayton, 1964). The ice is not exposed and there is no morphological evidence to indicate that rapid ablation is occurring. Calculations of theoretical geothermal heat flow indicate that the average melting rate at the top of the ice has probably increased during the last 50–60 years but remains low at a maximum value of *c.* 2.4 cm year^{-1} (Hanisch *et al.*, 1999).

The dam at Thulagi is considered relatively stable due to the large size of the ice body and the insulating properties of the overlying thick sediment cover. The 500 m wide dam is less vulnerable to overtopping by displacement waves than a narrow end-moraine dam. Breaching is only likely through accelerated widespread ablation or through external factors such as seismic activity. It is unlikely that the immature thermokarst development and low general ablation rates at Thulagi will have a negative impact on such an extensive ice mass in the foreseeable future.

DISCUSSION

Processes of moraine degradation

In the examples presented here, the ice-cored moraine dams were formed during stagnation of debris-covered glaciers. During periods of wastage, ice at the glacier margins may be insulated by the thick debris and can become incorporated within end-moraines to form substantial ice cores. Degradation of the moraine dam may then occur by ablation of the ice body beneath the debris cover, by localized thermokarst development within the buried ice and by slope failure in the moraine sediments.

Widespread lowering of the moraine surfaces at Hualcán and Tsho Rolpa is attributed to ablation of buried ice beneath the supraglacial debris. The resulting subsidence of the moraine surface produces characteristic hummocky topography that may be bounded by active scarps and gullies. Measured subsidence rates are of the order of 1–2 m year^{-1}. These rates are consistent with published values of ablation on debris-covered stagnating glacier ice elsewhere (e.g. Watanabe *et al.*, 1995). It is known that debris thickness and lithology type can influence ablation rate (Inoue & Yoshida, 1980; Nakawo & Young, 1981; Nakawo *et al.*, 1999), but the variation in rates does not appear significant in terms of hazard development.

The development of thermokarst features such as sinkholes helps to accelerate moraine degradation. Proto-thermokarst features are expressed as linear and circular depressions in the moraine surface (Fig. 8(a)). These occur over water- and debris-filled crevasses as interpreted from geophysical investigations. The crevasses may act as meltwater conduits that aid differential melting of the sinkholes and lead to exposure of the ice core. Once the ice is exposed to solar radiation the melting accelerates and the backwasting ice slope steepens to form a cliff (Fig. 8(b)). If ponding occurs in the sinkhole, undercutting of the ice cliff may lead to Reeh-type calving (Reeh, 1968) (Fig. 8(c)). Water from icemelt and snowmelt may also collect in

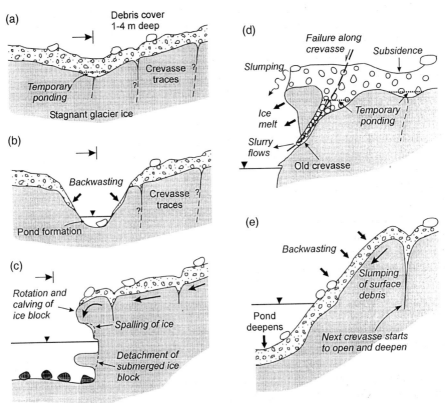

Fig. 8 Model of sinkhole formation within an ice-cored moraine dam. See text for discussion.

sub-moraine supraglacial ponds and may pass through crevasses exacerbating the degradation (Fig. 8(d)). In time, the rotating ice block fails leaving a lower angle slope that may be insulated by debris (Fig. 8(e)). Backwasting may then continue until the next set of structures within the ice is exploited mechanically. Exposed ice may disintegrate as rapidly as 22 m year^{-1} as witnessed at Tsho Rolpa. Similar degradation rates were observed at Donjek Glacier, Canada, where Johnson (1971) reported erosion of exposed ice by an average of 0.6 m per week.

Slope failures on the inner slope of a moraine dam have been observed at Tsho Rolpa adjacent to the buried ice body. It is thought that the buried ice mass beneath the lake may support the toe of sediments in the moraine ridge. As the ice mass melts, this support is removed and the moraine sediments are able to slide. Rates of movement have been inferred from time series photographs and are of the order of centimetres per year. A similar process also occurs in moraines adjacent to active glaciers (MacDonald, 1989).

Role of degradation processes in hazard development

Moraine ridges containing ice cores are potentially unstable, leading to unstable moraine-dammed lakes. Degradation causes moraine subsidence and reduces the structural integrity of the dam. Subsidence of relatively narrow end-moraine dams (e.g. Hualcán and Tsho Rolpa) leaves the dam vulnerable to overtopping by displacement waves from ice avalanches or by rising lake waters. Overtopping is one of the most common causes of historical outburst floods from moraine-dammed glacial lakes (Richardson & Reynolds, 2000). Relict glacier structures may fragment ice cores and reduce the cryostatic and lithostatic strength of the dam relative to the hydrostatic pressure of the lake. Structures within the ice core also provide possible conduits for lake water to percolate deep into the moraine core leading to the steepening of hydrostatic gradients thereby effectively reducing the width of the dam.

Dams containing thick and extensive bodies of debris-covered ice (e.g. Thulagi) are generally more stable than well-defined narrow end-moraine dams. Extensive ice bodies are less likely to be breached rapidly by the hydrostatic pressure of the lake or by erosion from displacement waves or rivers flowing over the ice and debris surface. Where ice is exposed by meltwater any downcutting will be gradual and lowering of the lake will be in a controlled manner.

CONCLUSIONS

Supraglacial lake formation on downwasting debris-covered glaciers may lead to the separation of a stagnant ice mass from the upper reaches of the glacier to form an ice-cored moraine dam. Moraine dams may subsequently degrade by: (a) ablation beneath a debris cover occurring at rates of a few centimetres to a few metres per year, (b) thermokarst development resulting in localized formation of kettle forms with subsidence rates of tens of metres per year, and (c) mass movement of the moraine sediments related to the wasting ice core and due to the saturation of sediment at the ice–moraine interface.

Relict glacier structures probably play a vital role in moraine degradation. Proto-thermokarst features may start as air- and water-filled voids at the ice–debris interface above old structures, which act as conduits for meltwater and lead to differential melting and exposure of the ice core. Degradation accelerates once the ice core has been exposed through the combined affects of solar radiation and mechanical failure due to the rheological response of the ice to deepening kettle forms.

Moraine dams containing ice cores are potentially unstable, leading to unstable moraine-dammed lakes. Degradation of the ice core causes moraine subsidence and lowers the lake freeboard, leaving narrow dams vulnerable to displacement waves from ice and/or rock avalanches into the lake. Structures within ice cores may also provide conduits for lake water to percolate deep into the moraine thereby threatening its structural integrity.

Acknowledgements The authors wish to thank Dr B. Rana (Department of Hydrology and Meteorology, His Majesty's Government of Nepal, Kathmandu) and S. Pant (Geophysical Research and Consultancy Service, Kathmandu, Nepal) for provision of the GPR (Fig. 5(a)) and electrical resistivity data (Fig. 5(b)), respectively. Thanks are also due to Eng. C. Portocarrero (Unidad de Glaciología y Recursos Hídricos, Huaraz, Peru) for Fig. 2.

REFERENCES

Clague, J. J & Evans, S. G. (1994) Formation and failure of natural dams in the Canadian Cordillera. *Geol. Soc. Can. Bull. 464.*

Clayton, L. (1964) Karst topography on stagnant glaciers. *J. Glaciol.* **5**(37), 107–112.

Hanisch, J., Delisle, G., Pokhrel, A. P., Dixit, A. M., Reynolds, J. M. & Grabs, W. E. (1998) The Thulagi glacier lake, Manaslu Himal, Nepal—hazard assessment of a potential outburst. In: *Proceedings Eighth International Congress, International Association for Engineering Geology and the Environment* (21–25 September 1998, Vancouver, Canada), 2209–2215. Balkema, Rotterdam.

Hanisch, J., Pokhrel, A. P., Dixit, A. M., Grabs, W. E. & Reynolds, J. M. (1999) GLOF mitigation strategies—lessons learnt from studying the Thulagi glacier lake, Nepal (abstract). *J. Nepal Geol. Soc.* **20**, 163.

Healy, T. R. (1975) Thermokarst—a mechanism of de-icing ice-cored moraines. *Boreas* **4**, 19–23.

Inoue, J. & Yoshida, M. (1980) Ablation and heat exchange over the Khumbu Glacier. *J. Japan. Soc. Snow Ice (Seppyo)* **42**, 26–33.

Johnson, P. G. (1971) Ice cored moraine formation and degradation, Donjek Glacier, Yukon Territory, Canada. *Geogr. Ann.* **53A**, 198–202.

Lliboutry, L., Morales, B., Pautre, A. & Schneider, B. (1977) Glaciological problems set by the control of dangerous lakes in Cordillera Blanca, Peru. I: Historical failure of morainic dams, their causes and prevention. *J. Glaciol.* **18**(79), 239–254.

MacDonald, K. I. (1989) Impacts of glacier-related landslides on the settlement at Hopar, Karakoram Himalaya. *Ann. Glaciol.* **13**, 185–188.

Modder, S. & van Olden, Q. (1996) Engineering–geomorphological analysis of a moraine dam in the Nepal Himalayas. Unpub. MSc Thesis, Free University of Amsterdam.

Mool, P. K. (1995) Glacier lake outburst floods in Nepal. *J. Nepal Geol. Soc.* **11**, 273–280.

Nakawo, M. & Young, G. J. (1981) Field experiments to determine the effect of a debris layer on ablation of glacier ice. *Ann. Glaciol.* **2**, 85–91.

Nakawo, M., Yabuki, H. & Sakai, A. (1999) Characteristics of Khumbu Glacier, Nepal Himalaya: recent change in the debris-covered area. *Ann. Glaciol.* **28**, 118–122.

Rana, B., Reynolds, J. M., Shrestha, A. B., Aryal, R., Pokhrel, A. P. & Budathoki, K. P. (1999) Tsho Rolpa, Rolwaling Himal, Nepal: a case history of ongoing glacial hazard assessment and remediation (abstract). *J. Nepal Geol. Soc.* **20**, 242.

Reeh, N. (1968) On the calving of ice from floating glaciers and ice shelves. *J. Glaciol.* **7**(50), 215–232.

Reynolds, J. M. (1992) The identification and mitigation of glacier-related hazards: examples from the Cordillera Blanca, Peru. In: *Geohazards* (ed. by G. J. H. McCall, D. J. C. Laming & S. C. Scott), 143–157. Chapman and Hall, London.

Reynolds, J. M. (1998) High-altitude glacial lake hazard assessment and mitigation: a Himalayan perspective. In: *Geohazards in Engineering Geology* (ed. by J. G. Maund & M. Eddleston), 25–34. Geological Society, London, Engineering Geology Special Publ. no. 15.

Reynolds, J. M., Dolecki, A. & Portocarrero, C. (1998) Construction of a drainage tunnel as part of glacial lake hazard mitigation at Hualcán, Cordillera Blanca, Peru. In: *Geohazards in Engineering Geology* (ed. by J. G. Maund & M. Eddleston), 41–48. Geological Society, London, Engineering Geology Special Publ. no. 15.

Richardson, S. D. & Reynolds, J. M. (2000) An overview of glacial hazards in the Himalayas. *Quatern. International* **65/66**, 31–47.

Watanabe, T., Kameyama, S. & Sato, T. (1995) Imja Glacier dead-ice melt rates and changes in a supraglacial lake, 1989–1994, Khumbu Himal, Nepal: danger of lake drainage. *Mountain Res. Develop.* **15**(4), 293–300.

Debris-Covered Glaciers (Proceedings of a workshop held at Seattle, Washington, USA, September 2000). IAHS Publ. no. 264, 2000.

Drainage of a glacial lake through an ice spillway

CHARLES F. RAYMOND

University of Washington, Geophysics Program, Box 351650, Seattle, Washington 98195-1650, USA

e-mail: charlie@geophys.washington.edu

MATT NOLAN

University of Alaska Fairbanks, Institute of Northern Engineering, Fairbanks, Alaska 99775-5860, USA

Abstract Debris cover on glacier surfaces forms topography that can trap water in surface lakes. Such lakes may overflow and drain by melting a gorge through a low point in the ice barrier. If the spillway elevation melts downward faster than the lake level drops, a rapid (unstable) discharge results. We show that unstable discharge will occur when the area of the lake exceeds a critical area evaluated in terms of the slope and width of the channel through the ice dam and the temperature of the water in the lake. If the lake water is at the freezing point, the critical area is large (order 1 km² or more) for typical slopes (order 0.1 or less) and unstable drainage is unlikely. Modest warming of the lake water (order 1°C) can reduce the critical area significantly and promote unstable drainage. The filling of depressions and subsequent drainage, whether fast or slow, is one mode of water storage change on a glacier that affects the timing of runoff. These theoretical concepts are used to explain observations from Black Rapids Glacier, Alaska, where a marginal lake drained through a lateral moraine onto the surface of the glacier with an initial unstable phase lasting about one day followed by a stable multi-day gradual drainage.

INTRODUCTION

Lakes impounded behind ice barriers can drain in a variety ways. Most well known are glacier outbursts (jökulhlaups) that are associated with catastrophic drainage of lakes by rapid thermal enlargement of subsurface tunnels. This phenomenon has been examined extensively through observations and theory (Björnsson, 1974; Nye, 1976; Clarke, 1982; Spring & Hutter, 1981; Björnsson, 1992). Ice-dammed lakes sometimes drain by mechanical collapse of the ice dam. Discharge through gaps between the wall of the enclosing valley and the ice can accelerate by sideward back melting and calving of the ice to increase the width of the channel (Walder & Costa, 1996).

Lakes often form in depressions on the irregular surface of debris-covered glaciers. Commonly, such lakes do not drain through pressurized tunnels or marginal moats, but instead drain over an ice floored spillway either on the ice surface or in a partially filled, near-surface tunnel. Ice cored moraine may also dam lakes that drain over spillways. This paper explores the potential for rapid, unstable discharges from a lake, when the lake overflows a spillway and the discharge water melts the floor of the spillway downward faster than the level of the lake drops. We also examine stable drainage of such lakes, when the spillway floor and lake level drop more or less in unison. Both the unstable and stable modes of drainage are of interest with regard to the evolution of surface water storage.

We illustrate features associated with drainage over a spillway with data from a marginal lake on the Black Rapids Glacier, Alaska. This lake drained with both unstable and stable phases through a gorge that was deepened by the discharge water.

DRAINAGE OF A LAKE ON BLACK RAPIDS GLACIER

We observed the 1993 drainage of a lake (latitude 63°29.5′N, longitude 146°31.0′W) on the north margin of the Black Rapids Glacier. The lake forms just upstream from the tributary entering from the east side of Aurora Peak (Fig. 1). We refer to this lake as "Aurora Lake". The depression that contained the lake was formed by a combination of factors associated with dynamic thickening of the trunk/tributary junction and with differential melting caused by debris cover and proximity to the rock slopes of the valley. Outburst-like discharges from this lake onto the ice surface have been observed on several occasions (Sturm & Cosgrove, 1990).

Discharge started sometime on 13 June 1993. At this time the surface of the glacier was still covered with a snow thickness of about 1 m. The lake had ice and snow slush floating in it. The water released from the lake ran several hundred metres through an ice gorge breaching the ice dam into a number of snow-bounded channels. Some of these channels were ice floored and flowed about 1 km downslope from the lake before dissipating into the snow or descending into the glacier. Figure 1 gives an over view of the lake and gorge.

The exact timing of the onset of drainage and the peak discharge are not known directly from observation. The drainage started to affect the speed of the glacier during

Fig. 1 View looking south across the eastern part of Aurora Lake and Black Rapids Glacier before the drainage started. Note the pre-existing gorge though which drainage occurred. "Pot holes" in the background are related to the drainage of other lakes (Sturm & Cosgrove, 1990).

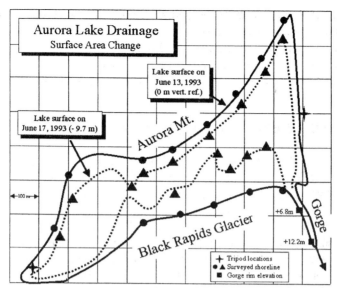

Fig. 2 Map of shorelines of Aurora Lake in local coordinates on 13 and 17 June 1993.

the night of 13–14 June (Nolan & Echelmeyer, 1999). Flooding of the surface suggested a peak discharge about midday on 14 June. At 17:00 h on 14 June the discharge in the main downslope drainage path below the gorge was roughly 12 m³ s⁻¹, but this may not account for possible drainage in other smaller streams beneath the snow cover. The discharge from the lake was distinctly higher at sometime before 17:00 h as evidenced by high water lines in the channels cut in the snow.

On the afternoon of 17 June we surveyed the shoreline of the remaining lake and the initial high shoreline of 13 June marked in the snow (Fig. 2). The survey shows that the initial area of the lake was 0.15 km². By 17 June the lake level had dropped 9.6 m and the area was reduced to 0.07 km² or about half the initial area. The lake was long and narrow with relatively uniformly sloped side banks. Therefore, we assume a linear relationship between lake area A_l and lake surface elevation h_l (Fig. 3) given by $A_l(h_l) = 0.80 \times 10^4 \, h_l$, where $h_l = 0$ m, 9.2 m and 18.8 m are respectively the bottom of the lake, the surface on 17 June and the surface on 13 June. The implied volume released from 13 to 17 June was 1.1×10^6 m³.

Figure 4 shows the gorge through which water was discharged from the lake. A sequence of water levels is clearly marked on the walls of the gorge. On 22 June at

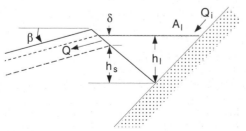

Fig. 3 Descriptive cross-section of lake and spillway.

Fig. 4 View looking into the gorge that formed the spillway for Aurora Lake. Note the series of water levels cut in the walls of the gorge.

18:00 h we measured the elevations of the water level marks. The number of levels corresponded to the number of days since the peak of discharge on 14 June. Subsequent visits to the gorge showed the creation of one new level mark each day. The measurements, therefore, enable the reconstruction of the history of the lake level and corresponding discharge on a daily basis (Fig. 5). Most of the water stored in the lake prior to 13 June was released rapidly in a 2-day interval. Subsequently water was released from the lake much more slowly at a relatively steady rate.

SPILLWAY MODEL

Figure 3 defines variables associated with an idealized geometry of a lake and spillway that forms the basis for the following analysis. The following relationships are introduced to predict the time evolution of drainage through the spillway.

Lake geometry relates height h_l of the lake surface to the lake volume V_l:

$$\frac{dV_l}{dt} = A_l(h_l)\frac{dh_l}{dt} \tag{1}$$

where A_l is the area of the lake surface.

Water volume conservation relates spillway discharge Q_s to change in storage in the lake and in flow rate Q_i:

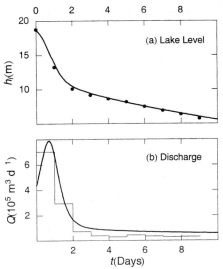

Fig. 5 History of water level (a) and rate of volume loss (b) for the lake. Data points in (a) and step plot in (b) show observations from Aurora Lake. Curves show the simulations described in the text.

$$Q_s = -\frac{dV_l}{dt} + Q_i \tag{2}$$

Hydraulics of the spillway relates Q_s, the lake level h_l relative to the spillway threshold h_s, width W_s and channel slope β:

$$Q_s = k\beta^{1/2}W_s(h_l - h_s)^{5/3}, \qquad h_l > h_s \tag{3}$$

where k is a channel discharge parameter depending on the roughness n and channel cross-section shape. Equation (3) corresponds to standard theory for steady open channel flow with $k = 1/n$ when the channel width is much larger than the water depth $\delta = h_l - h_s$. When $h_l < h_s$ there is no drainage from the lake ($Q_s = 0$). If the spillway were very steep or the width of the flow were not constrained down-flow from a breach, then the discharge would be limited by a transition to critical flow very close to the lake (e.g. Walder & Costa, 1996). Those conditions give a somewhat different flow relation with slightly different power (3/2 instead of 5/3) and substantially higher discharge unless β is quite large in equation (3). Because of the substantial length (~1 km) and modest slope (~0.1) of the gorge, it is appropriate to assume in this case that the flow is limited by the discharge through the channel.

Energy conservation relates melting of the spillway floor to the energy loss in the water flow:

$$\rho_i L W_s \frac{dh_s}{dt} = \left(\rho_w C_w \frac{d\theta}{ds} - \rho_w g\beta\right)Q_s = \rho_w g(\beta + \gamma)Q_s \tag{4}$$

ρ_i and ρ_w are densities of ice and water respectively; L is the latent heat of fusion per unit mass; C_w is the heat capacity per unit mass of water; $d\theta/ds$ is the change in water temperature per unit distance s along the spillway. To simplify the expression of equation (4), we introduce $\gamma \equiv (C_w d\theta/ds)/g \approx C_w \Delta\theta/gl$ and regard $d\theta/ds$ as an input approximated by the temperature of the lake water above freezing $\Delta\theta$ divided by the distance l along the spillway over which the temperature drops to freezing. To determine the actual temperature of the water in the spillway would require introduction of a heat transfer equation. We instead assume that the potential energy conversion to heat and thermal energy relative to the melting point are transferred to the ice floor of the spillway uniformly over its length according to the average slope and rate of water cooling.

Inputs to these four equations are $A_l(h)$, β, γ, W_s, k and Q_i. They can be solved for the four unknowns $h_l(t)$, $h_s(t)$, $Q_s(t)$ and $V_l(t)$.

It is useful to focus first on $h_l(t)$ and $h_s(t)$. Substitution of equation (3) into equation (4) gives:

$$\frac{dh_s}{dt} = -\frac{\rho_w g k \beta^{\frac{1}{2}}}{\rho_i L}(\beta + \gamma)(h_l - h_s)^{\frac{5}{3}} \tag{5}$$

Substitution of equations (2) and (3) into equation (1) to eliminate $Q_s(t)$ and $V_l(t)$ gives:

$$\frac{dh_l}{dt} = -\frac{k\beta^{\frac{1}{2}}W_s}{A_l(h_l)}(h_l - h_s)^{\frac{5}{3}} + \frac{Q_i}{A_l(h_l)} \tag{6}$$

The condition for unstable drainage is that the spillway elevation drops faster than the lake elevation ($dh_s/dt < dh_l/dt$ accounting for the signs of dh/dt). When inflow Q_i is neglected, equations (5) and (6) show that this condition holds when:

$$\frac{A_l(\beta + \gamma)}{W_s} > \frac{\rho_i L}{\rho_w g} \equiv H^* \tag{7}$$

The quantity $H^* = 3.0 \times 10^4$ m is the distance that a piece of ice at the melting point must fall under Earth's gravity g such that the potential energy loss is sufficient to melt the ice. It follows from equation (7) that unstable drainage requires that the lake area at the height of the spillway exceed a critical area A_0 given by:

$$A_0 \equiv \frac{H^* W_s}{\beta + \gamma} = \frac{\rho_i L W_s}{\rho_w g (\beta + \gamma)} \tag{8}$$

To further illustrate the stable vs unstable behaviour of this system, it is useful to consider explicitly the height difference $\delta = h_l - h_s$ that controls the discharge. Subtraction of equation (5) from equation (6) gives:

$$\frac{d\delta}{dt} \equiv k\beta^{\frac{1}{2}}W_s\left(\frac{1}{A_0} - \frac{1}{A_l(h_l)}\right)\delta^m + \frac{Q_i}{A_l(h_l)} \tag{9}$$

This equation shows that δ grows in a semi-exponential fashion when $A_l(h_l) > A_0$. When $A_l(h_l) < A_0$, then δ declines in a semi-exponential fashion. A time independent δ and corresponding discharge can be achieved when $d\delta/dt = 0$, which occurs when $\delta = [Q_i A_0/k\beta^{\frac{1}{2}}W_s(A_0 - A_l)]^{3/5}$ and $dh_l/dt = dh_s/dt = Q_i/(A_0 - A_l)$.

To examine the theoretical behaviour more generally it is useful to introduce the additional scales: height H, such that $A_l(H) = A_0$; time $T = A_0/(k\beta^{\frac{1}{2}}W_s H^{5/3})$; discharge

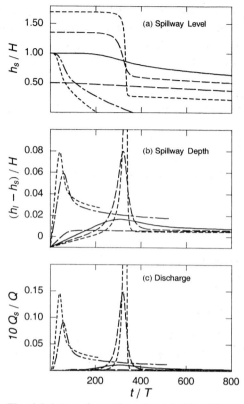

Fig. 6 Solutions for spillway level h_s (a), spillway depth $h_l - h_s$ (b) and discharge Q_s (c) displayed in dimensionless form using scales described in the text. A linear relation between lake area and lake surface height is assumed. Four initial spillway heights $h_s = 0.5H$ (long dashes), $h_s = 1.0H$ (solid), $h_s = 1.35H$ (intermediate dashes) and $h_s = 1.7H$ (short dashes) are considered, all starting with lake level 0.01 below the spillway and with dimensionless input flux 10^{-4}. Dimensionless input fluxes of 0.0014 (long-short dashes) and 0.0025 (short dashes) are also calculated for the case of initial $h_s = 1.0H$.

rate $Q = HA_0/T$. For example, with a channel slope of $\beta = 0.1$, freezing lake water ($\gamma = 0$) and a spillway width $W_s = 3$ m, the critical lake area A_0 is 9×10^5 m^2 (about 1 km^2). If the lake water is warm ($\gamma > 0$), then A_0 is smaller. Typical values for the other scales are H order 10 m, T order a few minutes and Q order 10^4 m^3 s^{-1}. These scales are used to display solutions to equations (5) and (6) for h_l, h_s and Q_s.

Figure 6 shows situations where the initial height of the spillway corresponds to a lake area that is more or less than A_0 (equation (8)). These solutions are started at $t = 0$ with a lake level $0.01H$ below the spillway. The drainage is started by a constant inflow Q_i that gradually raises the lake level above the spillway height. When the lake area is above critical, there is an initial acceleration of discharge associated with down melting of the spillway faster than the lake surface drops. When the lake area is smaller than critical, a gradual lowering of the spillway releases water from the lake, which augments the input discharge. When the lake area is close to critical, the behaviour is sensitive to the input; high input rate tends to cause initial instability.

INTERPRETATION OF OBSERVATIONS

We now examine the characteristics of the lake drainage observed on the Black Rapids Glacier using the theoretical model for spillway evolution. We use $A_l(h_l) = 0.80 \times 10^4$ h_l m, $W_s = 3$ m and an initial lake level $h_l = 18.8$ m as inputs that are relatively well known from observations. Since β, γ, Q_i and initial h_s were not well known from observations, we adjusted them to produce a fit with the observations of lake level *vs* time (Fig. 5). The curves shown in Fig. 5 show the model prediction with $\beta = 0.06$, $\gamma = 0.63$, $W_s = 3$ m, $k = 1/n = 10$, $Q_i = 0.38 \times 10^5$ m^3 day^{-1} and initial $h_s = 18.0$ m. The gradual steady drop in lake level during the later part of the observation period is controlled primarily by the combination of $(\beta + \gamma)Q_i$. The amount of lake level drop in the initial phases is controlled primarily by $(\beta + \gamma)$ in combination with the known lake area. The combination of $k\beta^{1/2}$ controls the time scale for the initial phase. Through these rather distinct controls the measurements appear to constrain the input variables quite closely. The values for these parameters imposed by the fit are quite reasonable in terms of independent information on the slope of the spillway and expected roughness of an ice channel. Starting the simulation with an initial spillway level equal to the initial lake level about 2 days prior to the peak of the discharge also can fit the known lake level data. However, it is also possible and probably more likely that the pre-existing gorge was locally blocked with snow that failed and was quickly blown out of the gorge thus suddenly exposing its ice base to a fairly thick water flow.

The large value of γ (0.63) in comparison to β (0.06) indicates that the thermal energy stored in the lake played a dominant role in the lowering of the spillway height by melting. This conclusion is forced by the continued lowering of the spillway with a rather low discharge of water and small rate of potential energy release. The value of γ = 0.63 is produced with a lake temperature $\Delta\theta$ about 0.7°C above freezing and a drop to freezing over about 500 m. The combined value of $\beta + \gamma = 0.7$ gives a critical lake level of $A_0 = 1.3 \times 10^5$ m^2 (equation (8)), which is slightly less than the initial lake area at the onset of discharge. If the lake water had not been warmed above freezing, then A_0 would have been much larger and the unstable discharge would not have happened.

DISCUSSION

Although the model is simplified, its success in simulating the Black Rapids Glacier lake drainage suggests its basic physical foundations are applicable. One may, therefore, expect a range of potential behaviour as illustrated in Fig. 6. A question that arises more generally is what determines the input variables. The lake area in comparison to A_0 is a crucial factor. The area of basins that can trap water on a glacier will be related in some way to characteristics of the debris cover among other things. A_0 itself depends on the channel width W_s, the spillway slope β, and the lake temperature $\Delta\theta$ (equation (8)). All of these variables could be quite different from one circumstance to another depending on the shape of the ice barrier, the surface slope of the glacier and heat balance history of the lake. A steep spillway slope lowers A_0, but it is less likely to have large lakes on steep slopes. Thus, we expect that warming a lake and resultant lowering of A_0 is crucial for unstable drainage in most circumstances.

Lakes can become very warm (several degrees Celsius) when they are floored by debris (Sakai *et al.*, 2000).

Most lakes and ponds formed on glacier surfaces will be too small and cold to drain unstably. Nevertheless they comprise one mode of liquid water storage. They will reduce runoff in comparison to melt as they are filling during the early melt season. Later they will enhance runoff as they overflow and spillways are melting downward.

Seasonal snow may play an important role in the early melt season drainage of these lakes and can result in rapid unstable discharges, and should be an important consideration in the analysis of outburst hazard.

Acknowledgement This research was supported by National Science Foundation Grants no. OPP9122540 and no. OPP-9122783.

REFERENCES

Björnsson, H. (1974) The explanation of jökulhlaups from Grímsvötn, Vatnajökull, Iceland. *Jökull* **24**, 1–26.

Björnsson, H. (1992) Jökulhlaups in Iceland: prediction, characteristics and simulation. *Ann. Glaciol.* **16**, 95–106.

Clarke, G. K. C. (1982) Glacier outburst flood from "Hazard Lake", Yukon Territory, and the problem of flood magnitude prediction. *J. Glaciol.* **28**(98), 3–21.

Nolan, M. & Echelmeyer, K. (1999) Seismic detection of transient changes beneath Black Rapids Glacier, Alaska, USA: I. Techniques and observations. *J. Glaciol.* **45**(149), 119–131.

Nye, J. F. (1976) Water flow in glaciers: jökulhlaups, tunnels and veins. *J. Glaciol.* **17**(76) 181–207.

Sakai, A., Takeuchi, N., Fujita, K. & Nakawo, M. (2000) Role of supraglacial ponds in the ablation process of a debris-covered glacier in the Nepal Himalayas. In: *Debris-Covered Glaciers* (ed. by M. Nakawo, C. F. Raymond & A. Fountain) (Proc. Seattle Workshop, September 2000). IAHS Publ. no. 264 (this volume).

Spring, U. & Hutter, K. (1981) Numerical studies of Jökulhlaups. *Cold Regions Sci. Technol.* **4**, 221–244.

Sturm, M. & Cosgrove, D. M. (1990) Correspondence. An unusual jökulhlaup involving potholes on Black Rapids Glacier, Alaska Range, Alaska. *J. Glaciol.* **36**(122), 125–126.

Walder, J. S. & Costa, J. E. (1996) Outburst floods from glacier-dammed lakes; the effect of mode of lake drainage on flood magnitude. *Earth Surf. Processes and Landforms* **21**(8), 701–723.

5 Climate Variations

Debris-Covered Glaciers (Proceedings of a workshop held at Seattle, Washington, USA, September 2000).
IAHS Publ. no. 264, 2000.

Ice-marginal geomorphology and Holocene expansion of debris-covered Tasman Glacier, New Zealand

MARTIN P. KIRKBRIDE

Department of Geography, University of Dundee, Dundee DD1 4HN, UK
e-mail: m.p.kirkbride@dundee.ac.uk

Abstract The Neoglacial evolution of the Tasman Glacier is reconstructed from the distribution of ice-marginal moraines and from the subglacial topography. The glacier has overridden its margins, creating two shelves of thin ice by *c.* 3700 years before present (BP) and *c.* 2000 years BP. The proglacial foreland is dominated by outwash aggradation and lacks pre-nineteenth century terminal moraines. The glacier has experienced successively larger expansions over the Neoglacial period (*c.* 5000 years), prior to drastic twentieth-century thinning and retreat. Over the same period, uncovered glaciers have shown progressively smaller re-advances. The expansionary tendency of the debris-covered glacier is interpreted as a response to long-term (millennial) accumulation of both subglacial and supraglacial debris. Subglacial aggradation has probably raised the bed of the glacier, promoting debris cover growth and reducing ablation even as less favourable balance regimes developed. Comparison with other glaciers shows that the expansionary tendency is widespread but may be manifest in a variety of sediment-landform associations.

INTRODUCTION

Supraglacial debris covers reverse the ablation gradient and reduce the equilibrium accumulation area ratio, and covered glaciers are often associated with elevated subglacial beds. The longer-term glaciological effects are obscure, yet are important for understanding the climatic significance of dated moraines (Kirkbride & Brazier, 1998), the survival of low-altitude ice tongues, and the evolution of their outwash plains. This paper interprets Neoglacial ice-marginal environments of Tasman Glacier in terms of changes to the 20 km^2 debris-covered ablation area. Fluctuations of uncovered glaciers in the region provide a control sample. The aim is to understand how a persistent debris cover has influenced the magnitude of terminus fluctuations and the style of ice-marginal sedimentation over a period of multiple mass-balance cycles.

ICE-MARGINAL GEOMORPHOLOGY

A schematic view of the lower Tasman Glacier (Fig. 1) has been made from available topographic, velocity and geophysical surveys, and from dated moraines. In Fig. 1, inset sections are based on field observations and interpretation of geophysical profiles.

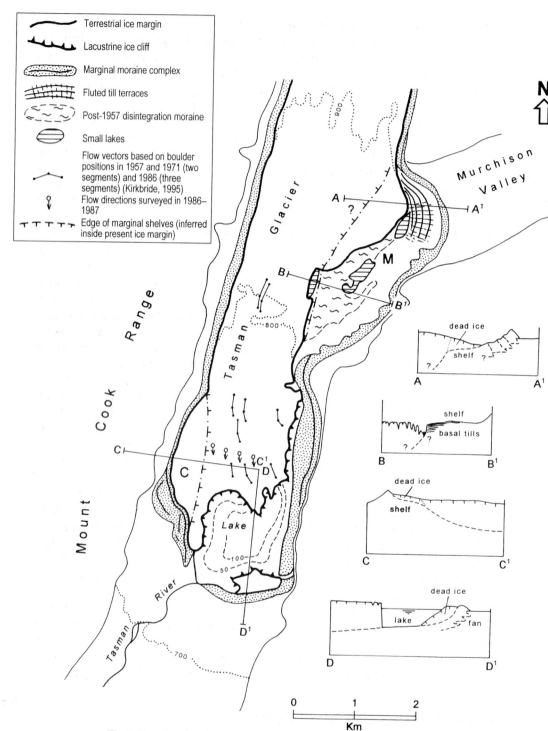

Fig. 1 Map showing the spatial relationships between the present Tasman Glacier and ice-marginal sediment-landform associations, compiled from various sources (see text). Lake bathymetry from Hochstein *et al.* (1995). Inset sections based on 1:50 000 NZMS 260 topomap, with 2.5× vertical exaggeration.

The glacier occupies a trough in the centre of the valley, bounded along the margins by lateral moraines, beneath by subglacial till, and in the proglacial foreland by fluvioglacial sediments. The continuity of the lateral moraines is disrupted at two embayments, informally named the Murchison embayment (M in Fig. 1) and the Celmisia embayment (C in Fig. 1). Within each, surviving ice is thin and stagnant, and appears detached by shear zones from ice in the central trough.

The Murchison embayment has been deglaciated since 1957 aerial photography, revealing to its north end a flight of three fluted, till-mantled benches, and to the south chaotic disintegration moraine (Kirkbride, 1995). Recently deposited tills in the southern area are couplets of a basal melt-out till overlain by supraglacial melt-out till, apparently laid down by post-1957 stagnant-ice wastage. In the northern area where flutes ornament the till surface, deglaciation involved active retreat of mobile ice. The embayment forms a shelf distal to the central trough, created by Tasman ice invading the mouth of the tributary Murchison Valley. The inner shelf edge forms a 40 m cliff of stratified lodgement and basal melt-out tills above a marginal lake (section B–B[1]), interpreted as evidence of mobilization/stagnation cycles as the invasive ice thickened and thinned repeatedly. The till benches are interpreted as former lateral moraines behind which aggradation of the Murchison River raised the sandur surface as the Tasman Glacier encroached into the Murchison Valley (see section A–A[1] for interpreted facies structure). Each terrace connects to the north with a bouldery horizon within the lateral moraine, dated by Gellatly *et al.* (1985). Their dates demonstrate moraine building over about the last 3700 ^{14}C years, culminating in the late nineteenth century before drastic thinning of the main glacier. Lateral correlation with the till terraces implies construction of lateral moraines at roughly 3700, 3300, 1600 and <1000 years before present (BP), each being overridden to form a terrace by successive advances until *c.* 100 years BP.

Celmisia embayment (C in Fig. 1) is comparable in form to the Murchison embayment, but remains ice-filled. Velocity surveys up to 1986 detected no significant ice motion (Kirkbride, 1995), and radar survey places the shelf edge beneath the present glacier (section C–C[1]) (Hochstein *et al.*, 1995). Weathering-rind dating of lateral moraines provides a minimum age for formation of the embayment of 2160 ± 562 years BP (Gellatly, 1984). The form indicates overfilling of the main trough by Tasman Glacier, causing a thin ice lobe to extend beyond the former glacier margin.

The glacier terminus is an outwash head, in which nearly all the debris from the glacier has been redistributed to form the proglacial fan at the expense of moraine construction. No moraines lie beyond the AD 1890 terminus, from which retreat has only recently begun (section D–D[1]). The new proglacial lake is ponded by the ice-contact slope of the outwash head, and in 1995 reached >130 m depth (Hochstein *et al.*, 1995). Moraines are preserved only in a latero-frontal position, and are dated to post 1490 ± 387 years BP (Gellatly, 1984). The terminus environment is one of aggradation of moraines and outwash around the sluggish glacier tongue, which reached its maximum Neoglacial length *c.* AD 1890, but which has oscillated close to this limit for about 1500–2000 years.

MODEL OF NEOGLACIAL EVOLUTION

Evidence for long-term expansion of Tasman Glacier contrasts with chronologies of uncovered glaciers in the region, whose early Neoglacial moraines (*c.* 4000–4500 years BP) lie up to 3.0 km downvalley of the late-nineteenth century ice margins (Wardle, 1973). Samples of 26 uncovered and seven debris-covered glaciers show that the distance between early Neoglacial and late-nineteenth century moraines is less at debris-covered glaciers with a 0.01 significance level. It is proposed that the presence of the debris cover is primarily responsible for these long-term contrasts in climatic response.

If Tasman Glacier has expanded over millennia, coeval with shrinkage of uncovered glaciers, not only is a debris cover necessary to reduce ablation but the cover must itself have expanded. In periods of positive mass balance, faster ice flow and lower bare-ice ablation (*transport-dominant* conditions) cause the cover to contract towards the terminus. Under negative balance, reduced flow and increased ablation (*ablation-dominant* conditions) favour the upstream spread of the debris cover. If, over multiple balance cycles, the covered area oscillates about an "average" state, the glacier would not expand. Therefore, the increase in debris cover under negative balance must have exceeded its shrinkage under positive balance: there must have been a long-term accumulation of supraglacial debris.

Expansion over millennia implies that ablation under the debris cover was not just reduced below that of uncovered ice, but continued to decrease even though the climate became less favourable for glacier survival at low altitudes (as evinced by the retreats of uncovered glaciers). Declining ablation would be achieved by thickening and extension of the debris cover, in turn reflecting some combination of continued addition to the base of the debris cover by englacial melt-out; by strain thickening under longitudinal compression, and by upglacier growth of the cover as englacial particle paths are re-oriented in the evolving glacier tongue (Kirkbride & Warren, 1999). Over multiple mass balance cycles, debris cover growth would be reversed under transport-dominant conditions, and enhanced during ablation-dominant conditions: but over time the effects of growth would exceed those of shrinkage as the glacier itself became longer, gentler and less sensitive to mass balance perturbations.

The model is illustrated in Fig. 2. Growth of the debris cover is related to oscillating transport- and ablation-dominant conditions (Fig. 2(a)). An initial wedge-shaped form (unit 1) is shortened by faster flow, and bare ice extends further downglacier until flow decelerates. Melt-out of englacial debris (unit 2) replaces older debris-cover material which has been transported downstream (unit 1). A return to transport-dominance accretes unit 2 to the thickening debris wedge near the terminus. The process repeats over multiple cycles (units 3–5 *et seq.*), but over time the supraglacial load near the terminus increases as long as marginal deposition is exceeded by additions to the base and upstream edge of the debris layer. The ablational effect will be to lengthen the glacier tongue and reduce surface gradient, promoting further supraglacial debris accumulation. A parallel interpretation is that, if equilibrium mass balance were maintained throughout, long-term supraglacial debris accumulation would cause glacier volume to increase.

Subglacial bed aggradation might also have contributed to a long-term reduction in glacier gradient and increased length, by elevating the glacier bed and inducing a positive mass balance/altitude feedback. Elevated beds are apparent from the morphology of many moraine-dammed glaciers, and have been revealed elsewhere by geophysical surveys (Lliboutry, 1977). Geophysical surveys have shown that the lower

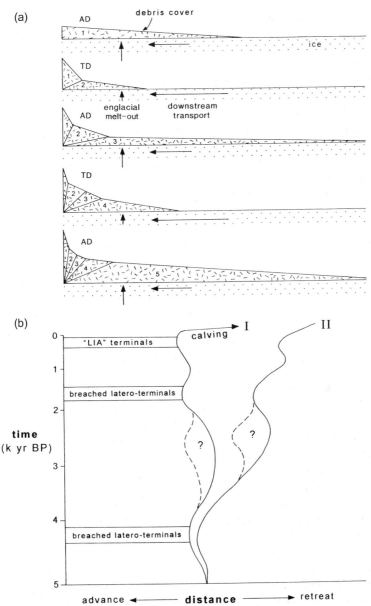

Fig. 2 Schematic evolution of a debris-cover tongue over multiple mass-balance cycles, showing net debris accumulation and glacier expansion.

(a) Incremental accretion to the debris cover under oscillating transport- and ablation-dominance (TD and (AD). Most debris (odd-numbered increments) melts out when mass balance is negative and ablation enhanced, then is accreted to the debris cover by higher ice velocities during positive balance (transport-dominant) phases. The resultant debris cover grows over time, and thickens increasingly towards the terminus. As long as low terminus velocities mean that losses by ice-marginal deposition are exceeded by additions to the debris cover, a lengthening glacier will increasingly favour long-term accumulation.

(b) Comparative distance–time paths for length variations and moraine spacing for debris-covered (line I) and uncovered (II) glaciers. Timing of major advance–retreat phases are tentatively based on published chronologies.

10 km of Tasman Glacier rests on a debris bed of unknown thickness (Broadbent, 1973). For a moraine-dammed glacier to remain constrained by its lateral moraines, the moraine crests must build at least as rapidly as basal aggradation elevates the bed. By implication, long-term thickening of the glacier probably occurs, associated with the supraglacial processes outlined by the model and promoted by the reduced surface gradient of the elevated tongue.

The expansionary model concords with the simplified interpretation of Neoglacial length variations for covered and uncovered glaciers (Fig. 2(b)), whose responses to millennial-scale climate perturbations may follow a similar temporal pattern, but produce the contrasting pattern of moraine spacing.

EVIDENCE FOR EXPANSION OF OTHER DEBRIS-COVERED GLACIERS

It is instructive to examine the margins of debris-covered glaciers in other climatic regions to see whether the expansionary model based on Tasman Glacier has wider applicability. Three types of debris-covered glacier terminus are recognized as evidence of a long-term expansion: (a) outwash heads, exemplified by Tasman Glacier and found in other maritime regions where large glaciers terminate in wide, gentle valleys (e.g. Alaska); (b) elevated, moraine-dammed glaciers exemplified by Hatunraju, Peru (Lliboutry, 1977), and widespread in the Himalaya-Karakoram chain and elsewhere; (c) ice-cored rock glaciers such as Nautardalur, Iceland (Whalley *et al.*, 1995), occurring widely throughout drier alpine areas. The nature of the dynamic differences between types is not fully known, but types will be separated by thresholds related to the competence of outwash to evacuate sediment from the glacier margin (a function of catchment size and climate), and to the ability of the expanding glacier to override its marginal moraines. The first threshold distinguishes the outwash-head type from the other two. The second threshold separates the rock glacier lobe (at which the marginal apron of sediment is being continually overridden) from the moraine-dammed glacier (at which marginal deposition has constructed an obstacle against further expansion). In the latter case, the expansion is accommodated by localized breaching of the moraine dam and formation of overspill lobes. Complex multi-lobed termini can evolve from the basic type. Such lobes are the morphological equivalents in drier areas of the shelf embayments at Tasman Glacier.

The fundamental dynamic of long-term supraglacial debris-cover growth causing glacier expansion appears to be widespread. The main influence on many ice-marginal sediment-landform assemblages appears to have been the dynamics of the individual glaciers rather than climate oscillations in the later Holocene. Individual glaciers express their expansionary tendency as different morphological outcomes, depending on the nature of the linkage between glacial and proglacial sediment transport and moraine construction. Future research should uncover the complex responses of such glaciers within the framework of Holocene climate change.

REFERENCES

Broadbent, M. (1973) A preliminary report on seismic and gravity surveys on the Tasman Glacier, 1971–2. *Geophysics Division, DSIR, Wellington, K/6/2/1*.

Gellatly, A. F. (1984) The use of rock weathering-rind thickness to redate moraines in Mount Cook National Park, New Zealand. *Arctic Alpine Res.* **16**, 225–232.

Gellatly, A. F., Röthlisberger, F. & Geyh, M. A. (1985) Holocene glacier variations in New Zealand (South Island). *Z. Gletscherk. und Glazialgeol.* **21**, 265–273.

Hochstein, M. P., Claridge, D., Henrys, S. A., Pyne, A., Nobes, D. C. & Leary, S. (1995) Downwasting of the Tasman Glacier, South Island, New Zealand: changes in the terminus region between 1971 and 1993. *NZ J. Geol. Geophys.* **38**, 1–16.

Kirkbride, M. (1995) Ice flow vectors on the debris-mantled Tasman Glacier, 1957–1986. *Geogr. Ann.* **77A**, 147–157.

Kirkbride, M. P. & Brazier, V. (1998) A critical evaluation of the use of glacial chronologies in climatic reconstruction, with reference to New Zealand. *Quatern. Proc.* **6**, 55–64.

Kirkbride, M. P. & Warren, C. R. (1999) Tasman Glacier, New Zealand: 20th century thinning and predicted calving retreat. *Global Plan. Change* **22**, 11–28.

Lliboutry, L. (1977) Glaciological problems set by the control of dangerous lakes in the Cordillera Blanca, Peru. II. Movement of a covered glacier embedded within a rock glacier. *J. Glaciol.* **18**, 255–273.

Wardle, P. (1973) Variations of glaciers in Westland National Park and the Hooker Range, New Zealand. *NZ J. Bot.* **11**, 349–388.

Whalley, W. B., Hamilton, S. J., Palmer, C. F., Gordon, J. E. & Martin, H. E. (1995) The dynamics of rock glaciers: data from Tröllaskagi, north Iceland. In: *Steepland Geomorphology* (ed. by O. Slaymaker), 129–145. John Wiley, Chichester, UK.

Debris-Covered Glaciers (Proceedings of a workshop held at Seattle, Washington, USA, September 2000).
IAHS Publ. no. 264, 2000.

Twentieth century surface elevation change of the Miage Glacier, Italian Alps

M. H. THOMSON, M. P. KIRKBRIDE & B. W. BROCK

Department of Geography, University of Dundee, Dundee DD1 4HN, UK
e-mail: m.h.thomson@dundee.ac.uk

Abstract The 5 km debris-covered tongue of Miage Glacier has been studied to explore the effect of the debris cover on patterns of thickness change over an 86-year period (1913–1999). Changes in surface elevation and volume for four intervals of eight to 44 years' duration have been calculated from comparisons of digital terrain models (DTMs) derived from cartographic and topographic surveys. Thickness changes over successive periods show that parts of the ablation zone have thickened while other parts have thinned or maintained stable elevations. Zones of thickening migrated downstream to cause small advances of the terminus on two occasions. In contrast to nearby uncovered glaciers, Miage Glacier increased in volume over the entire period. Our results indicate that decadal-scale thickness changes are forced primarily by mass flux perturbations in synchrony with uncovered glaciers, and not by debris-mantle insulation. Century-scale volume and thickness changes differ from uncovered glaciers, due to the conservation of ice beneath the debris cover during prolonged periods of thinning.

INTRODUCTION

In contrast to "clean" glaciers, the response of debris-covered glaciers to climatic variation is commonly delayed, subdued and given topographic expression by thickening and thinning rather than by terminus advance and retreat, because reduced ablation beneath the debris cover allows "extended" ablation zones to evolve (Kirkbride & Warren, 1999). Changes to debris-covered glaciers over several decades have generally been measured during negative balance periods, and have involved comparison of only two surveys from which calculated average rates of change (of thickness, ablation, velocity) suggest steady, uniform evolution and an attenuated climatic response (e.g. Kirkbride & Warren, 1999; Nakawo *et al.*, 1999).

This paper traces changes to the surface elevation of the Miage Glacier, Italian Alps, using digital terrain models (DTMs) derived from five maps produced at eight to 44 year intervals between 1913 and 1999. The aim is to compare century-scale "average" rates of change to ice thickness with approximately decadal spatial and temporal patterns measured over several mass balance cycles, as far as historical data sources permit. A more detailed understanding of the relative roles of sub-debris insulation and ice flow on the topographic expression of climatic forcing may then be ascertained.

SETTING

The Miage Glacier (45°47′30″N, 6°52′00″E) is the largest ice mass on the southern side of the Mont Blanc massif. Three steep tributaries (~24°–33°) draining the western flank of Mont Blanc converge to form the gently inclined glacier tongue (~5°), which occupies a deeply incised trough (Fig. 1). This section, which contains two prominent medial moraines, divides to form two main terminal lobes, which descend more steeply (~11°) to ~1750 m. The lower ~5 km of the ice surface is buried beneath a continuous mantle of coarse, angular debris, delivered to the glacier by frequent rockfall and avalanche events. Spot depth measurements from 1999 show that the debris mantle is generally 5–20 cm thick on the tongue, increasing to >1 m thick approximately 0.5 km upglacier from the twin terminal lobes.

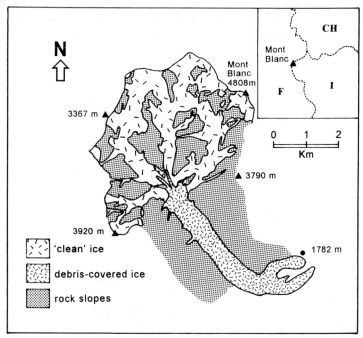

Fig. 1 Location and physical characteristics of Miage Glacier, Italian Alps. I = Italy; F = France; CH = Switzerland.

METHODS

Published cartographic data sources of the 1913, 1957, 1967 and 1975 glacier surface were supplemented by a topographic survey of the glacier surface in July 1999, using a Sokkia (Set 5a) total station. Because some maps fail to delineate terminus positions in sufficient detail, changes in the planimetric area of the glacier were not examined. Contour lines were digitized using manual point selection, producing a series of (*x*, *y*, *z*) coordinates from each map. The density of points varied largely as a function of the complexity of relief over the glacier surface, with areas of irregular relief containing a greater number of sampled points in comparison to homogeneous areas. Data were imported into the ARC/INFO software package, for conversion into triangulated irregular networks (TINs) based on the Delauney algorithm (ESRI, 1993). TINs were converted into 50-m grids using a linear interpolation routine, giving data attached to five sets of coincident nodes, allowing quantitative comparisons of the five DTMs. The difference in elevation between equivalent nodes of successive models was computed and displayed as polygon altitude difference maps (Figs 2 and 3).

To test the accuracy of the DTMs, the elevations of 125 control points, taken directly from the 1967 contour map of the glacier surface, were compared with corresponding estimates of elevation of the same points interpolated from the final DTM. The vertical root mean square error (RMSE) was calculated as <4 m over the study area. This value equates to a volume error of 1.1×10^6 m^3, which applies to comparisons between the DTMs. Due to the similarity in relief and density of sampled points, RMSEs were assumed to be of a similar magnitude for all DTMs. Given these error estimates, together with unknown errors inherent in the construction of the original maps, all thickness changes within the ±5 m interval were regarded as areas of little or no change.

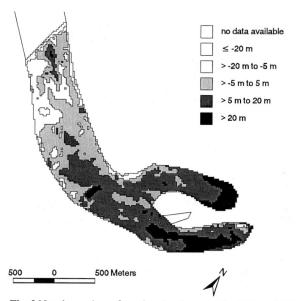

☐ no data available
☐ ≤ -20 m
☐ > -20 m to -5 m
▨ > -5 m to 5 m
▨ > 5 m to 20 m
■ > 20 m

500   0   500 Meters

Fig. 2 Net change in surface elevation between the 1913 and 1999 topographic surveys. Negative and positive values indicate areas of thinning and thickening respectively.

RESULTS

The overall change between 1913 and 1999 (Fig. 2) demonstrates a net increase in elevation on the lower parts of the glacier. On the left (northern) lobe, positive values are accentuated towards the terminus whilst a net decrease in elevation of the same magnitude has occurred over a small area at the terminus right (southern) lobe. Upglacier, large areas experienced little change (>–5 to 5 m). Net losses occur towards the upper limits of the study area, but with localized areas of thickening evident. The total change over the entire 1913–1999 period was a net volume gain of 1.3×10^6 m^3 (equivalent to a mean specific net balance of +5.7 m or +0.07 m year^{-1}).

Between 1913 and 1957 (Fig. 3(a)) the glacier shows a general thickening, which is more pronounced towards the termini of all lobes. Over this period the studied area

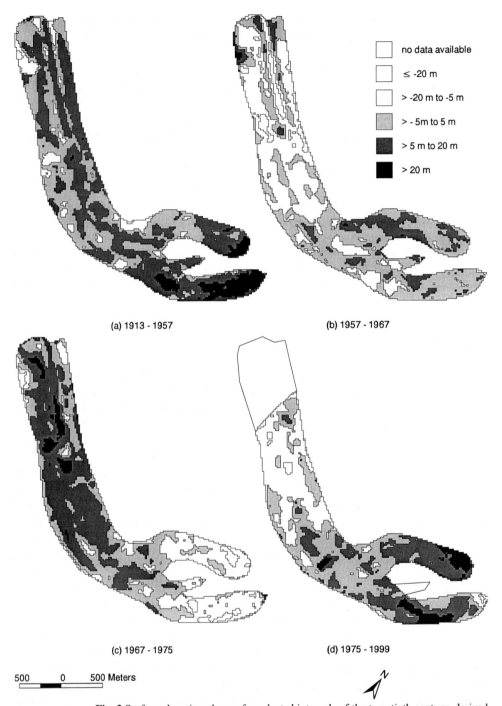

no data available

≤ -20 m

> -20 m to -5 m

> - 5m to 5 m

> 5 m to 20 m

> 20 m

(a) 1913 - 1957

(b) 1957 - 1967

(c) 1967 - 1975

(d) 1975 - 1999

500 0 500 Meters

Fig. 3 Surface elevation change for selected intervals of the twentieth century, derived from the following published maps: Porro (1913), 1:10 000 scale, 5-m contour interval; Comitato Glaciologico Italiano (1957), 1:5000, 5 m; Institute Geographique National (1967), 1:25 000, 10 m; Regione Autonoma della Valle d'Aosta (1975), 1:10 000, 10 m. The 1999 surface topography is from the authors' own survey. Negative and positive values indicate areas of thinning and thickening respectively.

underwent a net increase in volume of 1.73×10^6 m^3 (+5.98 m or +0.07 m year^{-1}). Upglacier, elevation increases are principally confined to the glacier centreline and to the crests of medial moraines.

During the period 1957–1967, the study area experienced a net loss of 1.11×10^6 m^3 (−3.83 m or −0.38 m year^{-1}). On the lower half of the glacier little net change in surface elevation occurred, although areas of increase of over 20 m occur, in particular on the left lobe (Fig. 3(b)). The majority of loss occurred over the tongue, although smaller scale changes are also apparent, such as the reversal in trend of medial moraine growth.

A general reversal in the pattern of thickness change occurred between 1967 and 1975, with a net loss in elevation of over 20 m on the glacier lobes (Fig. 3(c)). A striking increase in surface elevation is evident over almost the entire area of the tongue resulting in a net gain in volume of 0.54×10^6 m^3 (+1.9 m or +0.23 m year^{-1}) for the study area.

A further net increase in volumetric change of 0.25×10^6 m^3 (+1 m or +0.04 m year^{-1}) occurred between 1975 and 1999. Again, the general pattern shows a reversal of trend with positive values now concentrated on the lobes and a trend of decreasing thickness change farther upglacier.

DISCUSSION

The observed volume increase in the debris-covered tongue between 1913 and 1999 (Fig. 2) contrasts with recorded fluctuations of nearby glaciers, whose minor advances have punctuated a general twentieth-century volume decrease (Grove, 1988; Deline, 1999). The most plausible explanation is that the debris cover has reduced surface melting to conserve ice mass in the ablation zone. At shorter (decadal) time scales, the pattern of thickness change suggests that the debris cover is not the primary control on the distribution of thickness change (assuming the current spatial pattern of debris thickness has been similar throughout the study periods). Rather, zones of thickening appear to have migrated downstream on at least two occasions between measurement periods, indicating increased mass fluxes propagated to the terminus. The first "wave" probably resulted from a sustained increase in winter precipitation and lower mean annual temperatures between 1890 and 1940 (Orombelli & Porter, 1982), culminating in an advance of Miage Glacier around 1930 which deposited a prominent lateral and terminal moraine. The second was probably triggered by increased snowfall in the 1950s and 1960s, causing an advance culminating in the late 1980s (Deline, 1999).

In the 1913–1957 interval, most of the glacier experienced thickening, interpreted as the net effect of increased mass flux early in the period followed by a slow decrease in ice surface elevation after the *c.* 1930 highstand. The 44-year interval between surveys has been sufficient to mask any downstream propagation of the zone of greater flux, which instead shows as a general thickening throughout the tongue (Fig. 3(a)). The downstream transfer of a zone of thicker ice becomes apparent over shorter measurement intervals covering the subsequent positive balance perturbation. The leading edge of a zone of thickening, first apparent in the 1957–1967 period (Fig. 3(b)), migrated *c.* 2.5 km downstream by 1975 (Fig. 3(c)), to reach the terminus sometime between 1975 and 1999. By 1999 thinning had recommenced over most of

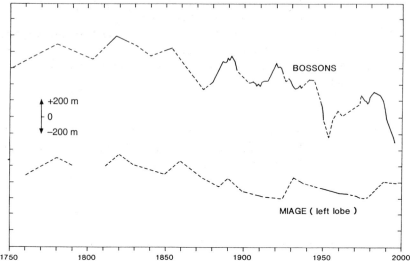

Fig. 4 Comparison of length changes of Miage Glacier and the uncovered Bossons Glacier, which shares an ice divide but flows north from Mont Blanc. Adapted from a synthesis by Deline (1999) from various sources. Solid lines indicate documented accounts of terminal advance/retreat. Dashed lines represent inferred terminal advance/retreat.

the ablation zone upstream of the "wave" (Fig. 3(d)). This spatial and temporal pattern is consistent with length changes synthesized by Deline (1999) (Fig. 4), if it is assumed that most thickening in the 1913–1957 interval occurred prior to the highstand and lateral moraine deposition in the early 1930s. Slow retreat of the left terminus between *c.* 1930 and *c.* 1976 corresponds to stable or decreasing surface elevations. The advance commencing in the mid 1970s, sustained throughout the 1980s, corresponds to the arrival of a zone of increased mass flux at the terminus evident from the comparison of Fig. 3(c) and (d). Accepting that Deline's length record can be interpreted as pulses of increased mass flux (kinematic waves) causing periodic advances, the passage of six waves between 1750 and the 1913 survey can be inferred in addition to the two identified from Fig. 3. The length record is broadly synchronous with fluctuations of nearby uncovered glaciers (Fig. 4), indicating a common climatic forcing.

In conclusion, the study has demonstrated the value of higher temporal resolution sampling of debris-covered glaciers, providing evidence of a more detailed picture of the interaction between the debris insulation effect and changes in ice flux. Detailed spatial patterns of thickness change for successive intervals show that waves of changing ice flux override any differential ablation associated with spatial variations in debris thickness. In addition, there exists a fundamental asymmetry of Miage Glacier and neighbouring uncovered glaciers during periods of advance and retreat. Both show a broadly synchronous response to positive mass balance perturbations imposed from upglacier. However, during periods of negative mass balance, terminus retreat of uncovered glaciers is more pronounced. The cumulative effect of this becomes more apparent at increasingly longer time scales. Whereas neighbouring uncovered glaciers in the Mont Blanc Range experienced a net decrease in volume over the twentieth century (Grove, 1988), the Miage sustained a net increase in volume. The difference is interpreted as the insulation of ice beneath the Miage debris cover, allowing more of the ice transported to the lower tongue of the glacier to be conserved, especially during warm summers. Thus, although detailed variations in thickness change are weakly related to differential ablation, this study has confirmed the overall importance of the debris insulation effect most strongly manifested at longer time scales.

Acknowledgements This study was supported by the Carnegie Trust for the Universities of Scotland. Special thanks to Bill Berry for advice on ARC/INFO, Nick Spedding and Alex Grindlay for assistance in the field.

REFERENCES

Deline, P. (1999) Les variations Holocènes récentes du glacier du Miage (Val Veny, Val d'Aoste). *Quaternaire* **10**(1), 5–13.

ESRI (1993) *Arc/Info User's Guide, Surface Modelling with TIN*. Environmental Research Systems Institute, Redlands, California, USA.

Grove, J. (1988) *The Little Ice Age*. Routledge, London.

Kirkbride, M. P. & Warren, C. R (1999) Tasman Glacier, New Zealand: twentieth-century thinning and predicted calving retreat. *Global and Planetary Change* **22**, 11–28.

Nakawo, M., Yabuki, H. & Sakai, A. (1999) Characteristics of Khumbu Glacier, Nepal Himalaya: recent changes in the debris-covered area. *Ann. Glaciol.* **28**, 118–122.

Orombelli, G. & Porter, S. C. (1982) Late Holocene fluctuations of the Brenva Glacier. *Geografia Fisica e Dinamica Quaternaria* **5**, 14–37.

Debris-Covered Glaciers (Proceedings of a workshop held at Seattle, Washington, USA, September 2000).
IAHS Publ. no. 264, 2000.

Recent areal and altimetric variations of Miage Glacier (Monte Bianco massif, Italian Alps)

CLAUDIO SMIRAGLIA, GUGLIELMINA DIOLAIUTI, DAVIDE CASATI

Dipartimento di Scienze della Terra, Università di Milano, Via Mangiagalli 34, I-20133 Milan, Italy
e-mail: claudio.smiraglia@unimi.it

MARTIN P. KIRKBRIDE

Department of Geography, University of Dundee, Dundee DD1 4HN, UK
e-mail: m.p.kirkbride@dundee.ac.uk

Abstract Changes in ice thickness and area of the debris-covered tongue of Miage Glacier have been measured using 1975 and 1991 aerial photographs, supplemented by measurements of ice flow from the displacement of 24 supraglacial boulders. Results show an increase in surface elevation of the lower glacier of >40 m, but thinning upstream. Overall ice volume increased in the study period, with negligible detectable change to terminus position and glacier area. The pattern of thickness variation is interpreted as a response to positive mass balance sometime after *c.* 1951. The debris cover may have prevented ablation from reducing the amplitude of a kinematic wave. Thus, the downstream amplification of thickening in the zone of compressive flow has been largely preserved. Debris-covered glaciers, whose termini are often held to be unresponsive to climatic variability, may actually magnify mass balance perturbations if ice remains mobile to the terminus.

INTRODUCTION

Debris-covered glaciers are widespread in the mountain chains of Asia, such as the Karakorum, the Himalaya (Moribayashi & Higuchi, 1977) and the Tien Shan. They are also common in New Zealand (Kirkbride & Warren, 1999) and Alaska. There are few examples of such glaciers in Europe. Two of the best-known (Miage and Brenva) drain the southwest and southeast slopes of Monte Bianco in Valle d'Aosta (western Alps). Miage Glacier (45°47′N, 06°52′E), with an area of *c.* 11 km^2, is Italy's third largest glacier. Morphologically, the glacier resembles the large Asian debris-covered glaciers (Fig. 1). The accumulation zone consists of several crevassed ice-fall tributaries descending from *c.* 4000 m to 2500–2700 m. The confluent tongue descends more gently for 6 km into Val Veny, bending abruptly northeast and dividing into two large lobes terminating at 1775 m, bounded by lateral moraines. The tongue is debris-covered below *c.* 2500 m, initially by medial moraines then more uniformly across the entire surface. Near the terminus, debris thickness exceeds 0.5 m.

Valle d'Aosta has a history of military strategy and trade, and has been explored for science since the observations of De Saussure in the eighteenth century. A long record of frontal variations exists, as well as reconstructions of lateral moraine formation (Baretti, 1880; Porro, 1914; Sacco, 1917; Capello, 1959; Lesca, 1974;

Deline, 1997, 1999a). The debris cover itself has received little attention. This paper interprets thickness change in the ablation zone over a 16-year period in terms of debris-cover insulation, velocity, and glacier response to mass balance change.

AREAL AND ALTIMETRIC VARIATION BETWEEN 1975 AND 1991

Method

Digital terrain models (DTMs) were prepared from aerial photographs taken for the Regional Government of Valle d'Aosta in 1975 (1:30 000 scale) and 1991 (1:26 000 scale). Aerial slides of Miage Glacier were not available. Photographs were scanned and the images so obtained were used to construct stereoscopic models for each photograph year. DTMs were obtained using digital video plotter (DVP) software, which uses scale, focal distance, aircraft altitude and recognizable homologous control points (HCPs) on both surveys. The points used to construct the DTMs were directly measured on the stereoscopic models. A Trimble Geoexplorer Differential GPS was used to locate 20 control points well spread around the glacier to georeference the absolute orientation of the photo images. The GPS master was located in Milan. In order to improve the georeferencing, another 15 control points visible on the aerial photographs were checked and identified on the regional technical map, at 1:10 000 scale (CTR Map, Regione Valle d'Aosta). For each image, a 40-m grid was created to generate the DTM. Spot elevations were interpolated to form a triangular irregular network (TIN), a mosaic of triangles overlapping the grid, and reproducing the morphology of the glacier and adjacent ice-free ground.

The accuracy of the calculated models has been evaluated as 6 m. The difficulties in the DEM generations at high elevation due to snow cover and associated loss of parallax were solved by a slight displacement of the acquisition point where no snow cover was present. Altimetric and volumetric variations of the glacier were calculated

Fig. 1 Wide-angle photograph of Miage Glacier, looking northwards. The southern lobe is in the foreground, and the calving cliff at Lake Miage visible on the right (west) margin of the glacier. Note supraglacial rock avalanche debris draped over a medial moraine in the left (western) part of the debris cover, and recent slope activity on the foreground lateral moraine due to thickening of the southern lobe.

by comparison of the 1975 and 1991 DTMs. HCPs visible in both the surveys (24 control points on the glacier surface) allowed the calculation of glacier surface velocity, by computing the displacement over 16 years of point coordinates on the two surveys. The accuracy of this calculation is controlled by the same factors, and comparable to that of the DTMs.

Results

The surface morphology changed little over the 16-year period, especially in the frontal area. No significant change to the terminus position was registered and the relief of the two main medial moraines increased. The area of the glacier tongue reduced very slightly from 4 461 334 m^2 in 1975 to 4 448 752 m^2 in 1991, a change of –12 582 m^2 (–0.3%). The only differences between the 1975 and 1991 surface areas were to the termini of the two main lobes and to the calving ice wall at Lake Miage (Fig. 1). The margins overlap perfectly for the rest of the glacier tongue. Most frontal retreat is associated with the main outwash portal of the north lobe. The terminus of the right lobe has remained unchanged, but the lobe has narrowed slightly.

Based on the premise that a variation in altitude corresponds to a variation in ice thickness, an altitudinal comparison of the DTMs (Fig. 2) indicates thickening of >40 m in the lower sector, particularly on the south lobe. Only at the southern terminus, where debris cover exceeds 0.5 m, was there no variation in thickness. The DTM surfaces converge upstream, so that the 1975–1991 altitude difference becomes zero near Lake Miage. Above *c.* 2100 m thinning of >40 m was recorded. There is no thinning around 2300 m altitude, where large landslide accumulations evidently reduce ablation (Fig. 1). Debris thickness decreases upstream to become thin and discontinous in the upper part of the glacier tongue.

In summary, thickening of the lower sector contrasts with thinning in the middle–upper sector, which has created a "swelling" in the terminal part of the glacier, as shown by topographic profiles (Fig. 3). Ice melted by ablation has been more than replaced by ice transported downglacier by flow. Across the whole tongue, a volumetric increase of *c.* 310 000 m^3 indicates a marginally positive balance. Only a very small part of this increase is attributable to an increase in debris thickness due to englacial melt-out and direct deposition on the glacier surface. Thickening of the terminal sector is consistent with observations along the glacier margins. The glacier has constructed new lateral moraine crests partially burying the "Little Ice Age" moraine crest, and at a lower gradient. Recent moraine superposition has been associated with numerous boulder falls down the distal moraine slopes of the south lobe (Fig. 1), creating a hazard on the road below the moraine (Mortara & Sorzara, 1987).

CALCULATION OF SURFACE VELOCITY

Displacement of 24 boulders visible on both aerial photographs allows surface velocity to be determined for the debris-covered area. Movement between 1975 and 1991 was calculated from coordinates using the DTMs. The results (Fig. 4) show a steady downstream decrease in mean annual velocity. In the middle–upper sector of the tongue,

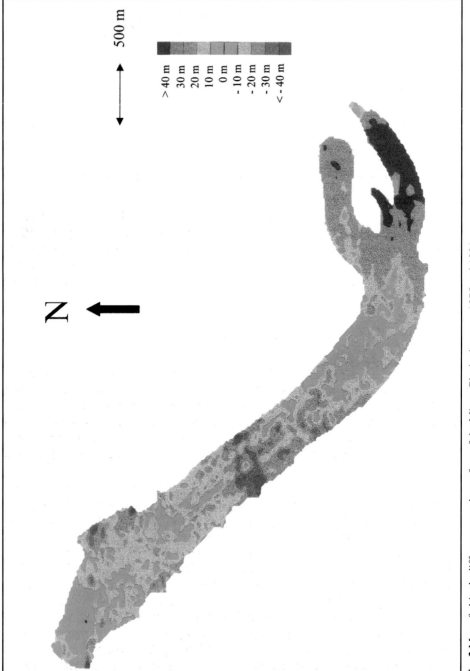

Fig. 2 Map of altitude differences on the surface of the Miage Glacier between 1975 and 1991.

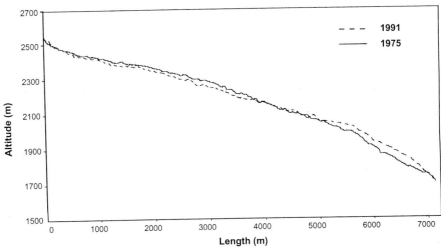

Fig. 3 Long profiles of the lower 7 km of Miage Glacier, showing the pattern of upstream thinning and downstream thickening between 1975 and 1991.

the velocity was *c.* 70 m year^{-1} (maximum of 78 m year^{-1}), slightly greater than the 61 m year^{-1} calculated by Cunietti (1961) using terrestrial photogrammetry. At 2100 m altitude the velocity is 60 m year^{-1}, decreasing to 30–40 m year^{-1} where the flow deviates eastward (2000 m), and to 15 m year^{-1} near the terminus. Velocity was less (6 m year^{-1}) on the outer edge of the south lobe, and there was no movement at a point on the right lateral moraine, employed as a control point.

GLACIER RESPONSE TO MASS BALANCE CHANGE

The unusual pattern of thickness change observed between 1975 and 1991 can be explained in terms of the expression of regional mass balance change by a debris-covered glacier with reversed ablation gradient. The observed upstream thinning and remarkable downstream thickening probably records the passage and amplification of a kinematic wave through the debris-covered tongue. The reversal of the ablation gradient would accentuate the effects of mass transfer from the accumulation basins to the ablation zone.

The Monte Bianco glaciers expanded during the 1962–1989 period (Cerutti, 1992). Since the late 1980s there has been a steady reduction in glacier lengths accompanied by a decrease in thickness that is more accentuated in the terminal sectors of the glaciers. Terminus changes at Miage Glacier indicate a slower, later response and lesser amplitude of frontal oscillation than at uncovered glaciers nearby (Deline, 1999b). Between 1954 and 1991, the Lex Blanche Glacier advanced by 740 m and the debris-covered Brenva Glacier advanced by 490 m, with an increase in volume of >57 million m^3. A 1977–1988 advance of 220 m of the north lobe is mentioned by Deline (1999b), consistent with the 1975–1991 thickening of the lobe (Fig. 2) but not with the retreat indicated by the photogrammetrically-based DTMs. Evidence for the extent of this advance is uncertain (Deline, 1999b, p. 8). Observations of frontal positions do not indicate such an advance in spite of the thickening, perhaps reflecting

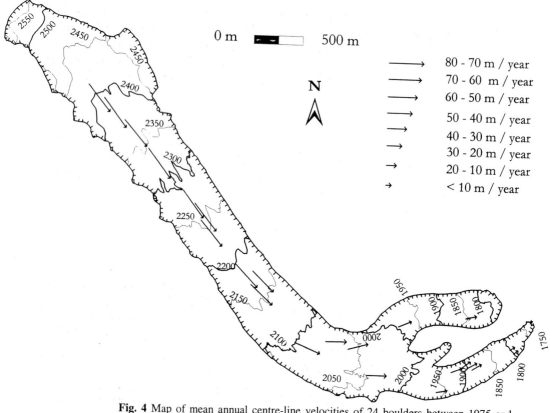

Fig. 4 Map of mean annual centre-line velocities of 24 boulders between 1975 and 1991.

thermal erosion and collapse around the main outwash portal. Significant thickening has not caused an advance of the southern terminus, because the zone of greatest thickening had not reached this terminus by 1991 due to the lower ice velocity (Fig. 4) and longer flow path of the south lobe.

The 1962–1989 advances were probably initiated by a drop in summer temperature. Between 1951 and 1960, mean summer temperature at Courmayeur was 0.65°C lower than the 1936–1983 mean, and 0.2°C cooler between 1961 and 1970. Cooling was accompanied by increased annual precipitation, which peaked between 1976 and 1980 (+303 mm compared to the 1936–1983 mean). Increased net accumulation probably generated the thickening above the equilibrium line initially during the 1950s, which has since propagated downstream. Theoretically, it is well known that the thickening generated in any cross-section is magnified downstream in a zone of longitudinal compression (Nye, 1968; Paterson, 1994). Normally the thickening would be partly offset by ablational loss of ice. On Miage Glacier, ablation decreases towards the terminus, therefore the downstream amplification of the wave has not been damped and the effect is manifested as the observed increase in surface elevation. If the mass redistribution was by passage of a kinematic wave travelling at about four to five times the ice velocity, a response time of *c.* 30–40 years is estimated, consistent with the timing of the observed thickening, and with a slightly faster response of the north lobe. Thomson *et al.* (2000) use map-based reconstructions since 1913 to demonstrate similar behaviour of the lower Miage Glacier on other earlier occasions. Thus, debris-covered glaciers which are commonly held to be unresponsive to climate change may, in fact, amplify a climatically-induced mass balance perturbation due to the insulation and preservation of ice transported into the lower ablation zone.

Acknowledgements We thank Giuseppe Stella for work on the photogrammetric comparison. Fieldwork was partly funded by ENEL (Italian Energy Company). This study was part of the research programme "Alpine Glaciers and Environmental Variations" (MURST 1999). MPK acknowledges the assistance of the Carnegie Trust for the Universities of Scotland.

REFERENCES

Baretti, M. (1880) Il ghiacciaio del Miage. Versante italiano del gruppo del Monte Bianco (The Miage Glacier, Italian flank of the Monte Bianco Group). *Memorie Regia Accademia delle Scienze di Torino* II **34**, 3–36.

Capello, C. F. (1959) Cenni illustrativi sul ghiacciaio del Miage e studi compiuti sino all'anno 1957 (Some remarks on Miage Glacier and research carried out up to 1957). *Bollettino Comitato Glaciologico Italiano* II **9/I**, 47–56.

Cerutti, A. V. (1992) L'espansione dei ghiacciai italiani del Monte Bianco fra il 1962 e il 1989 (Expansion of the Italian Glaciers of Monte Bianco from 1962 to 1989). *Geografia Fisica Dinamica Quaternaria* **15**, 67–74

Cunietti, M. (1961) Rilevamenti di ghiacciai e studi glaciologici in occasione dell'anno geofisico (Ghiacciaio del Miage): rilievo fotogrammetrico (Survey and glaciological research for Geophysical Year (Miage Glacier): photogrammetric survey). *Bollettino Comitato Glaciologico Italiano* II **9/1**, 59–85.

Deline, P. (1997) Les variations Holocènes récentes du Glacier du Miage (Val Veny); contribution à la prévision du risque glaciaire (Recent Holocene variations of Miage Glacier (Val Veny); a contribution to glacial risk assessment). *Mémoire DEA*, Univ. Savoie.

Deline, P. (1999a) La mise en place de l'amphithéâtre morainique du Miage (Val Veny, Val d'Aoste). *Géomorphologie: Relief, Processus, Environnement* 1999, no. 1, 59–72.

Deline, P. (1999b) Les variations Holocènes récentes du Glacier du Miage (Val Veny, Val d'Aoste). *Quaternaire* **10**, 5–13.

Kirkbride, M. P. & Warren, C. R. (1999) Tasman Glacier, New Zealand: 20th-century thinning and predicted calving retreat. *Global and Planetary Change* **22**, 11–28.

Lesca, C. (1974) Méthode topographique de précision pour la détermination de la vitesse superficielle des glaciers (A precise topographical method for determining the surface velocity of glaciers). *Bollettino Comitato Glaciologico Italiano* II **22**, 153–168.

Moribayashi, S. & Higuchi, K. (1977) Characteristics of glaciers in the Khumbu region and their recent variations. *J. Japan. Soc. Snow Ice (Seppyo)* **39**, special issue, 3–6.

Mortara, G. & Sorzana, P. F. (1987) Situazioni di rischio idrogeologico connesse all'espansione recente del ghiacciaio del Miage ed all'instabilità dei versanti in alta Val Veny (Hydrological risk and slope instability in upper Val Veny associated with the recent expansion of Miage Glacier). *Revue Valdotaine Histoire Naturelle* **41**, 111–118.

Nye, J. F. (1968) The response of glaciers and ice sheets to seasonal and climatic changes. *Proc. Roy. Soc. Lond.* series A **256**, 559–584.

Paterson, W. S. B. (1994) *Physics of Glaciers*, third edn. Pergamon Press, Oxford.

Porro, F. (1914) Primi studi topografici sul Ghiacciaio del Miage (The first topographic study of Miage Glacier). *Bollettino Comitato Glaciologico Italiano* **1**, 31–44.

Sacco, F. (1917) L'apparato morenico del ghiacciaio del Miage (The morainic complex of Miage Glacier). *Bollettino Società Geologica Italiana* **36**, 323–354.

Thomson, M. H., Kirkbride, M. P. & Brock, B. W. (2000) Twentieth-century surface elevation change of the Miage Glacier, Italian Alps. In: *Debris-Covered Glaciers* (ed. by M. Nakawo, C. F. Raymond & A. Fountain) (Proc. Seattle Workshop, September 2000). IAHS Publ. no. 264 (this volume).

Debris-Covered Glaciers (Proceedings of a workshop held at Seattle, Washington, USA, September 2000).
IAHS Publ. no. 264, 2000.

Shrinkage of the Khumbu Glacier, east Nepal from 1978 to 1995

TSUTOMU KADOTA

Frontier Observational Research System for Global Change, Sumitomo Hamamatsu-cho Building 4F, 1-8-16 Hamamatsu-cho, Minato-ku, Tokyo 105-0013, Japan
e-mail: kadota@frontier.esto.or.jp

KATSUMOTO SEKO*

Institute for Hydrospheric–Atmospheric Sciences, Nagoya University, Furo-cho, Chikusa-ku, Nagoya 464-01, Japan

TATSUTO AOKI

Department of Geography, University of Tokyo, Bunkyo-ku, Tokyo 113-0033, Japan

SHUJI IWATA

Department of Geography, Tokyo Metropolitan University, Hachioji, Tokyo 192-0397, Japan

SATORU YAMAGUCHI

Institute of Low Temperature Science, Hokkaido University, Kita-ku, Sapporo 060-0819, Japan

Abstract Surface lowering of the Khumbu Glacier, a large debris-covered glacier in the Nepal Himalayas, was detected by means of ground surveying in 1978 and in 1995. Over this interval the surface of the glacier lowered about 10 m throughout the debris-covered ablation area. Lowering in the lowermost part of the glacier, where surface ablation may be negligible, might result from subglacial meltwater interaction. Indication that ice flow is slowing suggests that shrinkage may accelerate even if ablation conditions remain unchanged.

INTRODUCTION

Glaciers are retreating worldwide. In the Nepal Himalayas small glaciers have been shrinking since at least the late 1970s (e.g. Kadota, 1997). Small glaciers in the Himalayas are debris-free and changes in the positions of their termini are easily detected. On the other hand, ablation areas of large glaciers are covered with thick debris and the lowest parts of these glaciers are stagnant ice. Positions of their active termini are hard to define or detect. To evaluate the status of such glaciers, it is necessary to study changes in ice thickness.

The Khumbu Glacier is one of the large debris-covered glaciers in the Nepal Himalayas. In 1978 the "Debris Cover Project" (part of Glaciological Expedition of Nepal called GEN) conducted extensive studies and prepared large-scale topographic maps for four areas in the ablation area (Higuchi, 1980; Watanabe *et al.*, 1980). In 1995, a topographic survey was carried out in the same four areas as 1978, resulting in the production of new topographic maps.

---

* *Present address not known.*

This paper describes changes in surface level in the ablation area of the Khumbu Glacier from the 1978 and the 1995 maps, and discusses its spatial pattern relevant to supraglacial debris distributions.

KHUMBU GLACIER

Khumbu Glacier is situated in the Khumbu region, east Nepal (Fig. 1). The glacier starts from the basin surrounded by Mt Sagarmatha (Mt Everest, 8848 m), Lhotse (8501 m) and Nuptse (7861 m). The equilibrium line lies around 5600 m a.s.l. within the icefall and supraglacial debris appears at the foot of the icefall with increasing thickness towards the terminus. The distance from the foot of the icefall to the terminus is about 10 km.

Mapped areas are shown by four rectangles in Fig. 1, named sequentially from lowest to highest as I, II, III and IV. Descriptions of the areas (after Watanabe *et al.*, 1980) are as follows:

(a) *Area I*: fossil or stagnant ice area with rough surface topography; surface features with large boulder concentration and fluvial topography with partial covering of vegetation.

(b) *Area II*: the boundary zone between active and stagnant ice area; rough surface with steep ridges and troughs without water pools or glacier ponds. The most intensive subsidence of the glacier surface is in Area II, where the height difference from the crest of the lateral moraine to the glacier surface reaches a maximum of about 100 m.

(c) *Area III*: typical area of compound glacier, where one tributary glacier meets the trunk glacier, with varying roughness on different surfaces.

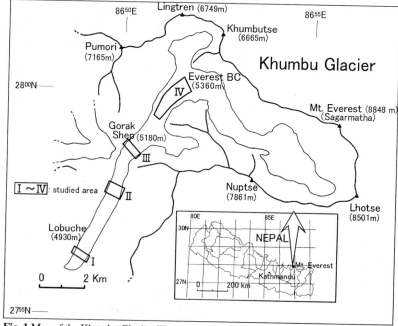

Fig. 1 Map of the Khumbu Glacier. The studied areas (I–IV) are shown by the rectangles.

(d) *Area IV*: surface topography characterized by transitional change from ogive form to ice pinnacle row. Significant debris first appears in Area IV.

SURVEYS

Data from 1978 were measured in the monsoon season (Iwata *et al.*, 1980). In Area I, Area II and Area III, contour maps were made at 1:1000 by surveying a grid with a Wild T2 theodolite and plane table. Area IV was mapped on a 1:2500 scale by tacheo-metry (using stadia readings). The 1995 survey used mostly the same benchmarks as in 1978. Angles and distances were measured with a theodolite (Wild T2) and an electro-nic distance meter (Sokkisya RED1A) as the main instruments. A transverse line set out in 1978 (*X–X'* in Fig. 2(a)) was resurveyed in Area I. In Area II ground photogrammetry was carried out. A pair of stereoscopic photographs of the area was taken from the crest of the each lateral moraine (total two pairs) using a camera (Pentax PAMS645) horizon-tally set on a tripod. Several ground control points together with camera positions were measured from a benchmark on the crest of the left lateral moraine. A topographic map (Fig. 3) was prepared using a plotter (Wild BC2) with contour interval 5 m (original scale 1:2000). Many locations were hidden behind high topography, especially the foot areas of the inside slopes of the lateral moraines. These areas could not be plotted. Broken lines in Fig. 3 represent hand-drawn elevations, which were approximately drawn with

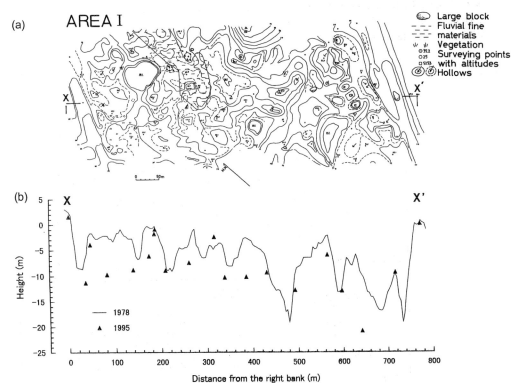

Fig. 2 (a) Topographic map of Area I in 1978 (after Watanabe *et al.*, 1980). A transverse line measured in 1978 and in 1995 is shown by *X–X'*. (b) Surface profiles along the line *X–X'* in 1978 (solid line) and in 1995 (solid triangles).

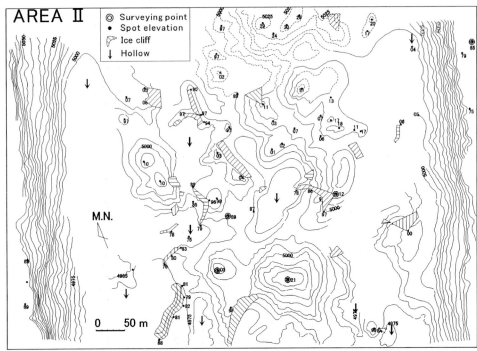

Fig. 3 Topographic map of Area II in 1995. The contour interval is 5 m. Broken lines represent hand-drawn elevations, which were not surveyed due to being hidden behind high convex topography. Solid circles show locations of spot elevations. The adjacent numbers (XX) give elevations with the following code: XX between 01 and 50 indicates 50XX m; XX between 51 and 99 indicates 49XX m. The surveying point on the crest of the left-hand lateral moraine is one of the benchmarks. Ground control points on the glacier are also shown as surveying points.

the aid of pictures taken during the survey. A survey of control points and plane table surveying were conducted in Area III. A topographic map (Fig. 4) was prepared with contour intervals of 5 m (original scale 1:2500). In Area IV traverse surveying was carried out. A topographic map (Fig. 5) was prepared with contour intervals of 10 m (original scale 1:5000). The surveyed area was limited to the lower part of the 1978 survey.

CHANGES IN SURFACE LEVEL FROM 1978 TO 1995

The surface topography of the glacier is extremely rough and evolves by both differential ablation and flow in Areas II, III and IV. Therefore, changes in surface elevations within these areas were investigated using several different statistical methods. In Area I, however, elevations along a transverse line were simply compared, because the 1995 survey showed no glacial flow in this area.

Area I

Elevations along a transverse line (X–X′ in Fig. 2(a)) were compared. Figure 2(b) shows the surface profiles in 1978 and in 1995 along the line X–X. The surface level had lowered by 5–8 m on the right-hand bank.

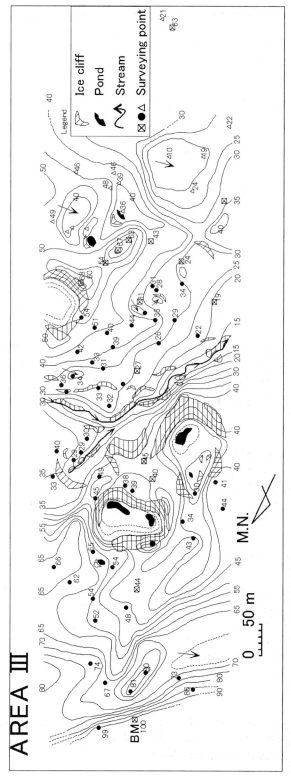

Fig. 4 Topographic map of Area III in 1995. The contour interval is 5 m. Elevations are shown according to the datum height set as 100 m at BM on the crest of the right-hand lateral moraine.

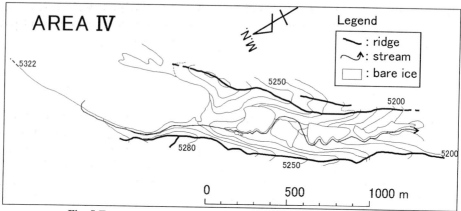

Fig. 5 Topographic map of Area IV in 1995. The contour interval is 10 m. The bare ice shown in this figure comprises ice pinnacles. The area of ice pinnacles was not surveyed.

Area II

Maximum and minimum elevations in each 50 m × 50 m mesh area obtained from the maps were used for comparison in Area II. Figure 6 shows frequency distributions of maximum and minimum elevations, and relative relief (maximum minus minimum) in 1978 and in 1995. The mean elevations of the maximum/minimum heights in 1978 and 1995 are 5019/4999 m and 5005/4989 m respectively. The surface level was 10–14 m

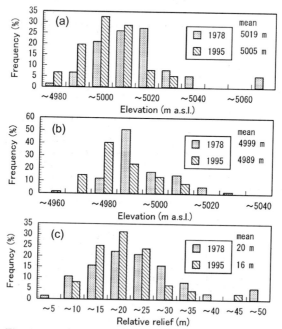

Fig. 6 Frequency distributions in Area II: (a) maximum elevations, (b) minimum elevations and (c) relative relief in 1978 and in 1995. A total number of samples (meshes: 50 m × 50 m each) is 77.

lower on average. The mean heights of the relative relief in 1978 and in 1995 are 20 m and 16 m respectively, indicating a slight decrease in surface roughness. Collapse of debris cones may account for the decrease the relative relief.

Area III

Maximum and minimum elevations in each 50 m × 50 m mesh area obtained from the maps were used for comparison in Area III. Figure 7 shows frequency distributions of maximum and minimum elevations, and relative relief in 1978 and 1995. The mean elevations of the maximum/minimum heights in 1978 and in 1995 are 5129/5116 m and 5123/5108 m respectively. The surface level lowered by 6–8 m on average. The mean heights of the relative relief in 1978 and in 1995 are 13 m and 15 m respectively, indicating a slight increase in surface roughness.

Area IV

Average elevations in each 50 m × 50 m mesh area obtained from the maps were used for comparison. The areas occupied by ice pinnacles (bare ice in Fig. 5) were excluded from the comparison because the 1995 survey did not obtain topographic data for the ice pinnacles. Figure 8 shows frequency distributions of average elevations in 1978 and 1995. The average elevations on the left/right-hand bank of the row of ice

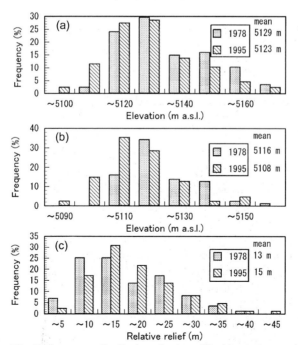

Fig. 7 Frequency distributions in Area III: (a) maximum elevations, (b) minimum elevations and (c) relative relief in 1978 and in 1995. The total number of samples (meshes: 50 m × 50 m each) is 88.

pinnacles in 1978 and in 1995 are 5260/5262 m and 5254/5244 m, respectively. The surface level lowered by 6 m on the left-hand side and 18 m on the right-hand side on average.

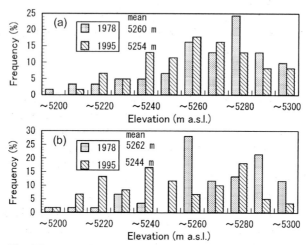

Fig. 8 Frequency distributions of average elevations in Area IV for 1978 and 1995: (a) left-hand bank, (b) right-hand side of the ice pinnacle row. The total number of samples (meshes: 50 m × 50 m each) is 62 on the left and 61 on the right.

DISCUSSION

Although supraglacial debris rapidly increases in thickness with downstream distance below Area IV (Nakawo *et al.*, 1986), there was a more or less uniform lowering of the surface along this stretch of the ablation area from 1978 to 1995. In fact, Inoue (1977) detected surface ablation over the full ablation area except near the apparent terminus where Area I lies. Although ablation under debris cover decreases as debris cover thickens, ablation on/around ice cliffs and ponds is so extensive that the aerial mean ablation rates in Areas II and III may be more or less comparable to that in Area IV where bare ice and thin debris cover are dominant (Inoue & Yoshida, 1980). In Area I, however, surface ablation may be negligibly small (Inoue & Yoshida, 1980). Surface lowering in this area could result from subsurface melting in meltwater passages.

Surface lowering along the ablation area was derived by Nakawo *et al.* (1999) using a simple continuity equation that accounts for ablation and flow divergence. Annual ablation rates were estimated using thermal data derived from satellite data and meteorological data obtained in the 1970s. This analysis suggests that the glacier would shrink under the same climatic conditions as in the 1970s.

Although no further information has been obtained on ablation conditions since the 1970s, there are some observations on recent ice flow conditions based on displacements of some identifiable topographic features in the time series of topographic maps and satellite images. Seko *et al.* (1998) found a trend of decreasing flow speed after the 1950s in the uppermost part of the ablation area where Area IV lies. Iwata *et al.* (2000) reported that on the right-hand side in the upper part of this area, at the confluence of the tributaries from Lingtren and Khumbtse (see Fig. 1), two large hollows emerged and that the relative relief became small between 1978 and 1995. This suggests that a decline of ice flow from the tributary may be responsible for the greater lowering on the right-hand bank (18 m on average) compared with that in the left -hand bank (6 m on average) in Area IV.

Surface lowering in the ablation area occurs when ablation exceeds inflow from upstream. Slowing of ice flow might accelerate shrinkage of the glacier even if ablation conditions remain unchanged.

Acknowledgements We are indebted to all of the members of "Debris Cover Project in Khumbu Glacier" for preparing the base maps. We thank Dr K. Moriwaki, National Institute for Polar Research, for advising on ground photogrammetry and plotting. We wish to thank Prof. Charles F. Raymond and two anonymous reviewers for their valuable suggestions to improve our first manuscript. We express our appreciation to the Department of Hydrology and Meteorology, Ministry of Science and Technology, His Majesty's Government of Nepal for their cooperation in our research in Nepal. This study was financially supported by Grant-in-Aid for Scientific Research (no. 06041051 and no. 09490018) from the Ministry of Education, Science, Sports and Culture, Japanese Government.

REFERENCES

Higuchi, K. (1980) Outline of the Glaciological Expedition of Nepal (4). *J. Japan. Soc. Snow Ice (Seppyo)* **41**, special issue, 1–4.

Inoue, J. (1977) Mass budget of Khumbu Glacier. *J. Japan. Soc. Snow Ice (Seppyo)* **39**, special issue, 15–19.

Inoue, J. & Yoshida, M. (1980) Ablation and heat exchange over Khumbu Glacier. *J. Japan. Soc. Snow Ice (Seppyo)* **41**, special issue, 26–33.

Iwata, S., Watanabe, O. & Fushimi, H. (1980) Surface morphology in the ablation area of the Khumbu Glacier. *J. Japan. Soc. Snow Ice (Seppyo)* **41**, special issue, 9–17.

Iwata, S., Aoki, T., Kadota, T., Seko, K. & Yamaguchi, S. (2000) Morphological evolution of the debris-cover on Khumbu Glacier, Nepal, between 1978 and 1995. In: *Debris-Covered Glaciers* (ed. by M. Nakawo, C. F. Raymond & A. Fountain) (Proc. Seattle Workshop, September 2000). IAHS Publ. no. 264 (this volume).

Kadota, T. (1997) On the recent shrinkage of small glaciers in the Nepal Himalayas. Doctoral Thesis, Nagoya University, Japan.

Nakawo, M., Iwata, S., Watanabe, O. & Yoshida, M. (1986) Processes which distribute supraglacial debris on the Khumbu Glacier, Nepal Himalaya. *Ann. Glaciol.* **8**, 129–131.

Nakawo, M., Yabuki, H. & Sakai, A. (1999) Characteristics of Khumbu Glacier, Nepal Himalaya: recent change in the debris-covered area. *Ann. Glaciol.* **28**, 118–122.

Seko, K., Yabuki, H., Nakawo, M., Sakai, A., Kadota, T. & Yamada, Y. (1998) Changing surface features of Khumbu Glacier, Nepal Himalayas revealed by SPOT images. *Bull. Glacier Res.* **16**, 33–41.

Watanabe, O., Fushimi, H., Ikegami, K., Tanaka, Y., Yoshida, M., Iwata, S., Inoue, J. & Upaday, B. P. (1980) Outline of studies on supraglacial debris of the Khumbu Glacier, Khumbu region. *J. Japan. Soc. Snow Ice (Seppyo)* **41**, special issue, 5–8.

Debris-Covered Glaciers (Proceedings of a workshop held at Seattle, Washington, USA, September 2000). IAHS Publ. no. 264, 2000.

Numerical simulation of recent shrinkage of Khumbu Glacier, Nepal Himalayas

NOZOMU NAITO, MASAYOSHI NAKAWO

Institute for Hydrospheric–Atmospheric Sciences, Nagoya University, Furo-cho, Chikusa-ku, Nagoya 464-8601, Japan
e-mail: naito@ihas.nagoya-u.ac.jp

TSUTOMU KADOTA

Frontier Observational Research System for Global Change, Sumitomo Hamamatsu-cho Building 4F, 1-8-16 Hamamatsu-cho, Minato-ku, Tokyo 105-0013, Japan

CHARLES F. RAYMOND

Geophysics Program, University of Washington, Box 351650, Seattle, Washington 98195-1650, USA

Abstract A new model for coupled mass balance and flow of a debris-covered glacier was developed to account for the effects of supraglacial debris on glacier evolution. The model is reasonably consistent with observations of recent shrinkage of the ablation area of Khumbu Glacier, Nepal Himalayas from 1978 to 1999. The model predicts formation and succeeding enlargement of a depression in the lower ablation area. This depression could result in the formation of a glacial lake. Potential improvements to the model for a debris-covered glacier are identified.

INTRODUCTION

The ablation areas of most large glaciers in the Himalayas are covered with thick supraglacial debris. It is, hence, important to know how these debris-covered glaciers in the Himalayas respond to climate change in order to predict consequences for local water resources and sea level rise.

Khumbu Glacier is one of the largest debris-covered glaciers in the Nepal Himalayas. It flows down from the slopes of Mts Everest (8848 m, Sagarmatha or Qomolangma), Lhotse (8511 m) and Nuptse (7861 m) (Fig. 1). Its total length is more than 15 km and its present terminus is located at about 4900 m a.s.l. The accumulation area, called the West Cwm, is nearly inaccessible due to an ice fall. The equilibrium line altitude (ELA) is located in this ice fall at about 5600 m a.s.l. More glaciological research has been undertaken on the ablation area than on any other debris-covered glacier in the Himalayas. Recent thinning of the glacier has been measured (Kadota *et al.*, 2000). This study establishes a new numerical model to simulate the recent shrinkage of the glacier accounting for supraglacial debris and its effects on ablation.

MODEL DESCRIPTION

The continuity equation coupling mass balance and glacier flow was formulated using the finite-volume method (Patankar, 1980; Lam & Dowdeswell, 1996):

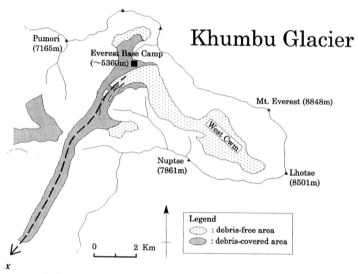

Fig. 1 Illustrated map of Khumbu Glacier. The study area is along a central flow line indicated as a dashed line with an arrow.

$$\frac{\Delta V}{\Delta t} = b\overline{W}\Delta x - \left(Q_{out} - Q_{in}\right) \tag{1}$$

where V, b, $\overline{W}$ and Q represent volume between fixed vertical cross-sections, mass balance rate, glacier surface width averaged between the sections, flux through the boundary cross-section to/from neighbouring control-volumes, respectively. Subscripts for Q refer to outgoing or incoming flux, t and x are time and horizontal distance along a flow line traced in Fig. 1. Time step, Δt, was 1/36 year (about 10 days), and the longitudinal length of each control-volume (grid space), Δx, was 500 m. Equation (1) was stepped forward in time using an implicit Crank-Nicholson scheme with calculations of mass balance and glacier flow described in the following subsections. The simulation, however, was limited to the ablation area with an assumption about flux through the upper boundary cross-section, which will be described later. A trapezoidal cross-section was assumed for the glacier channel with lateral slopes of 40° and 35° for the right and left bank sides, respectively, as compatible with a topographic survey by Glaciological Expedition of Nepal (1980). Glacier width was approximated with a linear variation to fit measurements from the topographic map published by the National Geographic Society (1988). The profile of the glacier bed was determined by ice thickness measurements with ice penetrating radar (Gades *et al.*, 2000) and topographic surveys in 1999.

Mass balance

Glaciers in the Himalayas are fed mostly in summer, and this summer-accumulation-type mass balance has to be taken into consideration. Empirical equations among air temperature T (°C), precipitation rate P (m day^{-1}), accumulation rate c (m day^{-1}) and ablation rate a (m day^{-1}) were obtained for a debris-free glacier in the Nepal Himalayas by Ageta (1983) and Ageta & Kadota (1992) as follows:

$$
\begin{aligned}
c &= P & \text{when } T < -0.6 \\
&= P(0.85 - 0.24T) & \text{when } -0.6 \le T \le 3.5 \\
&= 0 & \text{when } T > 3.5 \\
a &= 0 & \text{when } T < -3.0 \\
&= -0.0001(T + 3.0)^{3.2} & \text{when } -3.0 \le T \le 2.0 \\
&= -0.009T & \text{when } T > 2.0 \qquad\qquad (2)
\end{aligned}
$$

Seasonal variations in P and T were approximated by sinusoidal variations, having the same phase (i.e. high/low in summer/winter). Annual mean air temperature was set to be compatible with a measurement in 1973–1974 at Lhajung (0.5°C at 4420 m a.s.l.) (Inoue, 1976), accounting for a fixed altitudinal lapse rate of -6×10^{-3} °C m^{-1}. Annual range of air temperature and annual precipitation were assumed to be the same as at Lhajung (15°C and 540 mm, respectively) and independent of altitude. Lhajung is located at about 5 km southeast of the Khumbu Glacier terminus.

Effects of debris cover on the ablation have been examined in the following ways. Nakawo *et al.* (1999) estimated the longitudinal distribution of the ablation rate for the whole ablation area, using satellite data and meteorological data. As accumulation to the glacier ice body is negligible on the debris-covered ablation area, the estimated ablation rate was taken to be equivalent to the mass balance rate. They, however, implied that the magnitude of the mass balance rate may be in error due to uncertainty in meteorological data input. Surface lowering rate calculated by the continuity equation with observed surface flow speed was compared with that measured by Kadota *et al.* (2000). The comparison indicated that the calculated surface lowering rate was larger than the measurement on the lowest part of the glacier. The longitudinal distribution of mass balance rate, therefore, was slightly modified from the estimate by Nakawo *et al.* (1999) as shown in Fig. 2(a). A hypothetical mass balance rate for debris-free conditions is also shown in Fig. 2(a), which was calculated with equation (2) with the distribution and the seasonal variation of air temperature based on the surface altitude from the topographic surveys in 1978 (Watanabe *et al.*, 1980). The ratio r of the mass balance for debris-covered conditions to that for debris-free conditions was evaluated from the solid and dashed curves in Fig. 2(a). The longitudinal distribution of debris thickness H_d was measured by Nakawo *et al.* (1986) and Watanabe *et al.* (1986). The implied relationship between r and H_d is shown in Fig. 2(b).

As a result, net ablation (negative mass balance) on the debris-covered area can be calculated from c, a in equation (2) and r which depends on H_d (Fig. 2(b)). However, special attention must be given to the situation when supraglacial debris is covered with snow. If debris cover is buried by snow cover, water equivalent thickness of the snow cover H_s varies depending on $c + a$ in equation (2), and the mass of glacier ice beneath the debris cover does not change. There is no melt-out debris supply from glacier ice in this case. If net ablation exceeds an amount required to melt all the snow cover, however, extra ablation of glacier ice occurs according to the residual amount of net ablation, $(c + a)\Delta t + H_s$ (<0), and the ratio r in Fig. 2(b). Additional debris is, then, supplied as melt-out from the glacier ice. Then, the mass balance rate for glacier ice b is described as:

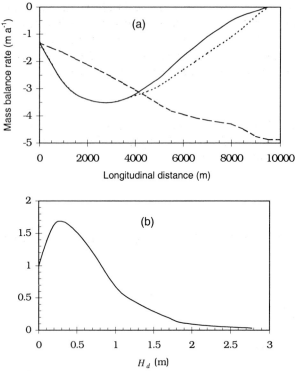

Fig. 2 (a) The mass balance rates on the ablation area of the Khumbu Glacier (dotted line) estimated by Nakawo *et al.* (1999) and (solid line) modified for this simulation with (dashed line) hypothesized for debris-free conditions. (b) The relation between debris thickness H_d and the ratio of mass balance on the debris-covered area to that for debris-free conditions r.

$$b = c + a \qquad\qquad \text{when } H_d = 0$$

$$= \frac{r\left[(c+a)\Delta t + H_s\right]}{\Delta t} \qquad \text{when } H_d > 0 \text{ and } (c + a)\Delta t + H_s < 0$$

$$= 0 \qquad\qquad \text{when } H_d > 0 \text{ and } (c + a)\Delta t + H_s \geq 0 \qquad (3)$$

Water equivalent thickness of snow cover H_s varies as:

$$\frac{\Delta H_s}{\Delta t} = c + a \qquad\qquad \text{when } H_d > 0 \text{ and } (c + a)\Delta t + H_s \geq 0$$

$$H_s = 0 \qquad\qquad \text{in the other cases} \qquad (4)$$

Debris thickness H_d varies according to the continuity equation for supraglacial debris:

$$\frac{\Delta H_d}{\Delta t} = \frac{C_d}{\rho_d}(-b) - \frac{D_{out} - D_{in}}{\overline{W}\Delta x} \quad \text{when } b < 0$$

$$= -\frac{D_{out} - D_{in}}{\overline{W}\Delta x} \qquad \text{when } b \geq 0 \qquad (5)$$

where C_d, ρ_d and D are concentration of debris in glacier ice, density of debris, and flux of supraglacial debris through a boundary between neighbouring control-volume, respectively. The concentration of debris C_d and the density ρ_d were assumed to be constants 0.1 kg m^{-3} and 1220 kg m^{-3} (Nakawo *et al.*, 1986), respectively. Subscripts for D refer to outgoing or incoming flux. The flux D is described as:

$$D = H_d \overline{W} U_s \qquad (6)$$

where U_s is surface flow speed, which is described by equation (7) in the next subsection. Note, here, each variable on the right side in equation (6) should be that at the boundary between control-volumes.

Glacier flow

Surface flow speed U_s and flux of glacier ice through a cross-section Q can be described as:

$$U_s = U_d + U_b \qquad (7)$$

$$Q = \left(f_2 U_d + U_b\right)S \qquad (8)$$

$$U_d = \frac{2A}{n+1}\left(-f_1 \rho g \sin \alpha\right)^n H^{n+1} \qquad (9)$$

U_d is a contribution of ice deformation to the surface flow speed. U_b represents a basal sliding. A and n (= 3) are parameters in the flow law of ice; ρ and g are the density of ice and the gravitational acceleration; α, H and S are the surface slope, the central ice thickness and the transversal cross-section area, respectively. f_1 and f_2 are so-called "shape factors", which account for lateral drag in equation (9) and ratio of cross-sectional average ice deformation to U_d in equation (8).

The value of A was assumed to be constant, 6.8×10^{-15} s^{-1} (kPa)$^{-3}$, which is a recommended value for ice temperature of 0°C by Paterson (1994). The value of the shape factor f_1 was approximated with

$$f_1 = 1 - \frac{0.33^{W/2H} + 0.78^{W/2H}}{2} \qquad (10)$$

which fits with the values obtained by Nye (1965) for a parabolic cross-section, as the value of f_1 should not be so different from that for a trapezoidal cross-section, which was used in this model. The flow speed ratio f_2 was assumed to be the same as for laminar flow, $n + 1/n + 2$ (= 0.8), which neglects variation in flow speed ratio across the flow. Then U_b was assumed to be distributed in the ablation area independent of time as shown in Fig. 3, which gives surface flow speed U_s consistent with observation (Kodama & Mae, 1976; Nakawo *et al.*, 1999). Inflow from the upper glacier area $Q_{in}(x = 0)$ was assumed to be constant as 5.6×10^9 kg year^{-1}. This value yields agreement between modelled and observed (Kadota *et al.*, 2000) surface lowering at $x = 0$, and is about 1.5 times that of an earlier rough estimate by Inoue (1977), which was based on the assumptions that precipitation on the accumulation area would be the same as at Lhajung independent of altitude and that the accumulation area was in a steady state.

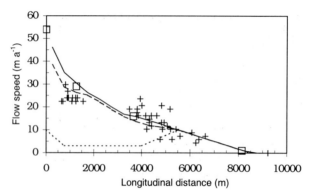

Fig. 3 Flow speeds on the Khumbu Glacier. Square and plus symbols are the observed surface speeds by Kodama & Mae (1976) in 1973–1974 and Nakawo *et al.* (1999) in 1987–1993, respectively. The solid curve represents the calculated surface speed based on the surveyed profile in 1978, and the dashed curve shows that based on a profile in 1990 estimated from topographic surveys in 1978 and 1999. Dotted curve is basal sliding U_b assumed in this study to tune the calculated surface speeds to the observations.

RESULTS OF SIMULATION

The initial conditions were the longitudinal profiles in 1978 of surface elevation (Watanabe *et al.*, 1980) and supraglacial debris thickness (Nakawo *et al.*, 1986; Watanabe *et al.*, 1986). Climate was assumed to be constant as in 1973–1974 (Inoue, 1976), since there are no available data about climate changes around the Khumbu Glacier. Furthermore, Kadota & Ageta (1992) succeeded in simulating shrinkage of a debris-free glacier near the Khumbu Glacier in 1978–1989 without significant climate change, which supports this assumption. Predictions for changes in surface elevation and debris thickness are shown in Fig. 4.

The longitudinal surface profile in 1999 is simulated quite reasonably (Fig. 4(a)). The succeeding simulation predicts that a depression would be formed at about $x = 5.5$ km around year 2020 and the ablation area would be divided into two parts around year 2040. Debris thickness H_d is predicted to decrease on the uppermost part, to increase on the lowest part and near the predicted terminus after the glacier division (Fig. 4(b)).

Sensitivity tests

Sensitivity tests for the simulation of the longitudinal surface profile were examined concerning three important parameters: incoming flux at the upper boundary, basal sliding, and the effect of debris on the mass balance. Figure 5 shows the simulated profiles for 1999 under three different conditions, together with the preceding result. Assuming the incoming flux $Q_{in} (x = 0) = 3.8 \times 10^9$ kg year^{-1} to be the same as Inoue's (1977) earlier rough estimate, the simulated glacier surface lowering during 1978–1999 was predicted to be about twice as large as the observation on the uppermost part. On the other hand, neglecting basal sliding U_b resulted in almost the same surface

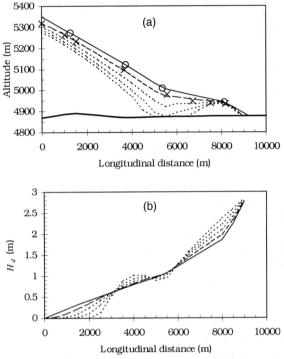

Fig. 4 The results of simulation from 1978. (a) Longitudinal profiles of glacier surface. (b) Longitudinal distributions of debris thickness.

Solid curves mean the initial profile and distribution in 1978. Dashed curves represent simulated results for 1999. Dotted curves are those for 2020, 2040 and 2060. A thick solid line, circle and cross symbols in (a) show the bed profile, and the surface positions estimated from the topographical surveys in 1978 and 1999, respectively.

lowering, although showing a slightly greater lowering on the lower part. Ignoring the effects of supraglacial debris on the mass balance, in other words calculating mass balance everywhere under debris-free conditions only with equation (2), the lowest part was simulated to disappear by 1999.

DISCUSSION

Surface topography of the debris-covered area is so heterogeneous (Iwata *et al.*, 1980) that it is difficult to determine a unique debris thickness depending on x. The debris thickness H_d used in this study should be just an indicator that represents an area average. It must be distinguished from a point debris thickness. The effect of point thickness on ablation has been examined extensively (e.g. Østrem, 1959; Mattson *et al.*, 1993), which shows that debris cover accelerates ablation most effectively at a thickness of a few centimetres, and suppresses it at greater thickness. The relation in this study between the thickness H_d and the mass balance ratio r shown in Fig. 2(b) gives a similar result, although the magnitude of the ratio is different. The present model takes the interaction between the debris thickness and the mass balance into

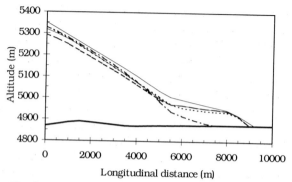

Fig. 5 The results of sensitivity tests for the longitudinal surface profile simulation during 1978–1999. A dashed curve is for $Q_{in}(x = 0) = 3.8 \times 10^9$ kg year^{-1} (Inoue, 1977), a dotted curve is for no basal sliding, and a chain curve is for debris-free conditions. The three curves represent simulation results for 1999. The initial profile in 1978 and the original simulation result in 1999 are also shown as in Fig. 4(a) with thin solid curves.

account in a very simplified way through debris conservation (equation (5)) and effects of debris thickness on mass balance (Fig. 2(b)). Without the effects of debris cover on mass balance, actual surface lowering of the glacier especially on the lowest part cannot be simulated as shown by the chain curve in Fig. 5.

Ice cliffs and supraglacial ponds accelerate ablation on the debris-covered area significantly (Inoue & Yoshida, 1980). The mass balance ratio r in Fig. 2(b) includes these effects, because it was based on an ablation rate estimated by Nakawo *et al.* (1999) which was derived as an area average through utilization of satellite data. The evolution of the cliffs and ponds depends on ablation. Sakai *et al.* (2000) argue that the evolution of cliffs and ponds would cause supraglacial debris to fall into the ponds, thus reducing the effective debris thickness. The model should be further improved to include interactions with cliffs and ponds, which are likely to be important.

The debris-free area on the uppermost part has decreased (Seko *et al.*, 1998), so apparently supraglacial debris should have increased on the uppermost part, contrary to the simulation (Fig. 4(b)). This failure of the model could result from neglecting melt-out debris on the upper glacier area and debris supply from lateral slopes. Nakawo *et al.* (1986) estimated that roughly half of the mass of the present supraglacial debris in the ablation area of the Khumbu Glacier was deposited by slope failure of the lateral moraines after the last expansion of the glacier. The present model should be revised to include debris supply from the lateral slopes.

As shown by the dashed curve in Fig. 5, the simulation result is fairly sensitive to the imposed incoming flux from the upper glacier area especially on the upper part. The flux was tuned to fit the observed surface lowering, because the earlier rough estimate by Inoue (1977) led to unreasonably large surface lowering. The tuned flux is about 1.5 times the earlier estimate, which suggests that Inoue (1977) underestimated the area of the upper glacier catchment, that more precipitation falls on the upper area than at Lhajung, and/or that more ice than net accumulation on the upper area flows into the ablation area and consequently the accumulation area is shrinking.

Kodama & Mae (1976) showed that surface flow speed on the ablation area had a seasonal variation, i.e. higher from May to August than the rest of the year. This seasonal variation should be caused by a variation in basal sliding and/or deformation of the subglacial till layer. Contributions to glacier flow from both of these processes were put together into a variable U_b, which was determined to depend only on location (x) as shown in Fig. 3, ignoring its seasonal and interannual variation. According to previous studies (e.g. Iken & Bindschadler, 1986; Boulton & Hindmarsh, 1987), water pressure at the bed layer should have an important role in both of these processes. Thus, inclusion of subglacial hydraulics could be important for accurate treatment. This defect in the model, however, seems to be minor and does not seriously effect the simulation results as shown by the dotted curve in Fig. 5.

The recent shrinkage of Khumbu Glacier was reasonably simulated in this study. Future projection predicted that stagnant ice in the lowest part would become separated from the main glacier body. This would imply that the Khumbu Glacier could develop a large glacial lake. In order to simulate the significant expansion in the past, e.g. in Little Ice Age, and the following shrinkage of the glacier, inclusion of the accumulation area into the model and long-term climate data would be required.

Acknowledgements This study is based on many contributions by Glaciological Expeditions in Nepal (GEN) activities; cooperation with Department of Hydrology and Meteorology (DHM), Ministry of Science and Technology, His Majesty's Government of Nepal. We would like to thank all members of GEN and the staff of DHM. Special thanks would be expressed to Prof. S. Iwata, Tokyo Metropolitan University, for providing information on topographic surveys in 1978. Grateful thanks also go to Prof. Y. Ageta, Nagoya University; Prof. E. D. Waddington and Dr. H. Conway, University of Washington, for their advice and for developing our numerical model in its formative stage. We would also like to thank Dr A. G. Fountain, Portland State University; Dr K. A. Brugger, University of Minnesota; and another anonymous reviewer for their valuable suggestions. This study was supported by Cooperative Research under the Japan–US Cooperative Science Program from the Japan Society for the Promotion of Science; US National Science Foundation Grant no. INT-9726704 from the National Science Foundation, USA; and a Grant-in-Aid for Scientific Research (no. 09490018) from the Ministry of Education, Science, Sports and Culture, Japanese Government.

REFERENCES

Ageta, Y. (1983) Characteristics of mass balance of the summer-accumulation type glacier in the Nepal Himalayas (in Japanese with an English abstract). *J. Japan. Soc. Snow Ice (Seppyo)* **45** (2), 81–105.

Ageta, Y. & Kadota, T. (1992) Predictions of changes of glacier mass balance in the Nepal Himalaya and Tibetan Plateau: a case study of air temperature increase for three glaciers. *Ann. Glaciol.* **16**, 89–94.

Boulton, G. S. & Hindmarsh, R. C. A. (1987) Sediment deformation beneath glaciers: rheology and geological consequences. *J. Geophys. Res.* **92**, 9059–9082.

Gades, A., Conway, H., Nereson, N., Naito, N. & Kadota, T. (2000) Radio echo-sounding through supraglacial debris on Lirung and Khumbu Glaciers, Nepal Himalayas. In: *Debris-Covered Glaciers* (ed. by M. Nakawo, C. F. Raymond & A. Fountain) (Proc. Seattle Workshop, September 2000). IAHS Publ. no. 264 (this volume).

Glaciological Expedition of Nepal (1980) Appendix 1. Glaciological data of the Khumbu Glacier in 1978. *J. Japan. Soc. Snow Ice (Seppyo)* **41**, special issue, 107–110 (with 5 separate sheets).

Iken, A. & Bindschadler, R. A. (1986) Combined measurements of subglacial water pressure and surface velocity of Findelengletscher, Switzerland: conclusions about drainage system and sliding mechanism. *J. Glaciol.* **32**, 101–119.

Inoue, J. (1976) Climate of Khumbu Himal. *J. Japan. Soc. Snow Ice (Seppyo)* **38**, special issue, 66–73.

Inoue, J. (1977) Mass budget of Khumbu Glacier. *J. Japan. Soc. Snow Ice (Seppyo)* **39**, special issue, 15–19.

Inoue, J. & Yoshida, M. (1980) Ablation and heat exchange over the Khumbu Glacier. *J. Japan. Soc. Snow Ice (Seppyo)* **41**, special issue, 26–33.

Iwata, S., Watanabe, O. & Fushimi, H. (1980) Surface morphology in the ablation area of the Khumbu Glacier. *J. Japan. Soc. Snow Ice (Seppyo)* **41**, special issue, 9–17.

Kadota, T. & Ageta, Y. (1992) On the relation between climate and retreat of Glacier AX010 in the Nepal Himalaya from 1978 to 1989. *Bull. Glacier Res.* **10**, 1–10.

Kadota, T., Seko, K., Aoki, T., Iwata, S. & Yamaguchi, S. (2000) Shrinkage of the Khumbu Glacier, east Nepal from 1978 to 1995. In: *Debris-Covered Glaciers* (ed. by M. Nakawo, C. F. Raymond & A. Fountain) (Proc. Seattle Workshop, September 2000). IAHS Publ. no. 264 (this volume).

Kodama, H. & Mae, S. (1976) The flow of glaciers in the Khumbu region. *J. Japan. Soc. Snow Ice (Seppyo)* **38**, special issue, 31–36.

Lam, J. K.-W. & Dowdeswell, J. A. (1996) An adaptive-grid finite-volume model of glacier-terminus fluctuations. *Ann. Glaciol.* **23**, 86–93.

Mattson, L. E., Gardner, J. S. & Young, G. J. (1993) Ablation on debris covered glaciers: an example from the Rakhiot Glacier, Punjab, Himalaya. In: *Snow and Glacier Hydrology* (ed. by G. J. Young) (Proc. Kathmandu Symp., November 1992), 289–296. IAHS Publ. no. 218.

Nakawo, M., Iwata, S., Watanabe, O. & Yoshida, M. (1986) Processes which distribute supraglacial debris on the Khumbu Glacier, Nepal Himalaya. *Ann. Glaciol.* **8**, 129–131.

Nakawo, M., Yabuki, H. & Sakai, A. (1999) Characteristics of Khumbu Glacier, Nepal Himalaya: recent change in the debris-covered area. *Ann. Glaciol.* **28**, 118–122.

National Geographic Society (1988) *Mount Everest*. National Geographic Society, Washington, DC.

Nye, J. F. (1965) The flow of a glacier in a channel of rectangular, elliptic or parabolic cross-section. *J. Glaciol.* **5**, 661–690.

Østrem, G. (1959) Ice melting under a thin layer of moraine, and the existence of ice cores in moraine ridges. *Geogr. Ann.* **41**, 228–230.

Patankar, S. V. (1980) *Numerical Heat Transfer and Fluid Flow*. Hemisphere, New York.

Paterson, W. S. B. (1994) *The Physics of Glaciers*, 3rd edn. Elsevier, Oxford.

Sakai, A., Takeuchi, N., Fujita, K. & Nakawo, M. (2000) Role of supraglacial ponds in the ablation process of a debris-covered glacier in the Nepal Himalayas. In: *Debris-Covered Glaciers* (ed. by M. Nakawo, C. F. Raymond & A. Fountain) (Proc. Seattle Workshop, September 2000). IAHS Publ. no. 264 (this volume).

Seko, K., Yabuki, H., Nakawo, M., Sakai, A., Kadota, T. & Yamada Y. (1998) Changing surface of Khumbu Glacier, Nepal Himalayas revealed by SPOT images. *Bull. Glacier Res.* **16**, 33–41.

Watanabe, O., Fushimi, H., Inoue, J., Iwata, S., Ikegami, K., Tanaka, Y., Yoshida, M. & Upadhyay, B. P. (1980) Outline of debris cover project in Khumbu Glacier. *J. Japan. Soc. Snow Ice (Seppyo)* **41**, special issue, 5–8.

Watanabe, O., Iwata, S. & Fushimi, H. (1986) Topographic characteristics in the ablation area of the Khumbu Glacier, Nepal Himalaya. *Ann. Glaciol.* **8**, 177–180.

Debris-Covered Glaciers (Proceedings of a workshop held at Seattle, Washington, USA, September 2000). IAHS Publ. no. 264, 2000.

Steady-state flow model of debris-covered glaciers (rock glaciers)

SARAH K. KONRAD & NEIL F. HUMPHREY

Department of Geology and Geophysics, University of Wyoming, PO Box 3006, Laramie, Wyoming 82071, USA

e-mail: skon@uwyo.edu

Abstract A two-dimensional, steady-state, flow line model of a debris-covered glacier is developed using mass conservation of debris and ice. Ice deformation is driven by shear stress, estimated from the local ice and debris overburden. Input variables are altitude-dependant ice mass balance, debris mass balance, and a function that modifies the ice mass balance with respect to the amount of surface debris; the model is solved numerically. The model demonstrates that a debris-covered glacier in steady state must be infinitely long and implies that existing debris-covered glaciers are not in steady state. The terminus of a debris-covered glacier is a critical, dynamic region that must constantly advance. The amount of debris input into the model strongly influences the form of the resultant glacier. A relatively large amount of debris produces a debris-covered glacier with a significant amount of ice beneath the debris, a morphology shared by many ice-cored rock glaciers. Less debris input into the system results in a thicker debris cover on top of a thinner layer of ice. Preliminary model results are consistent with observations from the Galena Creek rock glacier, Wyoming.

NOTATION

$a_d(x)$ = debris mass balance
$a_i(x)$ = ice mass balance
b = ablation function constant
A = flow law constant
$d(x)$ = depth of debris
D = debris mass balance coefficient
E = x-coordinate of the ELA
g = gravitational acceleration
$h(x)$ = depth of ice
M = ice mass balance coefficient
n = flow law constant

$Q_d(x)$ = surface debris flux
$Q_i(x)$ = ice flux
$v_{av}(x)$ = average longitudinal ice velocity
$v_s(x)$ = longitudinal ice velocity at surface
$v_x(x,z)$ = longitudinal ice velocity
$v_z(x,z)$ = surface-normal ice velocity
x = distance downglacier
z = distance below ice surface
θ = surface slope of ice
ρ_d = density of debris
ρ_i = density of ice

INTRODUCTION

This paper develops a simple, steady-state, flow line model of a debris-covered glacier. The objective is to increase understanding of the physical dynamics of these poorly understood glaciers. Although the morphology of debris-covered glaciers is well studied (e.g. Nakawo, 1979; Nakawo *et al.*, 1986; Clark *et al.*, 1994), their flow

dynamics have received little detailed attention. We are motivated in part by our
continuing work (Potter, 1972; Steig *et al.*, 1998; Konrad *et al.*, 1999) on the ice-cored
Galena Creek rock glacier (GCRG) of the Absaroka Mountains, Wyoming (Fig. 1).
Drilling on that glacier (and similar observations from the Murtèl I rock glacier in
Switzerland by Haeberli *et al.*, 1988) reveals up to 25 m of continuous ice underneath

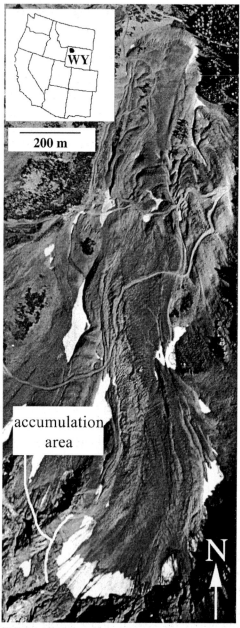

Fig. 1 Aerial photograph of Galena Creek rock glacier (August, 1985). Note relatively
small size of the accumulation area.

about a metre of loose surface debris. Although the ice contains entrained debris, including some debris layers, the overall percentage of debris is small (Potter *et al.*, 1998). We assume that the ice will deform with the same stress/strain relationship as glacier ice, and consequently base our model on standard glaciological flow laws.

The flow law assumption implies dynamic similarities between debris-covered glaciers and typical alpine glaciers. However, the surface debris cover complicates the system in two ways: (a) by adding an additional overburden stress, and (b) by inhibiting ablation (if the debris layer is more than several centimetres thick) (Østrem, 1959; Loomis, 1970; Lundstrom *et al.*, 1993). The mass balance patterns of typical alpine glaciers and debris-covered glaciers are distinctly different. The accumulation area comprises about two-thirds of the entire surface area of a steady-state alpine glacier, but much less of a debris-covered glacier (Clark *et al.*, 1994). For example, the accumulation area of GCRG represents only about 10% of the glacier surface (Fig. 1). On a typical, steady-state glacier, annual mass balance decreases with elevation. The mass balance of a debris-covered glacier is strongly influenced by the spatial variation of surface debris. Generally, the surface debris thickens in the downglacier direction (Nakawo, 1979; Konrad *et al.*, 1999), causing the net annual ablation to *decrease* from near the ELA to the terminus, the reverse of the ablation pattern observed on a typical glacier (Fig. 2).

Our model explores the effects of the "reversed" mass balance, and describes the physical behaviour of both debris-covered glaciers and ice-cored rock glaciers, provided that they consist of relatively clean, continuous ice overlain by surface debris. Although lacking many refinements, the model captures the essence of debris-covered glacier dynamics, and will act as a guide to future work.

MODEL

The steady-state flow model is two-dimensional in a vertical section along the centre flow line, with a surface-parallel coordinate system (Fig. 3). The model imposes

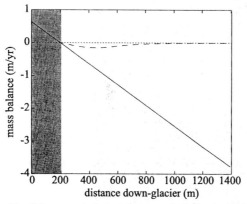

Fig. 2 Ice mass balance of a normal glacier (solid line) compared to a debris-covered glacier (dashed line). Dotted line is zero mass balance. A steady-state debris-free glacier under these conditions is 400 m long, whereas a steady-state debris-covered glacier is infinite in length. The solid line represents the mass balance function without debris, $M = 0.6$ m year^{-1}. The dashed line gives the mass balance inclusive of the insulating effects of the debris, a_i. The accumulation area is shaded.

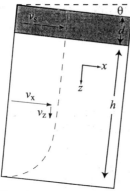

Fig. 3 Schematic illustration of the coordinate system and basic variables of the debris-covered glacier system. x is measured from the top (headwall) of the glacier; z is measured from the ice surface. Surface debris is shaded.

conservation of both ice and debris and uses a simplified force balance based upon the parallel-sided slab ice flow model which ignores effects of ice coupling along the glacier axis or transverse to the flow (Paterson, 1994). The ice deformation at any point depends on the shear stress generated by the downslope component of the overburden weight of ice and debris. Ice coupling transverse to flow is minor if the width of the glacier is much greater than the depth (Nye, 1965). Ignoring longitudinal ice coupling is more problematic since slope, depth, and velocity vary rapidly in the accumulation area; consequently we expect our model to apply poorly in this region. Our model should accurately describe the flow dynamics in the debris-covered region, where gradients in depth and velocity are relatively small. We assume that the surface debris is transported by the underlying ice, with no internal movement of its own (reasonable for low-angle slopes). Additionally, we assume no basal sliding, which is in keeping with observations from GCRG (Konrad *et al.*, 1999).

Our model is a general one, designed to provide insight into the dynamic effects of debris cover on ice. In order to maintain simplicity, we make certain assumptions, such as no basal sliding and restricting the surface debris input to the ELA. We justify the assumptions with observations from GCRG, and note that they may need to be altered in order to fit other debris-covered glaciers. In all cases we choose simple input values (constant or linear in space) and loosely base the numeric choice on observations from GCRG.

Governing functions

Our model is based on conservation of ice and debris; changes in ice or debris flux must be caused by external sources or sinks. The following mass balance equations are based on flux per unit width:

$$\frac{dQ_d}{dx} = \frac{d(dv_s)}{dx} = a_d \tag{1}$$

$$\frac{dQ_i}{dx} = \frac{d(hv_{av})}{dx} = a_i \tag{2}$$

Equation (2) assumes that there is no basal melt or accumulation, as the ice mass balance, a_i, refers to surface processes. Expansion of (2) leads to the differential equation:

$$\frac{dh}{dx} = \frac{a_i}{v_{av}} - \frac{h}{v_{av}}\left(\frac{dv_{av}}{dx}\right) \tag{3}$$

We derive the longitudinal velocity by modifying the parallel-sided flow model to account for the weight of the debris (after Konrad *et al.*, 1999):

$$v_x(z) = \frac{2A(\rho_i g \sin\theta)^n}{(n+1)}\left[\left(h + \frac{\rho_d}{\rho_i}d\right)^{(n+1)} - \left(z + \frac{\rho_d}{\rho_i}d\right)^{(n+1)}\right] \tag{4}$$

Note that $v_s = v_x(0)$. Integration of equation (4) in z gives the average ice velocity:

$$v_{av} = \frac{2A(\rho_i g \sin\theta)^n}{(n+1)(n+2)h}\left[h(n+2)\left(h + \frac{\rho_d}{\rho_i}d\right)^{(n+1)} + \left(\frac{\rho_d}{\rho_i}d\right)^{(n+2)} - \left(h + \frac{\rho_d}{\rho_i}d\right)^{(n+2)}\right] \tag{5}$$

Equations (1) and (3)–(5) form a complete set of four equations and four unknowns (h, d, v_s, v_{av}). We use a second-order Runge-Kutta technique to solve this equation set, starting at the cirque and working downglacier. We use the following values for the constants: $A = 4.0 \times 10^{-24}$ s^{-1} Pa^{-3} (for $-1°$C ice, Paterson, 1994), $n = 3$, $\rho_i = 900$ kg m^{-3}, $\rho_d = 1800$ kg m^{-3}, $g = 9.8$ m^2 s^{-1}, and use a constant surface slope, $\theta = 15°$, that reflects the average GCRG slope. Note that the model input is the surface slope, as opposed to the unknown bedrock slope. The only input variables are the ice mass balance, a_i, and the debris mass balance, a_d. The model outputs are ice depth, debris depth, and consequently the bedrock profile.

We justify our choice of a constant surface slope in that it reduces the model's complexity, albeit at the expense of poorly modelling the typically steep accumulation area. However, we are primarily interested in the behaviour of the debris-covered ablation area. A more subtle consequence of our assumption is that the glacier bed profile must adjust to contain the steady-state amounts of ice and debris determined by the model. In most models, the surface slope adjusts to fit a specified bedrock profile. We note that when the glacier depth varies rapidly (such as in the accumulation area), the assumption of a constant surface slope generates unlikely bedrock profiles.

As a final step, we generate flow lines and isochrons within the debris-covered glacier. In order to do this, we assume incompressibility of ice to calculate the vertical velocity from (4):

$$v_z = -\int_h^z \frac{\partial v_x}{\partial x}dz \tag{6}$$

Boundary conditions

We start the integration at $x = 0$, at the top of the accumulation zone, where we specify $h(0)$ as a finite depth close to zero, and $d(0) = 0$. The ice mass balance is a function both of elevation (or x in the case of constant surface slope) and of the amount of surface debris. A typical, linear mass balance function that decreases with elevation describes the mass balance without the debris cover. Observations from GCRG suggest that the mass balance is close to zero on the lower rock glacier, where the debris cover is more than several metres deep (Konrad *et al.*, 1999). Higher on the rock glacier, ablation is greater, reaching a maximum slightly downglacier from the accumulation area, in a region of approximately 1 m of surface debris. Operating under the assumption that several metres of debris severely inhibits ablation, but that significant ablation still occurs beneath a metre of debris, we define annual mass balance as:

$$a_i = M\left(1 - \frac{x}{E}\right)\left(e^{-bd}\right) \tag{7}$$

M is the mass balance coefficient, which may be regarded as the ice equivalent of the snow fall/avalanche net contribution at the glacier head, while b is an exponential decay factor describing the insulating effect of debris thickness. Only M varies in our model, with the x-coordinate of the ELA, E, remaining fixed at 200 m, and b at 2 m^{-1}. The linear relationship of a_i to M implies that a reduction in accumulation must be accompanied by a reduction in ablation. We note however, that the ablation rates are largely controlled by debris thickness and not by elevation (Fig. 2). Values of M used in this study vary from 0.6 to 1.2 m year^{-1}.

The ice mass balance function is a schematic approximation: the linear dependence on altitude is only approximate, and the response to the debris cover is an extrapolation of numerous studies (summarized by Clark *et al.*, 1994). Nevertheless, this form of the function captures the "reversed" mass balance pattern observed on debris-covered glaciers in dry environments (Fig. 2). It is probable that this function would be more complex in a wet environment where water can directly advect heat through the debris cover.

The accumulation area of most debris-covered glaciers is primarily debris-free, as debris deposited here will not remain on the surface due to the positive ice mass

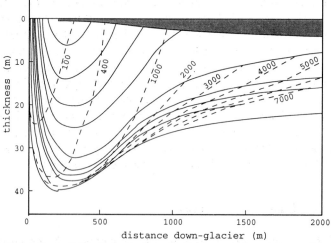

Fig. 4 Typical debris-covered glacier as generated by the model. In this particular case, $M = 0.6$ m year^{-1} and $D = 1.3$ m year^{-1}. Flow lines are solid and isochrons are dashed, ages are shown in years. The surface debris is shaded.

balance. Most debris is transported across the accumulation area by avalanche processes, and accumulates on the surface as the slope lessens away from the cirque (Potter, 1972). The downglacier steady-state flux of debris must be constant in both space and time as there are no other significant sources or sinks for rock debris. We represent this debris input pattern as a single point source at the ELA:

$$a_d = D\delta(E) \tag{8}$$

where $\delta(E)$ is the Dirac delta function at $x = E$. D is the debris balance coefficient, and represents the amount of debris added to the system at the ELA. In test runs, we allow D to vary from 1.3 to 2.6 m year^{-1}. An additional possible debris source derives from ice ablation, as any debris within the ice will be added to the bottom of the surface debris layer as the ice melts. At GCRG, it is reasonable to ignore this debris source, as the debris content of the ice is relatively low (Potter *et al.*, 1998). For the purposes of modelling debris-covered glaciers in which a large portion of the debris comes from ice ablation, (8) can be modified to be a function of ablation rates and debris content of the ice (e.g. Nakawo *et al.*, 1986).

RESULTS AND DISCUSSION

A typical debris-covered glacier generated by our model is shown in Fig. 4. Ice is significantly thicker in the accumulation area than in the ablation area, this is in part due to the assumption of constant surface slope. Debris cover gradually thickens down-valley, as the ice depth gradually thins. Within the accumulation area, the ice follows flow lines similar to those of a typical glacier. However, the flow paths in the ablation area are quite different: instead of curving up to meet the surface as in a debris-free glacier, the flow initially curves towards the surface (where ablation rates are relatively high) but turns back to parallel the surface further down-valley (where ablation rates approach zero). Predicted flow velocities are slow (~0.6 m year^{-1} on the majority of the debris-covered region), resulting in old ice underneath the debris cover. Ice older than ~1000 years is not expected in typical alpine glaciers: our model helps to explain the ice ages of 1600 and 2200 years measured on the upper reaches of GCRG (Konrad *et al.*, 1999).

The most striking result is that the glacier does not have a defined terminus: in steady state, because the debris cover forces the ablation to approach zero, the ice continues to flow down-valley. This is predicted by a comparison of the mass balance functions in Fig. 2. In order for the glacier to be in steady state, the area under the curves in the accumulation area and the ablation area must be equal. In the debris-free case, the steady-state glacier will be 400 m long. Because the area under the curve in the ablation area of the debris-covered glacier is highly bounded, the glacier must be infinite in length for the total ablation to equal the total accumulation.

Effects of varying input mass balances

The form of the resulting debris-covered glacier varies with the specified ice and debris mass balances, controlled by the coefficients M and D, respectively (Fig. 5). A large D and small M cause the majority of the ice mass to be found in the debris-covered tongue (Fig. 5(c)). For a given *M*, if *D* is increased, the result is both a thickening and speeding up of the debris-covered tongue. The maximum glacier depth does not change, but the total amount of ice is greater (compare Fig. 5(a) and (b)with 5(c) and (d), respectively). The increase in *D* results in a thinner layer of surface debris: this anti-intuitive result is caused by the increased ice velocity. For a given *D*, an increase of *M* actually results in less ice, although the maximum depth increases slightly (compare Fig. 5(a) and (c) with 5(b) and (d), respectively). There are two explanations for this: (a) increasing *M* increases the ice velocity, causing the debris layer to thin and increasing ablation; and (b) an increase of *M* increases both accumulation in the accumulation area and ablation in the ablation area. In the extreme case of large *M* and small *D* (not pictured) we develop a cirque glacier, with a small debris-covered tongue. This approaches the form of a debris-free glacier, for which $D = 0$.

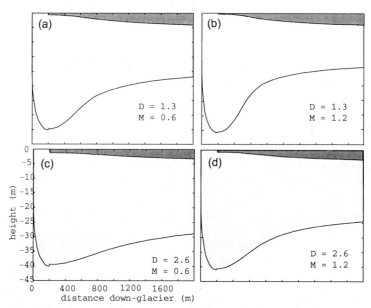

Fig. 5 Variations of glacier geometry with changes in ice mass balance (*M*, in m year^{-1}) and debris mass balance (*D*, in m year^{-1}).

Terminus region

Two conclusions immediately result from the observation that a debris-covered glacier cannot be in steady state: (a) the terminus of an active debris-covered glacier must advance, and (b) the length of the debris-covered glacier is some function of its age. Our model leaves the terminus region undefined: downglacier modelling is merely truncated. However, a conceptual examination is worthwhile. Imagine a debris-covered glacier that is not infinitely old and therefore has an advancing terminus located at a finite distance from the headwall. At the terminus, debris rests on top of ice that is now exposed (on the downglacier side) to the air and to ablation. The exposed ice quickly melts, causing the overlying debris to ravel down the face of the glacier, and start accumulating at the base of the ice face. The debris builds up along the ice face, again insulating it from ablation. However, the ice is still flowing forward, and overrides the fallen debris. The above processes of ablation, debris ravelling down the face, and the glacier advancing and overriding debris occur together as a continuous cycle as the terminus advances down-valley. The amount of debris underlying the glacier at any given point is directly related to processes at the terminus at the time at which the debris was overridden (essentially the ratio of longitudinal ice velocity to longitudinal ablation on the ice face). The underlying debris layer can also be thought of as a debris sink, or a way to remove debris from the debris-covered glacier system. We know from drilling at GCRG (Konrad *et al.*, 1999) and Murtèl I (Haeberli *et al.*, 1988) that debris (possibly ice-saturated) underlies the continuous ice layer. We have also observed debris ravelling down the steep terminus face of GCRG. Finally, the standard criterion used to identify an active rock glacier (as opposed to stagnant) is an advancing terminus (Wahrhaftig & Cox, 1959). All these observations support our conceptual model of the behaviour of the terminus.

Acknowledgements This research was supported by NSF Grant EAR-9710061, and a National Science Foundation Graduate Student Fellowship.

REFERENCES

Clark, D. H., Clark, M. M. & Gillespie, A. R. (1994) Debris-covered glaciers in the Sierra Nevada, California, and their implications for snowline reconstructions. *Quatern. Res.* **41**, 139–153.

Haeberli, W., Huder, J., Keusen, H. R., Pika, J. & Röthlisberger, H. (1988) Core drilling through rock glacier-permafrost. In: *Proceedings of the Fifth International Conference on Permafrost* (Trondheim, Norway) (ed. by Senneset-Kaare), vol. 2, 937–942. International Permafrost Association, Copenhagen, Denmark.

Konrad, S. K., Humphrey, N. F., Steig, E. J., Clark, D. H., Potter, N. Jr & Pfeffer, W. T. (1999) Rock glacier dynamics and paleoclimatic implications. *Geology* 27(12), 1131–1134.

Loomis, S. R. (1970) Morphology and ablation processes on glacier ice. Part I. Morphology and structure of an ice-cored medial moraine, Kaskawulsh Glacier, Yukon. *Arctic Inst. of N. Am. Res. Pap.* 57, 1–65.

Lundstrom, S. C., McCafferty, A. E. & Coe, J. A. (1993) Photogrammetric analysis of 1984–89 surface altitude change of the partially debris-covered Eliot Glacier, Mount Hood, Oregon, USA. *Ann. Glaciol.* 17, 167–170.

Nakawo, M. (1979) Supraglacial debris of G_2 Glacier in Hidden Valley, Mukut Himal, Nepal. *J. Glaciol.* 22(87), 273–283.

Nakawo, M., Iwata, S., Watanabe, O. & Yoshida, M. (1986) Processes which distribute supraglacial debris on the Khumbu Glacier, Nepal Himalaya. *Ann. Glaciol.* 8, 129–131.

Nye, J. F. (1965) The flow of a glacier in a channel of rectangular, elliptic or parabolic cross-section. *J. Glaciol.* 5, 661–690.

Østrem, G. (1959) Ice melting under a thin layer of moraine, and the existence of ice cores in moraine ridges. *Geogr. Ann.* 41, 228–230.

Paterson, W. S. B. (1994) *The Physics of Glaciers*, third edn. Pergamon Press, New York, USA.

Potter, N. Jr (1972) Ice-cored rock glacier, Galena Creek, Northern Absaroka Mountains, Wyoming. *Geol. Soc. Am. Bull.* **83**, 3025–3058.

Potter, N. Jr, Steig, E. J., Clark, D. H., Speece, M. A., Clark, G. M. & Updike, A. B. (1998) Galena Creek Rock Glacier revisited—new observations on an old controversy. *Geogr. Ann.* **80A**, 251–266.

Steig, E. J., Fitzpatrick, J. J., Potter, N. Jr & Clark, D. H. (1998) The geochemical record in rock glaciers. *Geogr. Ann.* **80A**, 277–286.

Wahrhaftig, C. & Cox, A. (1959) Rock glaciers in the Alaska Range. *Geol. Soc. Am. Bull.* **70**, 383–436.

6 Biology and Hydrology

Debris-Covered Glaciers (Proceedings of a workshop held at Seattle, Washington, USA, September 2000).
IAHS Publ. no. 264, 2000.   267

Effect of debris cover on species composition of living organisms in supraglacial lakes on a Himalayan glacier

NOZOMU TAKEUCHI∗ **& SHIRO KOHSHIMA**

Laboratory of Biology, Faculty of Bioscience and Biotechnology (c/o Faculty of Science), Tokyo Institute of Technology, 2-12-1, O-okayama, Meguro-ku, Tokyo 152-8551, Japan
e-mail: nozomu@iarc.uaf.edu

Abstract Supraglacial lakes on a Himalayan debris-covered glacier (Khumbu Glacier in east Nepal) were investigated to identify the organisms living in them. Two kinds of insects, a copepod, a branchiopod, and nine kinds of algae were observed in the lakes. The kinds of organisms identify three types of lakes. *Type A*: lakes with animals and algae; *Type B*: lakes with animals only; *Type C*: lakes without living organisms. Each type of lake had distinctly different water characteristics. Suspended sediment concentration of water in Type A lakes was significantly lower than that in Type B and Type C lakes. Electrical conductivity and surface temperature of lake water was highest in Type A lakes, followed by Type B and Type C lakes. Our results suggest that the species composition in supraglacial lakes is determined by water characteristics and the life span of the lake, which may be due to debris conditions around the lake.

INTRODUCTION

Glaciers are not anti-biotic environments. Recently, many kinds of cold-tolerant organisms have been found on glaciers of Himalayas, Tibet, Arctic, and Antarctic. For example, Kohshima (1984a,b, 1987a,b) found a specialized animal community consisting of cold-tolerant insects and copepods sustained on a Himalayan glacier by feeding on algae and bacteria growing in the near-surface snow and ice. He pointed out that the glacier is a unique freshwater ecosystem with a very simple and specialized biotic community based on the primary production of these algae.

Debris cover is extensive on mountain glaciers, especially those in the Himalaya. When the debris is thick, it is impossible for snow and ice algae to grow directly on the glacier surface. Some organisms inhabit the meltwater system of glaciers including ones with debris, for example in supraglacial lakes or meltwater channels on or beneath the surface (e.g. Clayton, 1964; Kohshima, 1985). However, few biological observations have been made, and the community in the meltwater systems of debris-covered glacier is still unexplored. Since community structure of living organisms is due to physical and chemical conditions of their habitat, the community in the meltwater systems, in particular in supraglacial lakes, may be largely affected by glacier surface conditions, such as debris thickness, debris characteristics, and/or glacial melting activity.

∗ *Now at*: Frontier Observational Research System for Global Change, International Arctic Research Center, University of Alaska at Fairbanks, 930 Koyukuk Drive, PO Box 757335, Fairbanks, Alaska, USA.

This study aims to determine species composition of living organisms in supraglacial lakes on a Himalayan debris-covered glacier (Khumbu Glacier in east Nepal). Physical, chemical, and biological characteristics of the lakes are described. The relationship of the diversity and quantity of organisms to the physical process acting on the glacier surface, in particular the role of debris depending on its thickness, is discussed.

STUDY SITE

The research was carried out from 20 October to 10 November 1995, in Khumbu Glacier, east Nepal (Fig. 1). This glacier flows from the top of Mt Everest (Mt Sagarmarta, 8848 m a.s.l.) down to 4900 m a.s.l. over a distance of more than 15 km in the Khumbu Valley. The ablation area of the glacier is 10 km long from 4900 m a.s.l. to 5200 m a.s.l. and is covered with debris. The debris area has complex surface morphologies including debris-covered cones, large hollows, ice cliffs, lakes, and streams (Iwata *et al.*, 1980).

On the debris-covered area, more than 100 supraglacial lakes and ponds were observed in the study period. For simplicity, all will be referred to as lakes. They ranged from approximately 2 to 100 m in diameter. Figure 2 shows the distribution of the lakes on the ablation area. Forty lakes with practical access were chosen for investigation.

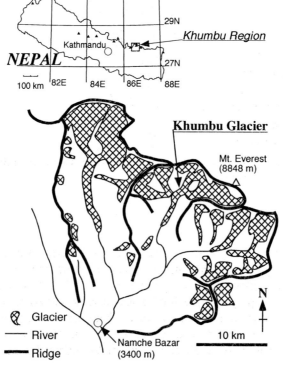

Fig. 1 Location of Khumbu Glacier in Nepal Himalayas.

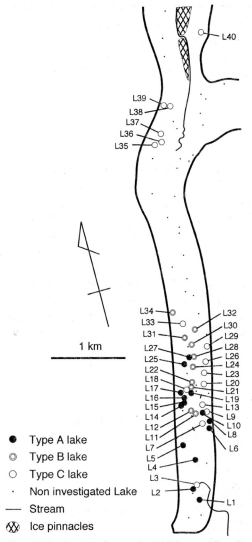

Fig. 2 Distribution of supraglacial lakes on Khumbu Glacier according to the species composition of each lake.

METHODS

Inhabitants of the 40 lakes were investigated in several ways. Insects and zooplanktons were sought in the lake bottom using a net of fine mesh. Lake water including benthos was collected by a pipette from the lakeside at each lake. The water was kept in 50 ml polyethylene bottles and was preserved as a 3% formalin solution. The samples were transported to Japan where organisms (microbes) in the water and benthos were analysed with a microscope. Bacteria were not analysed other than blue green bacteria (cyanobacteria), which are referred to here as algae for simplicity.

For each lake studied, the suspended sediment concentration (SSC, mg l^{-1}), water temperature (°C), and electrical conductivity (EC, μS cm^{-1}) were measured near the lake surface (5–10 cm in depth) at the lakeside. Measuring and sampling were done during the daytime (9:00–15:00) between 24 October and 7 November. Water temperature was measured with a thermistor thermometer (TAKARA D611). EC was measured with an EC meter (Model SC82, YOKOGAWA Co.). EC values were adjusted to 0°C. The water samples were transported to Japan and analysed at the Tokyo Institute of Technology. In order to measure SSC, 100 ml of sample water was first filtered through a pre-weighted membrane filter (Millipore HAWP047XX, pore size: 0.45 μm). Then, the filters were dried (65°C, 24 h), and the weight of the particles on the filter was measured with an electric balance (METTLER AE240, 0.01 mg resolution).

RESULTS

Living organisms in the supraglacial lakes

Two kinds of insect, a copepod, a branchiopod, and nine kinds of algae were observed. A list of the organisms is shown in Table 1. The insects, copepod, and branchiopod were at the bottom of the lakes. Algae were observed mainly in the benthos.

Table 1 List of living organisms found in supraglacial lakes of Khumbu Glacier.

	Family	Size (algae: cell size)	Remarks
Animal			
Stonefly	Capniidae	12–8 mm length, 1.8–2.0 mm width	Larva
Midge	Chironomidae	7–9 mm length, 0.7–0.9 mm width	Larva, black to yellow colour
Copepod	Diaptomidae	1.2–1.5 mm length, 0.4 mm width	red color
Branchiopod	Daphniadae	1.0–2.3 mm length, 0.8–1.0 mm width	*Daphnia* sp.
Plant			
Blue green alga 1	Oscillatoriaceae	1.5 µm length, 1.0 µm width	
Blue green alga 2	Oscillatoriaceae	1.5 µm length, 1.5 µm width	
Blue green alga 3	Chroococcaceae	3–10 µm in diameter	
Blue green alga 4	Nostocaceae	2–4 µm length, 2–4 µm width	*Anabaena* sp.
Green alga 1	Zygnemataceae	90–110 µm length, 16–18 µm width	
Green alga 2	Desmidiaceae	75–90 µm length, 70–80 µm width	*Cosmarium* sp.
Diatom 1	Fragilariaceae	15–20 µm length, 7–8 µm width	
Diatom 2	Naviculaceae	35–50 µm length, 8–10 µm width	
Diatom 3	Cymbellaceae	11–14 µm length, 3–4 µm width	

Species composition of the lakes

Table 2 shows the list of lakes and organisms observed in each lake. The species composition of the organisms was found to differ in the lakes. Fourteen of the 40 lakes were inhabited by algae and animals. Ten lakes were inhabited by only animals. Sixteen lakes were not inhabited by any organisms. Therefore, the lakes were divided

Table 2 List of investigated supraglacial lakes of Khumbu Glacier, showing water characteristics and living organism, and lake type.

Lake no.	Date	SSC (mg l⁻¹)	EC (μS cm⁻²)	Water temperature (°C)	Ice cliff	Type of species composition	Stonefly	Midge	Copepod	Branchiopod	Blue green alga 1	Blue green alga 2	Blue green alga 3	Blue green alga 4	Green alga 1	Green alga 2	Diatom 1	Diatom 2	Diatom 3
1	2 Nov.	0.0	75.3	6.7		A		+	+		+	+			+	+	+	+	+
2	27 Oct.	34.3	44.3	5.6		A	+	+	+	+	+								
3	27 Oct.	50.7	34.9	0.4		C													
4	28 Oct.	0.0	72.7	6.3		A	+	+	+		+	+			+				
5	28 Oct.	0.0	80.1	8.5		A		+			+	+	+	+	+	+	+	+	
6	28 Oct.	0.0	44.0	4.2		A		+	+		+						+	+	+
7	28 Oct.	15.2	22.4	1.6	+	C													
8	28 Oct.	0.0	25.9	5.3		A		+			+			+	+	+	+	+	
9	29 Oct.	49.7	17.5	0.7	+	C													
10	29 Oct.	0.0	32.7	0.6		A	+	+			+				+				
11	24 Oct.	57.9	22.2	5.8	+	B	+	+											
12	27 Oct.	30.1	36.4	5.1	+	B	+	+											
13	29 Oct.	10.1	45.9	0.5	+	C													
14	24 Oct.	0.0	80.0	6.0		A		+			+	+	+		+	+	+		
15	24 Oct.	0.0	71.2	6.3		A	+	+	+		+			+	+	+	+		+
16	28 Oct.	21.3	79.7	5.7		A	+	+	+		+				+				
17	28 Oct.	0.0	90.0	8.3		A		+	+		+	+	+	+	+		+	+	
18	28 Oct.	64.2	41.4	4.7	+	C													
19	30 Oct.	3.0	38.3	3.3		A		+			+				+				+
20	29 Oct.	59.5	17.7	0.7		C													
21	30 Oct.	58.6	18.3	1.9	+	B		+											
22	30 Oct.	23.2	66.2	6.4	+	B	+	+											
23	29 Oct.	41.4	10.0	2.0	+	C													
24	20 Oct.	40.1	39.0	3.1	+	B		+											
25	29 Oct.	0.0	63.8	7.7		A	+	+	+		+	+	+		+		+	+	
26	31 Oct.	9.0	25.0	0.4	+	C													
27	29 Oct.	9.6	30.9	1.3		A		+											+
28	29 Oct.	55.6	28.1	1.4		B		+											
29	31 Oct.	3.0	38.0	0.9		C													
30	31 Oct.	12.1	25.7	1.5		B		+											
31	1 Nov.	40.1	23.6	3.0	+	B		+											
32	1 Nov.	43.2	33.1	0.8	+	B	+	+											
33	1 Nov.	86.5	19.1	2.2	+	C													
34	1 Nov.	7.0	15.9	0.6		B	+	+											
35	4 Nov.	5.0	10.0	0.6	+	C													
36	4 Nov.	18.0	14.9	0.7	+	C													
37	4 Nov.	3.0	17.6	1.0	+	C													
38	5 Nov.	0.0	2.4	0.6		C													
39	7 Nov.	20.1	20.3	0.4		C													
40	7 Nov.	0.0	16.6	0.5	+	C													

into three types:

Type A: lakes with animals and algae;
Type B: lakes with animals only;
Type C: lakes without living organisms.

Microscopy of the benthos of the lakes revealed that the benthos of Type A lakes contained much amorphous organic matter and much algae. On the other hand, the benthos of Type B and Type C lakes contained only fine mineral particles and a little amorphous organic matter. A food source for the animals in Type B lakes is likely to be this organic matter that is probably transported to the lakes from the surrounding terrain by wind.

Figure 2 shows the distribution of each lake type. Type A lakes tended to be distributed in the margin of the downstream area of the glacier. Type B lakes tended to be in the centre of the glacier. Type C lakes tended to be farther upstream.

Water characteristics of the lakes

SSC, EC, and surface temperature of lake water varied between the lakes (Table 2).

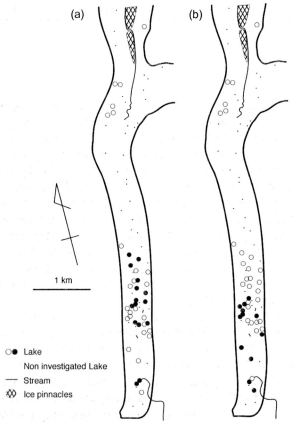

Fig. 3 Distribution of water characteristics of supraglacial lakes on Khumbu Glacier. (a) Suspended sediment concentration. ○: 0–30 mg l^{-1}; ●: > 30 mg l^{-1}. (b) Electrical conductivity. ○: 0–40 μS cm^{-2}; ●: > 40 μS cm^{-2}.

SSC of the lake water ranged from 0.0 to 86.5 mg l^{-1}. Mean SSC was 21.8 mg l^{-1}. The SSC of 12 lakes was 0.0 mg l^{-1}. EC of lake water ranged from 2.4 to 90.0 μS cm^{-2}. Mean EC was 37.3 μS cm^{-2}. Surface water temperature ranged from 0.4 to 8.5°C. Mean water temperature was 3.1°C.

Figure 3 shows the distribution of SSC and EC levels in the lakes. High SSC lakes (more than 30 mg l^{-1}) tended to lie toward the centre of the glacier. High EC lakes (more than 40 μS cm^{-2}) tended to be in the downstream area of the glacier.

Table 3 shows the characteristics of the water of each type of lake. SSC for Type B and Type C lakes was not significantly different (36.8 *vs* 27.2 mg l^{-1}, statistical *t*-test: $t = 2.06$, P (probability) $= 0.30 > 0.05$), but were significantly higher than Type A lakes (1.1 mg l^{-1}, Type A *vs* B: $t = 2.16$, $P = 0.00 < 0.05$; Type A *vs* C: $t = 2.09$, $P = 0.01 < 0.05$). Electrical conductivity and surface temperature of lake water were highest in Type A lakes, and lowest in Type C lakes.

Table 3 Water characteristics (mean values and standard error) for each lake type on Khumbu Glacier.

	Type A	Type B	Type C
SSC (mg l^{-1})	4.9 (±2.8)	36.8 (±5.8)	27.2 (±6.8)
EC (μS cm^{-2})	59.2 (±5.9)	30.9 (±4.6)	22.1 (±3.0)
Temperature (°C)	5.4 (±0.6)	3.0 (±0.7)	1.1 (±0.3)

DISCUSSION

The different characteristics of the water of the three lake types suggest that species composition is due to the characteristics of the lake water. Since suspended sediment particles in lake water decrease the transparency of the lake water, high SSC level of lake water inhibits the photosynthesis of algae and decreases algal growth. SSCs for most of Type A lakes were zero (10 of 14 lakes), and SSC for Type B and Type C lakes was significantly higher than that of Type A lakes. Therefore, lack of algae in communities of Type B and Type C lakes may be caused by the water turbidity. Nutrient conditions of the lake water must also affect species composition in the lakes, especially algal growth. High EC level of lake water indicates that the water is rich in solutes, which may include limiting nutrients. Since the EC level for lake water was the highest in Type A lakes, nutrient condition in Type A lakes may be relatively richer than in Type B lakes and in Type C lakes. Therefore, both SSC and EC play a role in the more abundant algae in Type A lakes.

Life span of lakes is also expected to affect species composition of the lakes. The lake distribution for 1995 on the glacier was different from the distribution in 1978 as reported by Iwata *et al.* (1980). This indicates that supraglacial lakes do not persist for a long time, but form and collapse repeatedly. This is probably due to changes of surface morphology caused by glacier flow and surface melting. Although the water characteristics of Type B and C lakes were similar, animals were observed only in Type B lakes. This is probably due to a difference in time since the formation of the lakes: Type B lakes may be older than Type C lakes and have been present long enough for colonization.

The lake water characteristics are probably affected by the debris condition around the lake. Meltwater from the glacier is the main water source for the lakes. Since the melting of debris-covered areas is concentrated at ice cliffs (Inoue & Yoshida, 1980), inflow to lakes with ice cliffs is relatively high. SSC of the lakes that had ice cliffs was significantly higher than the lakes without ice cliff (33.1 *vs* 12.6 mg l^{-1}; statistical *t*-test, $t = 2.945$, $P = 0.003 < 0.05$). This suggests that lake water with a high SSC level originates from an abundant meltwater supply. The meltwater may flow into the lakes carrying fine particles from the debris cover thus elevating the SSC. The distribution of lakes with low SSC also supports this idea. According to the debris thickness distribution on Khumbu Glacier compiled by Nakawo *et al.* (1986), the debris thickness in the downstream area of the glacier is more than 2 m on average. The lakes located in the downstream area had low SSC (less than 40 mg l^{-1}) except for L2 and L3 (Fig. 3(a)). Since the thick debris layer inhibits glacier melting (e.g. Nakawo & Young, 1981), the melting of glacier surface is likely to be slow in this area with consequent low inflow and generation of SSC. The high SSC lakes in this area (L2 and L3) were connected to a turbid meltwater stream that provided input of suspended sediment.

The distribution of high EC lakes suggests a solute source from organic soil debris around the lake. Lakes with high EC are distributed along the margin of downstream area of the glacier (Fig. 3(b)). According to Iwata *et al.* (1980), the debris of this area supports organic soil and vegetation patches. The lakes of this area are likely fed by water coming from or through organic soil. Since debris stability is required for the formation of organic soil, organic soil may develop only on areas of thick debris, where surface melting is strongly inhibited. Therefore, high EC lakes may form on thick and stable debris areas.

Thus, species composition of supraglacial lakes is likely to reflect the life span of the lakes and the debris condition around the lake. Type A lakes are formed in areas of stable and thick debris, Type B lakes are formed on thin debris area, Type C lakes are also formed on thin debris area, but have existed for a shorter time than Type B lakes.

According to Nakawo *et al.* (1986), supraglacial debris of this glacier has been forming for a period of the order of hundreds of years, since the last advance of the glacier. Numbers and distribution of each lake type might have changed with the debris formation. In the initial stage of debris formation, Type C lakes would have been dominant on the glacier surface when debris cover was thin, melting was intense, and surface morphology changed rapidly. As the debris became thicker, the number of Type B and Type A lakes might have increased. If the debris continues to thicken in the future, Type A lakes will eventually be dominant on the debris-covered area together with a more diverse ecology on the increasingly stable debris cover itself.

Acknowledgements We would like to express our thanks to the Department of Hydrology and Meteorology, Ministry of Water Resources, His Majesty's Government of Nepal. We thank all of the Sherpa people and the members of the Cryosphere Research Expedition in the Himalayas for their help to support our field work in Nepal. We also thank two anonymous reviewers for helpful suggestions on the manuscript. The expenses of this research were supported by a Grant-in-Aid for Scientific Research (no. 06041051, no. 09490018 and Aid for the Japan Society for the

Promotion of Science Research Fellow) from the Ministry of Education, Science, Sports and Culture, Japanese Government.

REFERENCES

Clayton, L. (1964) Karst topography on stagnant glaciers. *J. Glaciol.* **5**,107–112.

Inoue, J. & Yoshida, M. (1980) Ablation and heat exchange over the Khumbu Glacier. *J. Japan. Soc. Snow Ice (Seppyo)* **41**, special issue, 26–33.

Iwata, S., Watanabe O. & Fushimi, H. (1980) Surface morphology in the ablation area of the Khumbu Glacier. *J. Japan. Soc. Snow Ice (Seppyo)* **41**, special issue, 9–17.

Kohshima, S. (1984a) A novel cold-tolerant insect found in a Himalayan glacier. *Nature* **310**, 225–227.

Kohshima, S. (1984b) Living micro-plants in the dirt layer dust of Yala Glacier. In: *Glacial Studies in Langtang Valley* (ed. by K. Higuchi), 91–97. Data Centre for Glacier Research, Japanese Society of Snow and Ice Office, Nagoya, Japan.

Kohshima, S. (1985) Patagonian glaciers as insect habitats. In: *Glaciological Studies in Patagonia Northern Icefield 1983–1984* (ed. by C. Nakajima), 94–99. Data Centre for Glacier Research, Japanese Society of Snow and Ice Office, Nagoya.

Kohshima, S. (1987a) Glacial biology and biotic communities. In: *Evolution and Coadaptation in Biotic Communities* (ed. by S. Kawano, J. H. Connell & T. Hidaka), 77–92. Faculty of Science, Kyoto Univ., Kyoto.

Kohshima, S. (1987b) Formation of dirt layers and surface dust by micro-plant growth in Yala (Dakpatsen) Glacier, Nepal Himalayas. *Bull. Glacier Res.* **5**, 63–68.

Nakawo, M. & Young, G. J. (1981) Field experiments to determine the effect of a debris layer on ablation of glacier ice. *Ann. Glaciol.* **2**, 85–91.

Nakawo, M., Iwata, S., Watanabe, O. & Yoshida, M. (1986) Processes which distribute supraglacial debris on the Khumbu Glacier, Nepal Himalaya. *Ann. Glaciol.* **8**, 129–131.

Debris-Covered Glaciers (Proceedings of a workshop held at Seattle, Washington, USA, September 2000).
IAHS Publ. no. 264, 2000.

277

Seasonal changes in dissolved chemical composition and flux of meltwater draining from Lirung Glacier in the Nepal Himalayas

MAYA P. BHATT*, TOSHIYUKI MASUZAWA, MINEKO YAMAMOTO, AKIKO SAKAI & KOJI FUJITA

Institute for Hydrospheric–Atmospheric Sciences, Nagoya University, Furo-cho, Chikusa-ku, Nagoya 464-8601, Japan
e-mail: masuzawa@ihas.nahoya-u.ac.jp

Abstract Glacier meltwaters were sampled at approximately weekly intervals at the outlet of the debris-covered glacier, Lirung Glacier (28°12.9′N, 86°39.9′E; 4000 m a.m.s.l.), in the Nepal Himalayas from 16 May (pre-monsoon) to 26 October (post-monsoon) 1996. The average water discharge during the monsoon period (19 June–13 September) was 2.85±0.35 times higher than that during the pre- and post-monsoon periods. During the monsoon period the average TDS concentration was lower (0.57 times) and the average daily TDS flux was higher (1.63±0.23 times) than during the pre- and post-monsoon periods. The major cation and anion compositions in equivalent l^{-1} were Ca^{2+} >> Mg^{2+} ≥ Na^+ ≥ K^+ >> NH_4^+ and Alk > SO_4^{2-} >> NO_3^- > Cl^-, respectively. The composition of the major species was, however, quite constant throughout the observed period. The dominance of Ca^{2+}, Alk and SO_4^{2-} indicates that sulphide oxidation coupled with carbonate dissolution is the dominant chemical weathering processes occurring within the subglacial drainage system of this glacier as widely observed in other alpine glacierized basins. The monsoon season affected the weathering fluxes of solutes through the enhanced meltwater mass but not the weathering mechanism(s) within the subglacial drainage system of the glacier.

INTRODUCTION

Meltwaters from mountain glaciers of the Himalayas are one of the dominant water resources for Nepal. Understanding the associated geochemical processes for the development of their chemical composition is important. Glaciological and meteorological observations on glaciers and climate in the Nepal Himalayas have been carried out since 1973, and the Langtang Valley has been under observation since 1980 through the Glaciological Expedition of Nepal (Higuchi *et al.*, 1982). However, there are only limited data on the chemical composition of glacier meltwaters, pond waters and ice cores in the Nepal Himalayas (Watanabe *et al.*, 1984; Kamiyama, 1984; Reynolds *et al.*, 1995). There have been no measurements of seasonal changes in glacier meltwaters in the Nepal Himalayas although these data have been reported for other Himalayan areas (Hasnain & Thayyen, 1999; Collins, 1999). This study was undertaken to observe seasonal changes and fluxes of major chemical constituents in

* *Present address*: Environmental Sciences Division, School of Science, Kathmandu University, Dhulikhel, Kavre, Nepal

glacier meltwaters from the debris-covered glacier, Lirung Glacier. Data acquired through the pre- to post-monsoon season indicate that the principal weathering processes controlling the chemical composition of the glacier meltwaters is sulphide oxidation coupled with carbonate dissolution as widely observed in other alpine glacierized basins. The effect of surface debris cover on the chemical composition of discharge waters seems to be not significant.

STUDY AREA

Lirung Glacier (28°12.9′N, 86°39.9′E) is located 60 km north of Kathmandu in the Langtang Valley and is the headwater area of the Langtang–Narayani River system. Figure 1 shows a topographical map of Lirung Glacier basin (Sakai *et al.*, 1997). The

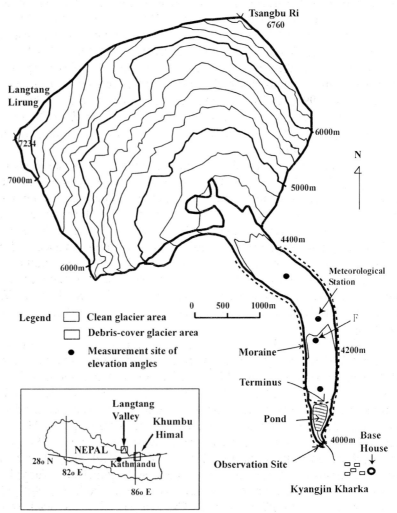

Fig. 1 Topographic map of Lirung Glacier basin in the Nepal Himalayas (after Sakai *et al.*, 1997).

altitude of the Lirung Himal is 7234 m and the lowest point of the basin, the outlet, is 4000 m a.m.s.l. The total area of the drainage basin is 13.8 km², of which 33% is steep bedrock walls, 16% debris-covered glacier and the remaining 51% debris-free ice (Fukushima *et al.*, 1987). Geologically, the Langtang Lirung area lies in a complex transition zone between the High Himalayan metasediments (south) and the Tethyan sedimentary series (north). The lithology mainly consists of high-grade metamorphic rocks with traces of igneous rocks including migmatites, gneisses, schists, phyllites and granites (Inger & Harris, 1992).

MATERIALS AND METHODS

Discharge waters were sampled at approximately weekly intervals from 16 May to 26 October 1996 at the outlet of Lirung Glacier (Fig. 1), as a part of the Cryosphere Research Expedition in the Himalayas in 1996 (Nakawo *et al.*, 1997; Fujita *et al.*, 1997; Sakai *et al.*, 1997). Hourly measurements of physical variables and tri-hourly sampling for chemical analyses were carried out for 30 h on 30–31 May and 29–30 September 1996 at the outlet to examine diurnal changes. Discharge at the outlet was observed from 8 May to 25 October 1996 except for a period from 29 June to 5 July (Sakai *et al.*, 1997). Daily precipitation was observed at the debris-covered area of Lirung Glacier (P_{LR}; 4190 m a.m.s.l.) and at Kyanjing Base House (P_{BH}; 3880 m a.m.s.l.; Fig. 1). Meteorological variables were measured during the same calendar interval in 1996 (Fujita *et al.*, 1997).

Each water sample was filtered with a pre-weighed 25-mm or 47-mm GELMAN Supor polyethersulfone filter with a 0.2-μm pore size by using a hand vacuum pump or a syringe just after sampling. The filter with the residue was stored in a petrislide. The filtrate was stored in a pre-washed Milli-Q-water-filled 50-ml polyethylene (PE) bottle for major species analyses (non-acidified) and a pre-washed 50-ml PE bottle filled with ultra-pure water prepared by sub-boiling distillation and added 0.5 ml of 6M HCl for PO_4-P and trace element analyses (acidified). The non-acidified samples were stored in a refrigerator and the acidified samples at room temperature until chemically analysed. Air temperature, water temperature, electrical conductivity (EC; Horiba B-173) and pH (Horiba B-212) of discharge waters were measured at the time of sampling.

Analytical methods used for the water samples were as follows: Suspended sediment (SS) was weighed with the filter after drying in a vacuum oven at 60°C for 48 h. Major cations (Na^+, K^+, Mg^{2+}, Ca^{2+} and NH_4^+) and anions (Cl^-, NO_2^-, NO_3^- and SO_4^{2-}) were determined by cation (DIONEX DX-100) and anion (DIONEX QIC) chromatography, respectively, relative to IAPSO international standard seawater as well as to standard solutions prepared from analytical reagents. Alkalinity (Alk) was determined by acid titration, and dissolved silica (SiO_2) and PO_4-P spectrophotometrically (Hitachi 124) by the standard molybdenum blue methods. Detection limits for SS and Alk were 1 mg l^{-1} and 1 μequivalent (μeq) l^{-1}, respectively, and analytical errors were <2% for Cl^-, NO_3^-, SO_4^{2-}, Na^+, K^+, Mg^{2+}, Ca^{2+} and SiO_2, <4% for NH_4^+ and <5% for PO_4-P. The analysis of a few blank solutions kept in washed PE bottles, which were carried to Nepal and then back to Japan, indicated that contamination of these chemical species was negligibly small during the processes of storage and transportation.

RESULTS AND DISCUSSION

Physical variables and chemical composition of the discharge waters are listed in Table 1 and shown in Figs 2 and 3. The monsoon season in 1996 was from 19 June (Julian day 170) to 13 September (Julian day 257) according to the precipitation data (Fujita *et al.*, 1997).

Two 30-h periods of hourly observations, one in May and one in September 1996, showed that discharge maxima occurred in the evening and minima in the morning. The ratios of maximum to minimum discharge were 1.38 and 2.13, respectively. Tri-hourly variations in concentrations and relative proportions of major dissolved species were, however, small compared with the large variation in discharge.

The concentrations of all measured dissolved species were lower during the monsoon period than those in the pre- and post-monsoon periods (Fig. 3). Conversely, daily discharge fluxes of these species were higher during the monsoon period than those in the pre- and post-monsoon periods (Fig. 4). The major cation and anion compositions in eq l^{-1} (Fig. 3) are $Ca^{2+} \gg Mg^{2+} \geq Na^{+} \geq K^{+} \gg NH_4^{+}$ and Alk $> SO_4^{2-} \gg NO_3^{-} > Cl^{-}$, respectively, and Ca^{2+}, Alk, most of which is as HCO_3^{-}, and SO_4^{2-} are the dominant ions.

For discussion below, the observation period is divided into three periods, pre- (9 May to 18 June; 41 days), actual (87 days) and post- (14 September to 25 October; 42 days) monsoon. Averages calculated and discussed below refer to these intervals.

Precipitation over Lirung Glacier basin (P_{LG}) is estimated based on altitude dependency of precipitation and area fractions for altitude zones (Rana *et al.*, 1997) as a function of P_{BH} (Fujita *et al.*, 1997). The P_{LG} value is separated into precipitation as snow (P_{SN}) and that as rain (P_{RA}) based on an air temperature of 2°C (Ageta *et al.*, 1980) set at an altitude estimated from the daily air temperature observed at Kyanjing Base House (Fujita *et al.*, 1997) and a laps rate of –0.6°C per 100 m. Cumulative P_{LG}, P_{SN} and P_{RA} values for the pre-, actual and post-monsoon periods in 1996 are given in Table 2. The estimated average percentages of P_{SN} relative to P_{LG} are 89, 69 and 89% for the pre-, actual and post-monsoon periods, respectively. Cumulative precipitation through the observed period (170 days) was 852 mm and accounts for 36% of cumulative discharge (2344 mm; Table 2). Since most of the annual precipitation and melting occur during this period, this suggests a strongly negative mass balance for Lirung Glacier similar to observations at Glacier AX010 in the east Nepal Himalayas (Kadota *et al.*, 1997).

Discharge (V_D) is given by the sum of meltwater (V_M) and rain (V_{RA}). Evaporation can be neglected due to very low temperature (Fukushima *et al.*, 1987). Changes in water storage are unknown, but are assumed to be negligible. Average concentration of species *i* in meltwater as a result of chemical weathering within the glacier system (C_{Mi}) is estimated by using a mass balance equation:

$$C_{Mi} = (V_D C_{Di} - V_{RA} C_{RAi})/V_M \tag{1}$$

Table 1 Seasonal changes in discharge, air temperature (T_a), water temperature (T_w), pH, electrical conductivity (EC), suspended sediment (SS) and chemical compositions of discharge waters at the outlet of Lirung Glacier from 16 May to 26 October 1996.

Name	Date	Time	Julian day	Discharge* (10^3 m³ day⁻¹)	T_a (°C)	T_w (°C)	pH	EC (µS cm⁻¹)	SS (mg l⁻¹)	Na (µmol l⁻¹)	NH_4 (µmol l⁻¹)	K (µmol l⁻¹)	Mg (µmol l⁻¹)	Ca (µmol l⁻¹)	Cl (µmol l⁻¹)	NO_3 (µmol l⁻¹)	SO_4 (µmol l⁻¹)	Alk (µeq l⁻¹)	PO_4 (µmol l⁻¹)	SiO_2 (µmol l⁻¹)	ΣAnion (µeq l⁻¹)	ΣCation (µeq l⁻¹)
LO-1	16/5/96	14:55	137	74.8	11.7	7.1	-	38	-	40.1	0.5	27.2	21.3	160.5	5.0	24.6	71.0	217	0.02	47.4	388	431
LO-2	17/5/96	11:00	138	66.4	9.4	5.1	7.2	28	-	37.8	0.4	27.7	20.4	154.3	4.5	24.1	67.4	213	0.02	46.0	376	415
LO-3	17/5/96	16:00	138	66.4	6.9	5.0	7.1	28	-	38.6	0.0	27.1	20.8	158.8	4.2	25.1	69.0	245	0.05	47.6	413	425
LO-4	18/5/96	08:00	139	75.2	5.4	0.7	-	34	-	36.9	0.0	27.1	20.3	152.9	4.1	24.5	65.8	201	0.01	45.6	362	410
LO-5	22/5/96	08:35	143	70.3	-	1.7	7.9	47	148	38.2	0.4	26.5	20.9	152.6	5.4	25.8	68.0	192	0.01	46.8	359	412
LO-6	22/5/96	15:10	143	70.3	-	5.6	8.1	50	42	40.3	1.9	26.7	21.2	154.7	7.2	25.6	68.2	204	0.07	47.3	374	421
LO-7	23/5/96	17:30	144	62.3	-	-	7.3	43	97	35.5	4.8	24.9	19.6	145.2	4.4	25.2	64.1	192	0.02	45.0	350	395
LO-8	26/5/96	09:30	147	120.9	-	2.9	6.4	30	375	28.2	2.2	23.2	14.1	107.1	7.6	21.9	42.1	145	0.07	32.5	259	296
LO-9	29/5/96	08:05	150	91.0	-	-	7.3	33	308	34.3	5.6	23.0	14.5	112.2	12.0	21.6	44.0	151	0.05	32.2	273	316
LO-10	30/5/96	09:00	151	76.4	-	3.6	7.1	34	158	28.8	1.0	22.1	15.7	120.1	5.0	24.5	50.0	160	0.09	36.7	290	324
LO-18	31/5/96	09:00	152	67.0	-	1.3	7.8	37	93	30.8	0.3	22.7	17.3	129.6	4.6	25.2	55.8	158	0.00	40.0	299	348
LO-22	02/6/96	09:35	154	62.6	-	-	7.6	42	93	35.3	0.4	23.2	18.9	140.9	4.2	26.5	61.3	178	0.00	44.9	331	379
LO-23	04/6/96	09:00	156	61.9	-	1.6	8.2	47	48	44.5	0.6	26.3	22.0	160.3	7.0	26.2	71.9	204	0.00	49.9	381	436
LO-24	06/6/96	13:30	158	70.8	-	-	7.6	52	218	51.7	0.4	28.8	23.8	174.1	8.3	24.8	80.6	235	0.20	56.6	429	477
LO-25	12/6/96	08:15	164	105.4	11.6	2.5	-	27	101	26.9	0.0	20.4	15.3	114.2	4.9	20.2	46.8	146	0.00	34.9	265	306
	16/6/96	-	168	126.5	-	-	-	-	122	20.7	0.0	17.7	12.6	97.6	3.0	21.0	36.2	124	0.00	29.4	221	259
LO-26	19/6/96	09:00	171	253.3	-	-	7.5	23	321	16.2	1.8	17.4	10.4	86.1	3.1	18.7	30.0	109	0.00	26.9	191	228
LO-27	29/6/96	11:00	181	-	8.3	2.3	8.5	25	115	14.4	0.8	14.0	9.0	74.7	2.2	12.5	26.7	92	0.00	23.1	161	196
LO-28	05/7/96	08:00	187	299.1	7.6	1.0	8.4	17	84	19.6	1.8	15.4	11.4	90.9	2.6	13.1	35.2	114	0.00	28.4	200	241
LO-29	13/7/96	07:50	195	282.5	8.2	0.8	8.6	20	140	14.0	1.3	14.3	8.9	72.7	1.8	8.8	24.7	94	0.00	23.3	153	193
LO-30	20/7/96	07:50	202	365.3	10.2	1.1	8.9	15	112	14.5	0.2	13.7	8.9	74.1	1.8	7.5	26.0	95	0.00	23.8	156	194
LO-31	28/7/96	10:05	210	318.1	11.8	2.2	8.4	20	86	14.8	1.1	13.2	8.9	74.2	1.7	6.9	26.2	97	0.00	23.1	158	195
LO-32	06/8/96	08:10	219	386.0	9.9	1.0	-	14	81	15.5	0.4	13.0	9.7	79.7	1.5	6.7	27.5	104	0.00	24.0	167	208
LO-33	13/8/96	08:50	226	244.6	10.7	1.0	-	26	436	12.9	0.0	14.2	8.4	70.9	1.8	5.6	26.8	96	0.00	21.1	157	186
LO-34	20/8/96	08:10	233	199.0	10.6	1.1	-	31	74	20.4	1.0	15.2	11.9	95.9	2.0	7.1	38.4	139	0.00	31.3	225	252
LO-35	26/8/96	09:30	239	271.1	-	-	-	26	71	24.8	0.5	17.5	13.9	108.1	2.2	7.6	46.8	151	0.00	35.9	252	287
LO-36	02/9/96	08:20	246	212.1	7.3	1.1	-	28	66	20.2	0.4	15.8	12.0	95.0	2.3	6.9	39.0	129	0.00	30.3	254	250
LO-37	09/9/96	11:20	253	137.9	9.8	5.2	-	33	60	24.1	0.0	17.3	13.9	108.2	2.3	7.5	46.8	144	0.00	35.3	216	286
LO-38	15/9/96	10:25	259	140.1	13.7	4.5	-	33	69	28.4	1.3	19.0	16.3	121.9	2.9	8.5	53.7	168	0.00	40.1	247	325
LO-39	22/9/96	07:30	266	205.6	7.4	1.2	-	35	64	30.3	1.3	20.0	16.4	121.8	3.0	10.2	53.4	168	0.00	40.2	286	328
LO-40	28/9/96	16:15	272	182.3	7.9	0.5	7.9	27	120	22.1	0.0	16.5	13.0	104.2	3.0	11.8	43.9	141	0.00	29.6	288	273
LO-41	29/9/96	09:00	273	122.4	11.7	2.8	7.8	46	63	23.5	0.2	16.8	13.4	106.5	2.9	11.5	43.4	142	0.02	28.2	243	280
LO-49	30/9/96	09:00	274	73.3	8.4	-0.6	7.8	57	39	32.8	0.4	20.2	16.0	124.6	5.1	12.8	53.9	177	0.00	41.6	244	335
LO-53	04/10/96	11:45	278	96.4	5.6	-0.3	7.5	53	29	41.6	0.0	24.5	21.7	157.1	5.8	13.5	74.0	227	0.00	53.7	302	424
LO-54	06/10/96	13:30	280	96.4	5.7	3.1	7.8	53	41	37.5	0.0	24.0	19.9	149.1	3.9	12.0	66.4	223	0.00	50.8	394	400
LO-55	06/10/96	14:30	280	73.0	6.1	1.4	8.3	42	67	44.1	1.5	25.4	20.3	151.2	10.1	12.8	67.4	224	0.01	51.4	372	414
LO-56	13/10/96	08:40	287	87.4	7.4	1.5	8.4	42	11	42.9	0.5	25.4	22.8	162.0	3.7	11.3	76.4	228	0.01	52.7	382	438
LO-57	19/10/96	14:30	293	64.2	9.7	5.3	9.6	31	15	47.2	0.5	26.6	24.1	172.8	4.1	8.8	82.5	231	0.09	54.4	396	468
LO-58	26/10/96	09:10	300		1.2	0.7	10.4		52	55.1	0.4	30.0	26.8	192.9	5.1	13.3	93.8	286		61.9	492	525

* Sakai *et al.* (1997).

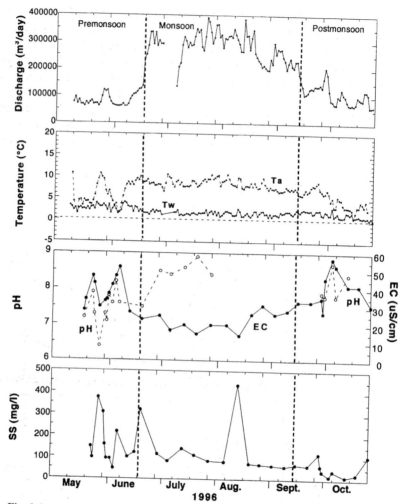

Fig. 2 Seasonal variations of discharge (Sakai *et al.*, 1997), water and air temperature, pH, electrical conductivity (EC) and concentration of suspended sediment (SS) of discharge waters at the outlet of Lirung Glacier in the Nepal Himalayas from May to October 1996.

where C_{Di} and C_{RAi} are average concentrations of species i in discharge water and rainwater, respectively. The C_{RAi} values as well as those of snow (C_{SNi}) for the pre-, actual and post-monsoon periods are assumed to be equal to average concentrations of snow pit samples collected at Yala Glacier (5450 m a.m.s.l.) on 20 May (245 cm deep), 3 August (158 cm deep) and 9 October (200 cm deep) 1996, respectively (Bhatt *et al.*, unpublished data). The C_{Di} (observed), C_{SNi} and C_{RAi} (assumed) and C_{Mi} (estimated) values for the three periods in 1996 are listed in Table 2. Average daily fluxes of dissolved species in discharge, rain and melt waters are estimated by multiplying the average concentrations with cumulative volumes of discharge, rain and melt waters, respectively, for the three periods, and are also shown in Table 2.

The average daily water discharge during the monsoon period was 3.2 and 2.5 times higher than those of pre- and post-monsoon periods, respectively (Table 2). The average

TDS concentration during the monsoon period was lower (0.57 times) than those during the pre- and post-monsoon periods. The average daily TDS flux during the monsoon period was 1.86 and 1.46 times higher than those during the pre- and post-monsoon periods. The total discharge of TDS through the observed period (170 days) was 597 t, and that during the monsoon period (87 days) was 63% of the total discharge (Table 2). The contributions of dissolved species from rain to discharge water were less than 1% by mass except for NH_4^+ (25%) and Cl^- (2.3%). This indicates that dissolved species in the discharge waters were derived from chemical weathering within the subglacial drainage system (Tranter *et al.*, 1993). During the monsoon period, the concentrations

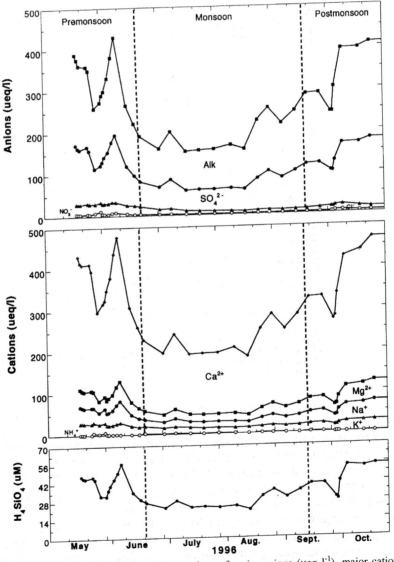

Fig. 3 Seasonal variations of concentrations of major anions (μeq l^{-1}), major cations (μeq l^{-1}) and dissolved silica (μmol l^{-1}) in discharge waters at the outlet of Lirung Glacier in the Nepal Himalayas from May to October 1996.

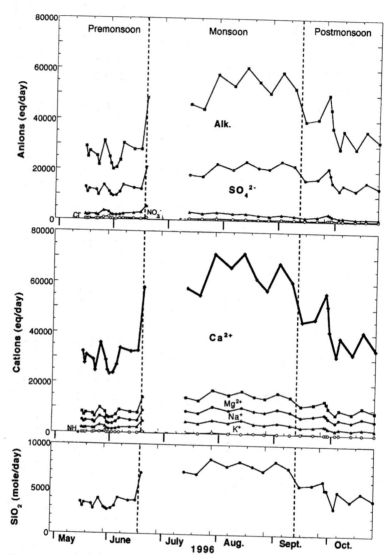

Fig. 4 Seasonal variations of discharge fluxes of anions, cations (eq day^{-1}) and dissolved silica (moles day^{-1}) at the outlet of Lirung Glacier in the Nepal Himalayas from May to October 1996.

were lower than those of the pre- and post-monsoon periods mainly by dilution from enhanced melting and rainfall (Fukushima *et al.*, 1987; Rana *et al.*, 1997). However, weathering activity was much higher during the monsoon period due to the larger melting water mass.

The dominance of Ca^{2+}, Alk and SO_4^{2-} in glacier meltwaters has been widely observed and considered to be due to sulphide oxidation (SO) coupled with calcium carbonate dissolution (CD) within the subglacial drainage system (Tranter & Raiswell, 1991; Tranter *et al.*, 1993; Hasnain & Thayyen, 1999). Linear relationships of cation and anion concentrations *vs* sulphate concentration (Tranter & Raiswell, 1991) are also observed at the outlet of Lirung Glacier.

Table 2 Water fluxes, average concentrations, daily average fluxes and sum of daily fluxes of eleven chemical species at the outlet of Lirung Glacier during the pre-monsoon (9 May to 18 June), monsoon (19 June to 13 September) and post-monsoon (14 September to 25 October) periods in 1996.

Season	Period (day)	Water flux (10^3 m³ day⁻¹)	Water flux (mm day⁻¹)	Na	NH_4	K	Mg	Ca	Cl	NO_3	SO_4	Alk (eq)	PO_4	SiO_2	ΣAnion (eq)	ΣCation (eq)	TDS (kg)
Concentrations (µmol l⁻¹ or µeq l⁻¹)																	
Discharge																	
Pre-monsoon	41	87.0	6.31	35.5	1.1	24.7	18.7	139.7	5.7	24.2	60.1	185.3	0.04	42.7	335.5	378.1	
Monsoon	87	277.8	20.13	17.6	0.8	15.1	10.6	85.9	2.1	9.1	32.8	113.6	0.00	27.2	190.4	226.4	
Post-monsoon	42	109.6	7.94	38.2	0.6	23.1	19.7	145.8	4.6	11.5	66.5	207.3	0.01	47.6	356.5	392.9	
Snow*																	
Pre-monsoon	41	14.4	1.35	0.55	4.08	0.27	0.16	2.47	1.03	2.12	0.67	0.00	0.02	0.14	4.5	10.2	
Monsoon	87	74.5	5.42	0.72	2.11	0.24	0.04	0.43	0.68	0.17	0.04	0.00	0.00	0.07	0.9	4.0	
Post-monsoon	42	34.5	2.32	0.07	0.07	0.06	0.02	0.04	0.40	0.72	0.10	0.00	0.00	0.05	1.3	0.3	
Rain*																	
Pre-monsoon	41	1.8	0.18	0.55	4.08	0.27	0.16	2.47	1.03	2.12	0.67	0.00	0.02	0.14	4.54	10.16	
Monsoon	87	32.7	2.43	0.72	2.11	0.24	0.04	0.43	0.68	0.17	0.04	0.00	0.00	0.07	0.94	4.01	
Post-monsoon	42	4.3	0.20	0.07	0.07	0.06	0.02	0.04	0.40	0.72	0.10	0.00	0.00	0.05	1.32	0.33	
Melwater																	
Pre-monsoon	41	85.2	6.12	36.3	1.1	25.2	19.0	142.6	5.8	24.6	61.4	189.1	0.0	43.6	342.4	385.7	
Monsoon	87	245.1	17.69	19.9	0.6	17.0	12.0	97.3	2.3	10.3	37.2	128.7	0.0	30.8	215.6	256.0	
Post-monsoon	42	105.3	7.74	39.8	0.6	24.1	20.5	151.7	4.8	11.9	69.3	215.8	0.0	49.6	371.0	408.9	
Daily fluxes (mol day⁻¹ or eq day⁻¹)																	
Discharge																	
Pre-monsoon	41	87.0	6.31	3 093	100	2 146	1 624	12 156	496	2 103	5 233	16 120	3.4	3 713	29 193	32 899	2 541
Monsoon	87	277.8	20.13	4 890	213	4 185	2 944	23 851	575	2 523	9 121	31 545	0.0	7 560	52 884	62 877	4 739
Post-monsoon	42	109.6	7.94	4 189	66	2 538	2 164	15 980	503	1 261	7 296	22 731	1.6	5 224	39 090	43 081	3 388
Sum	170	32 339	2 344	728 164	25 377	558 728	413 567	3 244 575	91 511	358 685	1 314 523	4 360 017	208	1 029 372	7 439 674	8 628 552	658 794
Rain																	
Pre-monsoon	41	1.8	0.18	1.0	7.2	0.5	0.3	4.4	1.8	3.7	1.2	0.0	0.0	0.2	8.0	18.0	1.13
Monsoon	87	32.7	2.43	23.4	69.0	7.8	1.3	14.2	22.2	5.5	1.4	0.0	0.0	2.2	30.6	131.1	4.20
Post-monsoon	42	4.3	0.20	0.3	0.3	0.3	0.1	0.2	1.7	3.1	0.4	0.0	0.0	0.2	5.7	1.4	0.22
Sum	170	3 096	228	2 086	711	6 31	126	1 418	2 080	765	192	0.0	1.3	215	3 233	12 198	421
Melwater																	
Pre-monsoon	41	85.2	6.12	3 092	93	2 146	1 624	12 152	494	2 100	5 232	16 120	3.4	3 713	29 185	32 881	2 540
Monsoon	87	245.1	17.69	4 866	144	4 178	2 942	23 837	553	2 517	9 120	31 545	0.0	7 558	52 854	62 746	4 735
Post-monsoon	42	105.3	7.74	4 189	65	2 538	2 164	15 980	502	1 258	7 295	22 731	1.6	5 224	39 085	43 079	3 387
Sum	170	29 243	2 116	726 078	19 062	558 017	413 441	3 243 157	89 431	357 919	1 314 330	4 360 017	206	1 029 158	7 436 441	8 616 353	658 374

* Average concentrations of snow and rain are assumed to be equal to those of pit work snow samples from Yala Glacier (5450 m a.s.l.) sampled at respective seasons in 1996 as shown in the text.

Figure 5 shows seasonal variations of relative proportions of anions to the sum of anions, those of cations to the sum of cations, and SiO_2/Alk ratio. They were quite constant throughout the pre- to post-monsoon period in 1996. For example, average relative proportions (+1 SD) of Alk, SO_4^{2-}, NO_3^- and Cl^- were $57.4 \pm 2.5\%$, $35.6 \pm 2.1\%$, $5.5 \pm 2.2\%$ and $1.43 \pm 0.67\%$, respectively, and those of Ca^{2+}, Mg^{2+}, Na^+, K^+ and NH_4^+ were $74.6 \pm 1.2\%$, $9.7 \pm 0.4\%$, $8.9 \pm 1.0\%$, $6.5 \pm 0.6\%$ and $0.29 \pm 0.37\%$, respectively. The constancy of chemical composition of meltwaters throughout the pre- to post-monsoon period suggests that the principal chemical weathering processes are not changed by the enhanced melting during the monsoon period.

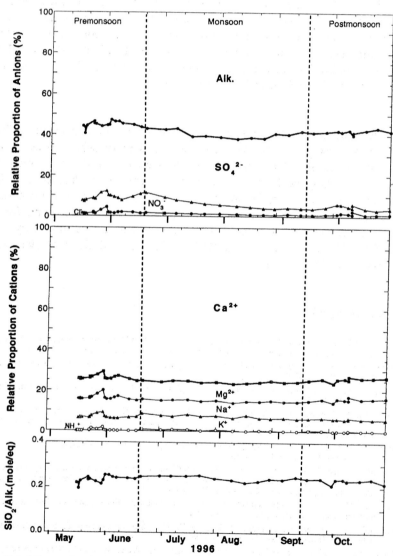

Fig. 5 Seasonal variations of relative proportions of anions (%), those of cations (%) and SiO_2/Alk ratio in discharge waters at the outlet of Lirung Glacier in the Nepal Himalayas from May to October 1996.

Impurities in pond waters on the debris-covered surface of Lirung Glacier showed that most of them were much more dilute than in the discharge waters (Masuzawa *et al.*, paper in preparation). Weathering of the surface debris may be relatively slow compared to the fresh rock flower introduced into the water at the base of the glacier. Furthermore, Rana *et al.* (1997) suggested the melting within the debris-covered area was about 10% of total melting of Lirung Glacier. So the effect of surface debris cover on the chemical composition of discharge water of Lirung Glacier seems to be not significant.

The cationic denudation rate (CDR) of the Lirung Glacier basin is estimated to be 740 meq m^{-2} year^{-1} based on assumptions that the water discharge from November to April is 12% of the annual discharge (Fukushima *et al*, 1987) and that average concentrations of dissolved species in discharge waters from November to April are equal to the average values for the pre- and post-monsoon periods in 1996 (Table 2). The estimated CDR for Lirung Glacier is about 1/6 of CDR found for Dokriani Glacier, Garhwal Himalayas, India, but is similar to CDR for European and North American glaciers (Hasnain & Thayyen, 1999).

Acknowledgements The authors would like to express their thanks to Prof. Y. Ageta and Dr M. Nakawo for allowing them to join the Cryosphere Research Expedition in the Himalayas in 1996. They thank all members of the expedition for their co-operation during the fieldwork. The interest shown by Prof. Mohan B. Gewali of Tribhuvan University in the preparation of this paper is greatly appreciated. They are indebted to two anonymous reviewers and Prof. C. F. Raymond for their critical reviews and valuable comments. This work was supported in part by a Grant-in-Aid for Scientific Research (no. 06041051) from the Ministry of Education, Science, Sports and Culture, Japan.

REFERENCES

Ageta, Y., Ohata, T., Tanaka, Y., Ikegami, K. & Higuchi, K. (1980) Mass balance of Glacier AX010 in Shorong Himal, East Nepal during the summer monsoon season. *J. Japan. Soc. Snow Ice (Seppyo)* **41**, 34–41.

Collins, D. N. (1999) Solute flux in meltwaters draining from a glacierized basin in the Karakoram mountains. *Hydrol. Processes* **13**, 3001–3015.

Fujita, K., Sakai, A. & Chhetri, T. B. (1997) Meteorological observation in Langtang Valley, Nepal Himalaya, 1996. *Bull. Glacier Res.* **15**, 71–78.

Fukushima, Y., Kawashima, K., Suzuki, M., Ohta, T., Motoyama, H., Kubota, H., Yamada, T. & Bajracharya, O. R. (1987) Runoff characteristics in three glacier-covered watershed of Langtang Valley, Nepal Himalayas. *Bull. Glacier Res.* **5**, 11–18.

Hasnain, S. I. & Thayyen, R. J. (1999) Controls on the major-ion chemistry of the Dokriani glacier meltwaters, Ganga basin, Garhwal Himalaya, India. *J. Glaciol.* **45**, 87–92.

Higuchi, K., Ageta, Y., Yasunari, T. & Inoue, J. (1982) Characteristics of precipitation during the monsoon season in high mountain areas of the Nepal Himalaya. In: *Hydrological Aspects of Alpine and High-Mountain Areas* (ed. by J. W. Glen) (Proc. Exeter Symp., July 1982), 21–30. IAHS Publ. no. 138.

Inger, S. & Harris, B. W. (1992) Tectonothermal evolution of the High Himalayan Crystalline Sequence, Langtang Valley, northern Nepal. *J. Metamorphic Geol.* **10**, 439–452.

Kadota, T., Fujita, K., Seko, K., Kayasta, R. & Ageta, Y. (1997) Monitoring and prediction of shrinkage of a small glacier in the Nepal Himalaya. *Ann. Glaciol.* **24**, 90–94.

Kamiyama, K. (1984) Lakes and their sediments around Yala Glacier. In: *Glacial Studies in Langtang Valley* (ed. by K. Higuchi), 85–89. Data Centre for Glacier Research, Water Res. Inst., Nagoya Univ., Nagoya, Japan.

Nakawo, M., Fujita, K., Ageta, Y., Shankar, K. & Pokhrel, A. P. (1997) Basic studies for assessing the impacts of the global worming on the Himalayan cryosphere, 1994–1996. *Bull. Glacier Res.* **15**, 53–58.

Rana, B., Nakawo, M., Fukushima, Y. & Ageta, Y. (1997) Application of a conceptual precipitation–runoff (HYCYMODEL) in the debris-covered glacierized basin of Langtang Valley, Nepal Himalaya. *Ann. Glaciol.* **25**, 226–231.

Reynolds, B., Chapman, P. J., French, M. C., Jenkins, A. & Wheater, H. S. (1995) Major, minor and trace element chemistry of surface waters in the Everest region of Nepal. In: *Biochemistry of Seasonally Snow-Covered Catchments* (ed. by K. A. Tonnessen, Mark W. Williams & Martyn Tranter), 405–412. IAHS Publ. no. 228.

Sakai, A., Fujita, K., Aoki, T., Asahi, K. & Nakawo, M. (1997) Water discharge from the Lirung Glacier in Langtang Valley, Nepal Himalaya, 1996. *Bull. Glacier Res.* **15**, 79–83.

Tranter, M. & Raiswell, R. (1991) The composition of the englacial and subglacial component in bulk meltwaters draining the Gornergletscher, Switzerland. *J. Glaciol.* **37**, 59–66

Tranter, M., Brown, G., Raiswell, R., Sharp, M. & Gurnell, A. (1993) A conceptual model of solute acquisition by Alpine glacial meltwaters. *J. Glaciol.* **39**, 573–581.

Watanbe, O., Takenaka, S., Iida, H., Kamiyama, K., Thapa, K. B. & Mulmi, D. D. (1984) First results from Himalayan Glacier Boring Project in 1981–1982: Part I. Stratigraphic analyses of full-depth cores from Yala Glacier, Langtang Himal, Nepal. In: *Glacial Studies in Langtang Valley* (ed. by K. Higuchi), 7–23. Data Centre for Glacier Research, Water Res. Inst., Nagoya Univ., Nagoya, Japan.